**Contemporary M**

***General Editor:* Ala**



# VECTORS : Pure and Applied

**David Holland and Terence Treeby**

**Edward Arnold**

First published 1977
by Edward Arnold (Publishers) Limited,
25 Hill Street
London W1X 8LL

ISBN: 0 7131 2625 6

Photoset and printed in Malta by Interprint (Malta) Ltd

# Editor's Preface

During the last fifteen years, the teaching of mathematics at schools and colleges has undergone a severe reappraisal. Not only have the *methods* of teaching changed considerably, but so have the *topics* which are taught. This is as it should be—the needs of our future mathematicians and scientists are constantly changing in the light of the technical developments of the twentieth century. It seems likely that the frontiers of science will be pushed further and further back in the coming years and the mathematics required must certainly keep abreast of these changes. If these developments are to continue rapidly, it is necessary for the students to meet and understand new ideas whilst in their last years at school and their first at college and university.

The 'Contemporary Mathematics' series of books has been written after several years' thought and experiment, and has been designed for these major purposes:

1. To produce texts to cover the new requirements of the major school mathematics syllabuses ('A' and 'S' level in Britain). Texts will provide the mathematical developments and cover the important applications (e.g. *Matrices: Pure and Applied*).
2. To provide an introduction to topics which are both contemporary and important, showing also how these might best be taught. (e.g. *Analogue Computers*).

It would seem sensible to develop and continue a number of the first examination ('O' level) topics—for example, Boolean Algebra, Matrices and Computers all combine in Boolean Matrices (the key to many computer circuits). Matrices, Vectors, Numerical Methods, Analogue and Digital Computing and Probability and Statistics are now part of every course.

It is hoped that these books will help students to appreciate at least a few of the current, most pressing applications which must soon be part of every mathematician's repertoire.

Wells
1976

Alan Sherlock

# Authors' Preface

This book is intended to be a text which an average Advanced Level student who has little previous experience of vectors can follow with minimal guidance. At all times we attempt to draw from the student's general experience, develop the appropriate theory, and then apply this as widely as possible. Accordingly, after an extensive introductory chapter, we first develop the essential work on vector spaces. The general ideas are investigated more fully in applications to geometry, kinematics, projectiles, and impulse-momentum problems. Following a detailed discussion of the scalar product is a long section on work, energy and power.

The material in this book is suitable for courses leading to most single and double subject advanced level examinations in both pure and applied mathematics. We include many exercises of both examination and routine practice type.

We would like to express our gratitude to our colleagues and pupils at St Dunstan's College, all of whom have helped with advice. Special thanks are due to Alan Sherlock for his patience and helpful suggestions.

We would also like to thank the following for permission to use their examination questions: Oxford and Cambridge Schools Examination Board Mathematics in Education and Industry (MEI) and School Mathematics Project (SMP); The Associated Examining Board (AEB); University of London Entrance and School Examinations Council (L); Joint Matriculation Board (JMB) and Midlands Mathematical Experiment (MME); University of Cambridge Local Examinations Syndicate (C); and Oxford Delegacy of Local Examinations (O).

1976

David Holland
Terence Treeby

# Contents

# List of Symbols

The page number quoted against each entry corresponds to the definition or first mention of the given symbol.

*(1) Vectors*

| | |
|---|---|
| $\overrightarrow{\mathrm{AB}}$ | directed line segment, 3 |
| $\mathbf{v}$ | free vector family, 3 |
| $\mathbf{a}$ | position vector $\overrightarrow{\mathrm{OA}}$, 5 |
| $\mathbf{0}$ | zero vector, 6 |
| $(-\mathbf{a})$ | negative vector, 6 |
| $u = \lvert\mathbf{u}\rvert$ | length or modulus of **u**, 9 |
| $\alpha\mathbf{u}$ | scalar multiple of **u**, 9 |
| $\hat{\mathbf{a}}$ | unit vector, 10 |
| $\hat{\mathbf{r}}, \hat{\boldsymbol{\theta}}$ | radial and transverse unit vectors, 15, 81 |
| $\mathbf{v}_{\mathrm{a}}$ | airspeed and course, 16 |
| $\mathbf{v}_{\mathrm{g}}$ | groundspeed and track, 16 |
| $\hat{\mathbf{i}}, \hat{\mathbf{j}}, \hat{\mathbf{k}}$ | directions of axes, 21, 35, 87, 89 |
| **PQ** | bound vector, 21 |
| $\overleftrightarrow{\mathbf{PQ}}$ | infinite line containing **PQ**, 22 |
| **PQ** | localized line vector, 22 |
| $\begin{pmatrix} a_1 \\ a_2 \\ a_3 \end{pmatrix}$ | column vector, 37 |

*(2) Real vector spaces*

| | |
|---|---|
| $V_3$ | vector space of free vector families, 4 |
| $P_3$ | vector space of position vectors, 5 |
| $R^3$ | vector space of column vectors with three entries, 37 |
| $R^2$ | vector space of column vectors with two entries, 43 |

*(3) Points and coordinates*

| | |
|---|---|
| O | origin, 5 |
| $(r, \theta)$ | plane polar coordinates, 14, 81 |
| G | centroid of triangle, 73 |
| G | centroid of tetrahedron, 74 |
| $(x, y)$ | plane cartesian coordinates, 87 |
| $(x, y, z)$ | three-dimensional Cartesian coordinates, 89 |

| | |
|---|---|
| $(r, \theta, z)$ | cylindrical polar coordinates, 93 |
| $(r, \theta, \phi)$ | spherical polar coordinates, 94 |

*(4) Mechanics*

| | |
|---|---|
| $t$ | time, 47 |
| $x$, $\mathbf{x}$ | displacement, 47, 54, 138 |
| $v$, $\mathbf{v}$, $\longrightarrow$ | velocity, 47, 54, 138 |
| $a$, $\mathbf{a}$, $\longrightarrow\!\!\!\!>$ | acceleration, 47, 55, 138 |
| $\mathbf{v} = \mathrm{d}\mathbf{r}/\mathrm{d}t$ | first derivative, velocity, 54 |
| $\mathbf{a} = \mathrm{d}^2\mathbf{r}/\mathrm{d}t^2$ | second derivative, acceleration, 55 |
| $\mathbf{v}_{BR}$ | velocity of R relative to B, 99 |
| $\mu$ | coefficient of friction, 115 |
| $G$ | universal gravitational constant, 123 |
| $g$, $\mathbf{g}$ | gravity, 123, 141 |
| $k$ | stiffness of string or spring, 131 |
| $\lambda$ | modulus of elasticity, 131 |
| $e$ | coefficient of restitution, 173 |
| $V(\mathbf{x})$ | potential energy, 223, 224 |

*(5) Products of vectors, and geometry*

| | |
|---|---|
| $\mathbf{a} \cdot \mathbf{b}$ | scalar product, 154 |
| $\mathbf{a} \wedge \mathbf{b}$ | vector product, 182 |
| $\hat{\mathbf{n}}$ | unit normal in equation $\mathbf{r} \cdot \hat{\mathbf{n}} = p$ of plane, 203 |
| $S$ | focus of conic, 211 |
| $e$ | eccentricity of conic, 214 |
| $l$ | half-length of latus rectum of conic, 214 |

*(6) SI units, and physical constants*

| | |
|---|---|
| length | 1 m (metre) |
| time | 1 s (second) |
| velocity | $1\ \mathrm{m\ s^{-1}}$ |
| acceleration | $1\ \mathrm{m\ s^{-2}}$ |
| mass | 1 kg (kilogram) |
| force | $1\ \mathrm{N} = 1\ \mathrm{kg\ m\ s^{-2}}$ (newton) |
| impulse, momentum | $1\ \mathrm{N\ s} = 1\ \mathrm{kg\ m\ s^{-1}}$ |
| work, energy | $1\ \mathrm{J} = 1\ \mathrm{N\ m}$ (joule) |
| power | $1\ \mathrm{W} = 1\ \mathrm{J\ s^{-1}} = 1\ \mathrm{N\ m\ s^{-1}}$ (watt) |
| standard gravity | $g \approx 9{\cdot}81\ \mathrm{m\ s^{-2}}$ (3S) |

# 1
# Vectors and Vector Quantities

## Introduction

This is a long and apparently formidable chapter, which needs to be viewed as a whole rather than as several sub-sections. For example, we pose a problem in Section 1.2 which we do not solve until Section 1.9. Reading the whole chapter through before attempting any detailed study will reveal that the intervening sections are concerned with formulating the mathematics naturally generated by the problem, but in rather greater detail than is needed for the problem itself. We would therefore recommend that you read through the whole chapter before you attempt a detailed study of any part of it. Some parts will necessarily be glossed over in this reading, but you should obtain a feel for the subject. Then go back to the beginning, and work through the chapter in a more usual manner, filling in the details and working the exercises.

Throughout this chapter we rely on a certain amount of intuition and knowledge of physical quantities, without being able to define and discuss them in detail. For example, the reader is expected to have some qualitative idea about such things as mass, velocity (speed and direction), acceleration (rate of change of velocity, again in a given direction), force, and momentum (the product of mass and velocity). Any more extensive properties are developed as and when needed.

## 1.1 Mathematical models

Some aspects of mathematical theory, which are often developed in abstract terms, may be used to describe real-life situations, either accurately or approximately. Such theories, when applied, are called *mathematical models*—even if the term is new, you are probably familiar with the idea, as the examples below may show. We form a mathematical model by considering an actual physical situation, and selecting a suitable piece of mathematics to describe it.

For example, we know that the earth is not a perfect sphere, but we assume that it *is* a sphere for many calculations, because the results obtained from this are often sufficiently accurate and involve simpler mathematics. The sphere, and its geometry and trigonometry, is taken as a mathematical model representing the earth. We also sometimes subscribe to the flat-earth theory: if we are dealing with only a small part of the earth's surface, we tend to assume that it is a plane—thus taking a plane as a mathematical model for part of the earth's surface (see, for instance, Chapter 8).

You may have met the equation $h = ut - (9{\cdot}8\, t^2/2)$ in connection with a stone being thrown vertically upwards with a speed of $u$, where $h$ is its height above the ground after time $t$, and the units of $u$, $h$ and $t$ are m $s^{-1}$, m and s respectively. This equation is only approximate, because it does not take account of air resistance, among other things, and because the value of 9·8 m $s^{-2}$ for the gravitational acceleration is not accurate. However, this equation serves as a reasonable mathematical model for stone-throwers.

More complicated models are used in connection with probability and statistics. Suppose we wish to investigate the numbers of boys and girls in families of four children, and their relative ages. If we assume that boys and girls are born in equal numbers, then we may represent our investigation by the experiment of tossing four coins: the sequence HTTT representing BGGG (with the eldest child a boy), for example. We may go further, and use the binomial distribution to predict what will happen in the coin-tossing experiment, and hence to postulate some hypotheses for the family situation.

In some cases, we do not even know that we are modelling. For instance, models are invented to represent the elementary particles of physics without knowing very much about elementary particles. Indeed, some elementary particles have only been discovered as the result of predictions from suitable models. More than one theoretical physicist has gained his Nobel prize for work in this field, almost entirely with models.

## 1.2 The need for vectors

Consider a boat, drifting powerless in an endless flat ocean. Suppose also that everywhere there is a current flowing due south, and a wind blowing from the east. For simplicity, we will assume that there are no waves, and that the motion of the boat is not influenced by any factors other than the current and the wind mentioned above. Then the boat will move neither due south with the current, nor due west with the wind, but somewhere in between.

Its exact direction will depend on the details of the wind and the current. But we notice that it will not depend at all on the exact location of the boat—just on the strength and direction of the two moving influences.

We will attempt to construct a mathematical model for this problem, and will see that this same model can be used for other situations. We would like a model which has quantities to represent the wind, the current, and the boat's drift. These representative quantities must therefore have *size* (or magnitude) to represent the speeds, and *direction*, to represent the directions. Further, we would like to be able to combine two such quantities to obtain a third single quantity. Here, we would like to combine the quantities representing the wind and the current to obtain that representing the boat's drift. The quantities we use to represent the velocities of the wind, the current, and the boat are called *vectors*. They will have magnitude and direction, and we will be able to combine two vectors to give another vector.

We start with the idea of a *directed line segment* $\overrightarrow{AB}$ and then extend this to give us the idea of a vector. We will also find it convenient to split our notion of 'direction' into two parts, which we will call *direction* and *sense*. For example the earth's axis (the straight line joining the north and south poles) is a direction. Northwards and southwards are the two possible senses associated with that direction. A directed line segment $\overrightarrow{AB}$ is a segment of a given straight line (which specifies a direction) in the sense A-to-B. It has magnitude, direction and sense, and therefore satisfies some of our qualifications for a vector.

We return to the problem of the boat later, when we have developed our model sufficiently to be able to solve it completely.

## 1.3 Directed line segments

A *directed line segment* $\overrightarrow{AB}$ is a line segment in space which has a definite sense attached, to distinguish it from $\overrightarrow{BA}$. For example, the top edge of this page becomes a directed line segment when we specify the sense, i.e. towards the spine, or away from the spine. Fig. 1.1 shows some directed line segments.

Directed line segments all have three properties: length, direction and sense. Some pairs of directed line segments share only some of these properties. For example, in Fig. 1.1, $\overrightarrow{AB}$ and $\overrightarrow{CD}$ have the same length but different directions; $\overrightarrow{AB}$ and $\overrightarrow{EF}$ have the same direction and sense, but different lengths; and $\overrightarrow{AB}$ and $\overrightarrow{GH}$ have the same length and direction, but opposite senses. Fig. 1.2 shows a number of different directed line segments all having the same direction, length *and* sense, although they have different locations. Thus for any directed line segment $\overrightarrow{AB}$, there is associated with it a whole family of directed line segments, each of which has the same direction, length and sense as $\overrightarrow{AB}$. These directed line segments are called *equivalent*. Thus, in the diagram, $\overrightarrow{AB}$ and $\overrightarrow{CD}$ form just one pair of equivalent directed line segments.

Let $V_3$ be the set of all such families of equivalent directed line segments. Let us give these families the names **a**, **b**, **c**, . . . . In handwriting, these will appear as underlined letters $\underset{\sim}{a}$, $\underset{\sim}{b}$, $\underset{\sim}{c}$, . . . . Then, for example, **v** may be the family of all directed line segments equivalent to $\overrightarrow{AB}$, that is $\mathbf{v} = \{\overrightarrow{XY} : \overrightarrow{XY} \text{ is equivalent to } \overrightarrow{AB}\}$. Fig. 1.2 shows some members of this family **v**.

Any such family **v** will be called a *free vector family*, and any member $\overrightarrow{AB}$ of **v** will be called a *free vector*. Many of the properties of free vector families are established by considering particular free vectors. For this reason, we often use

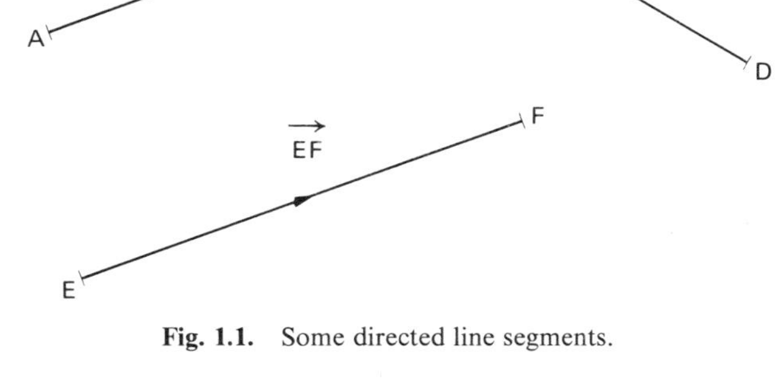

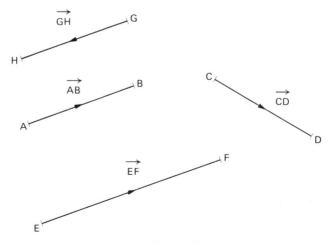

**Fig. 1.1.** Some directed line segments.

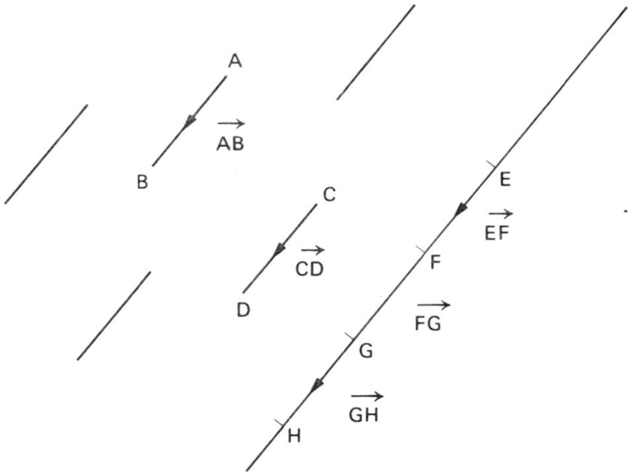


**Fig. 1.2.** Directed line segments with the same direction, length and sense, but different locations. These are called equivalent.

the term free vector to mean either the free vector $\overrightarrow{AB}$, or the corresponding family **v**, as appropriate. The set $V_3$ of all free vector families **v** is called a *vector space* because of the properties of its algebraic structure.

We now define a method of combining two free vectors **a** and **b** by addition to give a third free vector, which we will call **a** + **b**.

To form **a** + **b**, take *any* member $\overrightarrow{AB}$ of the family **a**.

Then there is a particular member $\overrightarrow{BC}$ of **b** which starts at the end-point B of $\overrightarrow{AB}$.

This defines a directed line segment $\overrightarrow{AC}$, which now defines a family of equivalent directed line segments. We will call this family **a** + **b**.

In practice, we usually create no confusion by labelling the actual free vectors (directed line segments) with the names of their families, as in Fig. 1.4. Remember that we are actually using representatives of families, and not the families themselves.

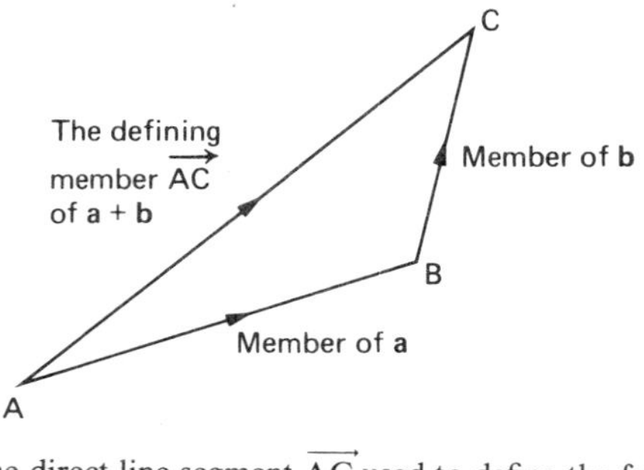


**Fig. 1.3.** The direct line segment $\overrightarrow{AC}$ used to define the family **a** + **b**.

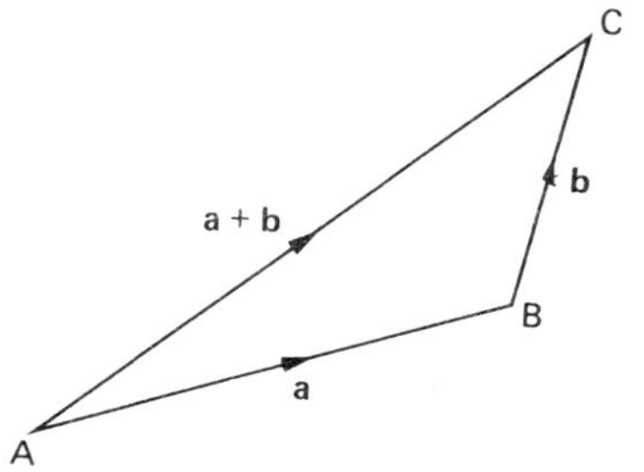


**Fig. 1.4.** A convenient notation for the diagram showing **a** + **b**.

## 1.4 Position vectors

Consider the set $V_3$ of families of free vectors in space. Choose in space an arbitrary fixed point O as *origin*. From each family **a** in $V_3$ select the particular member $\overrightarrow{OA}$ which starts at O, and call it $\underline{\underline{\mathbf{a}}}$. We will call $\underline{\underline{\mathbf{a}}}$ a *position vector*, since it determines the position of the point A relative to the origin O. It must not be confused with the point A itself; nor with the directed line segment $\overrightarrow{AO}$, which is not a position vector since it starts at A rather than at O. We now have an origin O and a set $P_3$ of position vectors $\underline{\underline{\mathbf{a}}}$, $\underline{\underline{\mathbf{b}}}$, $\underline{\underline{\mathbf{c}}}$, . . . .

We define an operation of addition in $P_3$ by referring back to $V_3$. To obtain $\underline{\underline{\mathbf{a}}} + \underline{\underline{\mathbf{b}}}$, consider the corresponding families **a** and **b** in $V_3$. Use these to find **c** = **a** + **b**, and then find the position vector $\underline{\underline{\mathbf{c}}}$ which belongs to this family. We then define $\underline{\underline{\mathbf{a}}} + \underline{\underline{\mathbf{b}}}$ to be the position vector $\underline{\underline{\mathbf{c}}}$. In Fig. 1.5, the dotted line shows the member of **b** used to find **a** + **b**.

The two sets $V_3$ and $P_3$, with their addition operations, are very closely related. In practice, it causes very little confusion to write both the family and the position vector as **a**. So **a** might be a free vector (directed line segment), or a family of free vectors, or the particular free vector $\overrightarrow{OA}$ (position vector). Also, **a** + **b** might be the sum of two position vectors, or of two free vectors, even though + has slightly different meanings. We often think of adding families in terms of adding particular members.

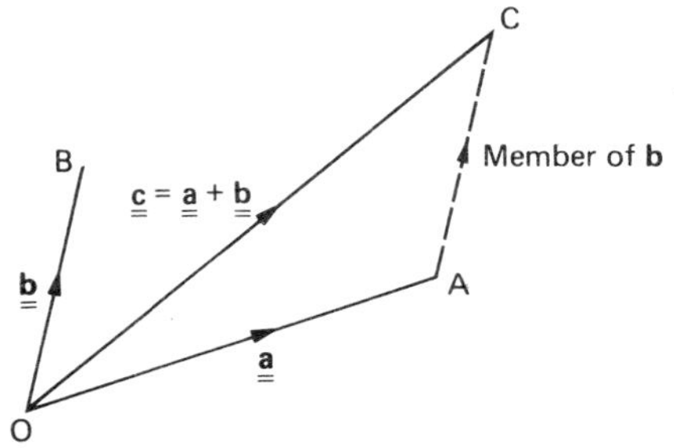


**Fig. 1.5.** The combination of position vectors $\underline{\underline{\mathbf{a}}}$ and $\underline{\underline{\mathbf{b}}}$ to give $\underline{\underline{\mathbf{c}}} = \underline{\underline{\mathbf{a}}} + \underline{\underline{\mathbf{b}}}$.

A special situation occurs if we add two position vectors which have the same direction.

Figures 1.6 and 1.7 show the two possible cases—when the given position vectors **a** and **b** have the same, and opposite, senses. In each case, we have added **a** and **b** by the usual method: we take the position vector **b**, or $\overrightarrow{OB}$, and then take the free vector $\overrightarrow{BC}$ equivalent to **a**. $\overrightarrow{OC}$ is then the position vector **a** + **b**. In both cases, **a** + **b** has the same direction as **a** and **b**, and the sense of the longer of **a** and **b**.

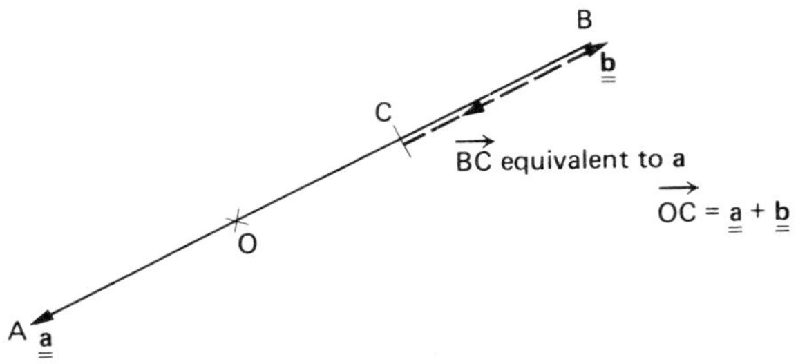


**Fig. 1.6.** Adding two position vectors with the same direction, and opposite senses.

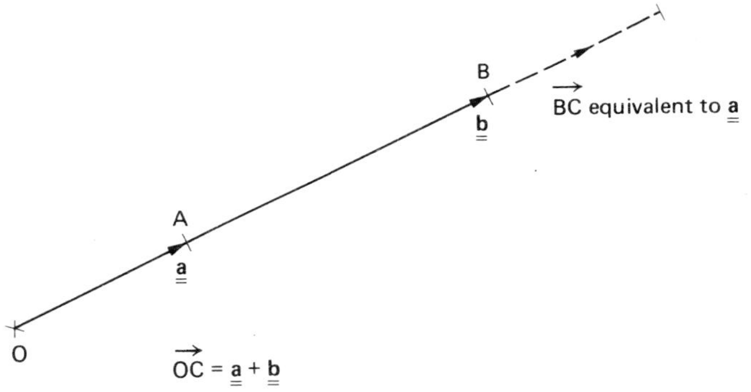


**Fig. 1.7.** Adding two position vectors with the same direction and sense.

A similar result is true for the addition of two free vectors in the same direction—their sum will be in the same direction.

The position vector $\overrightarrow{OO}$ is special—it has no length, and has arbitrary direction. We call it the *zero vector* **0** (more correctly, we should call it the zero position vector). The family of which this is a member is also called the zero vector (more correctly, the zero free vector family).

Now consider the position vector **a**, or $\overrightarrow{OA}$, and the position vector **b**, or $\overrightarrow{OB}$, having the same length and direction, but the opposite sense. Then we see that **a** + **b** = **0**. This corresponds to the property $a + (-a) = 0$ of real numbers. For this reason, we call the vector **b** the *negative* (−**a**) of **a**, so that

$$\mathbf{a} + (-\mathbf{a}) = (-\mathbf{a}) + \mathbf{a} = \mathbf{0} \qquad (1)$$

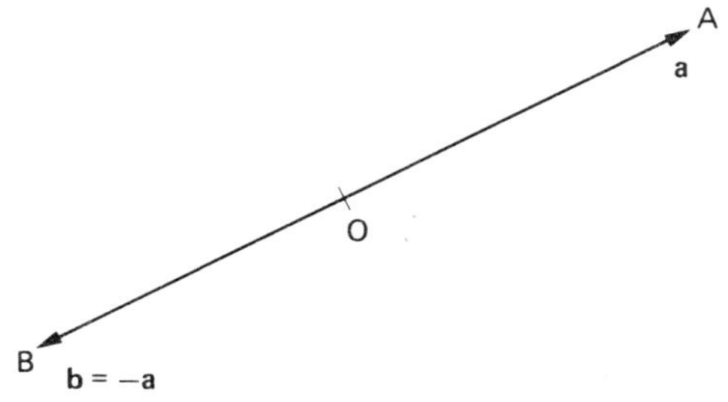


**Fig. 1.8.** The position vectors **a** and **b** = −**a**.

By extending this, we see that the position vectors **a** and −**a** define free vector families **a** and −**a** having the same property (1), and we have thus defined the free vector family −**a**.

## 1.5 Worked example

**Worked Example 1.1**

Referred to rectangular axes O$x$, O$y$ in a plane, the point A has coordinates (3, −2), B (2, −3) and C (−2, −5). Find the coordinates of the following points:

(i) D, where the position vector **d** is equivalent to $\overrightarrow{AB}$.

(ii) E, where the position vector **e** is the sum of the position vectors **a** and **b** of A and B.

(iii) F, where $\overrightarrow{FC}$ is equivalent to **a** + **b**.

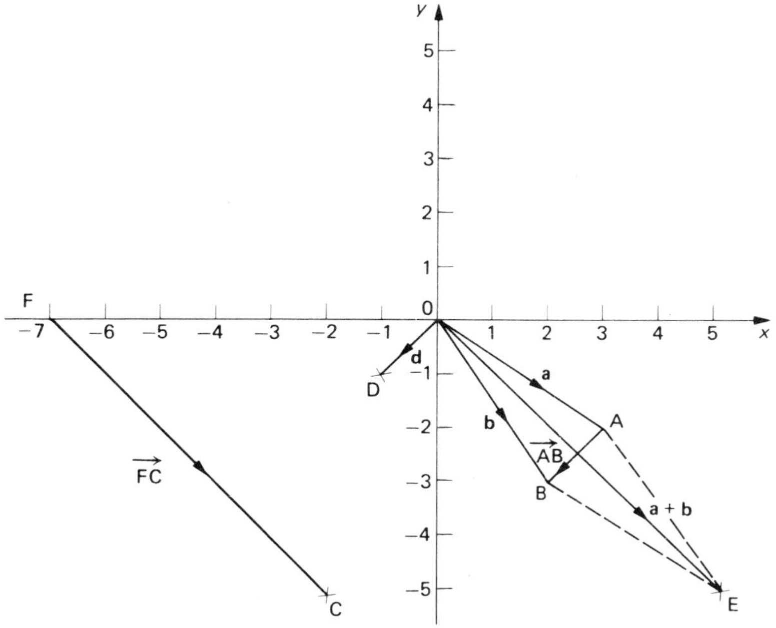


**Fig. 1.9.** Worked example 1.1.

*Solution*

A realistic diagram is helpful.

(i) $\overrightarrow{OD}$ is equivalent to $\overrightarrow{AB}$. Now B is 1 unit below A, and 1 unit to its left. Hence D is 1 unit below O, and 1 unit to its left. Hence the coordinates of D are $(-1, -1)$.

(ii) **a** and **b** are added as in the diagram, where $\overrightarrow{BE}$ is equivalent to $\overrightarrow{OA}$. Now A is 2 units below O, and 3 units to the right of O. Hence E is 2 units below B, and 3 units to the right of B. Hence the coordinates of E are $(5, -5)$.

(iii) $\overrightarrow{FC}$ is equivalent to $\overrightarrow{OE}$. Now O is 5 units above E, and 5 units to the left of E. Hence F is 5 units above C, and 5 units to the left of C. Hence the coordinates of F are $(-7, 0)$.

**Exercise 1*a***

1. Referred to rectangular axes O$x$, O$y$ the point A has coordinates (2, 3), B (2, 4), C (3, 5) and D (4, 4). Find the coordinates of the following points:
   (i) E, where the position vector **e** is equivalent to $\overrightarrow{BD}$.
   (ii) F, where the position vector **f** is equivalent to $\overrightarrow{AC}$.
   (iii) G, where the position vector **g** is the sum **e** + **f** of **e** and **f**.
   (iv) H, where $\overrightarrow{BH}$ is a member of the free vector family obtained by adding the families containing $\overrightarrow{AC}$ and $\overrightarrow{BD}$ respectively.

2. Referred to rectangular axes O$x$, O$y$, the point A has coordinates $(-1, 3)$ B $(-2, -4)$, C $(1, -5)$ and D $(-3, -3)$. Find the coordinates of the following points:
   (i) E, where $\overrightarrow{DE}$ is a member of the free vector family obtained by adding the families containing $\overrightarrow{AB}$ and $\overrightarrow{CD}$ respectively.
   (ii) F, where $\overrightarrow{EF}$ is a member of the free vector family obtained by adding the families containing $\overrightarrow{BC}$ and $\overrightarrow{DA}$.

## 1.6 Scalar multiples

Consider the line segment AC, with mid-point B. The directed line segments $\overrightarrow{AB}$ and $\overrightarrow{AC}$ have the same direction and sense, but $\overrightarrow{AC}$ is twice the length of $\overrightarrow{AB}$. Now take the family **u** of directed line segments equivalent to $\overrightarrow{AB}$. $\overrightarrow{DE}$ is another

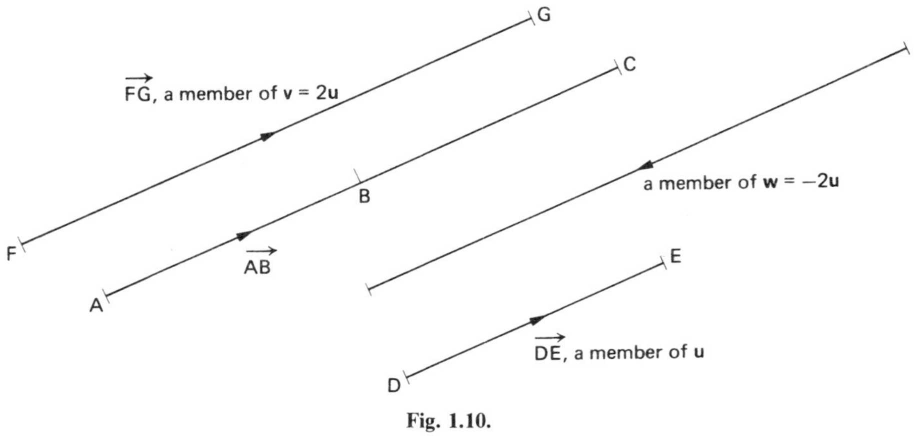


Fig. 1.10.

member of this free vector family **u**. Similarly, take the free vector family **v** of directed line segments equivalent to $\overrightarrow{AC}$, of which $\overrightarrow{FG}$ is another member. Then *any* member of **v** has the same direction and sense as *any* member of **u**, but twice the length.

From this connection between any member of **u** and any member of **v**, we have two new definitions. All the members of **u** have the same length: we will say that the *length of* **u** is equal to the length of any one of its members. We write $|\mathbf{u}|$ to mean the length of the free vector family **u**. Thus $|\mathbf{v}|$ is the length of **v**, and in the above example $|\mathbf{v}| = 2|\mathbf{u}|$. $|\mathbf{u}|$ is also called the *modulus* of **u**. We often write $u = |\mathbf{u}|$.

We also define a *scalar multiple* $\alpha\mathbf{u}$ of **u**, so that in the example we will be able to write $\mathbf{v} = 2\mathbf{u}$. Suppose **u** is a free vector family, and $\alpha$ is a real number. Then the vector $\alpha\mathbf{u}$ has the same direction as **u**, and

$$|\alpha\mathbf{u}| = |\alpha| \times |\mathbf{u}|,$$

where

$$|\alpha| = \begin{cases} \alpha & \text{for } \alpha > 0, \quad \text{in which case } \mathbf{u} \text{ and } \alpha\mathbf{u} \text{ have the same sense} \\ 0 & \text{for } \alpha = 0, \quad \text{in which case } \alpha\mathbf{u} = \mathbf{0} \\ -\alpha & \text{for } \alpha < 0, \quad \text{in which case } \mathbf{u} \text{ and } \alpha\mathbf{u} \text{ have opposite senses} \end{cases}$$

Now refer back to Fig. 1.10. We see that our definition gives us $\mathbf{v} = 2\mathbf{u}$. For another example, suppose that $\overrightarrow{CA}$ defines the free vector family **w**. Then $|\mathbf{w}| = 2|\mathbf{u}|$, but **w** and **u** have opposite senses. Hence $\mathbf{w} = -2\mathbf{u}$.

In Fig. 1.11, $2\mathbf{a}$ and $\frac{3}{2}\mathbf{a}$ have the same direction and sense as **a**, but $(-\frac{1}{2})\mathbf{a}$ is reversed in sense.

We use the same definition for the scalar multiple $\alpha\mathbf{u}$ of a position vector **u**—we specify that now $|\mathbf{u}|$ is the length of the actual position vector (directed line segment) rather than that of a member of the family.

Recall that we use the notation **u** for any type of vector—either free vector, or free vector family, or position vector. The definitions of $|\mathbf{u}|$ and of $\alpha\mathbf{u}$ are so closely connected that we may discuss properties of length and scalar multiples without reference to the type of vector under consideration. The definition following holds for all three types:

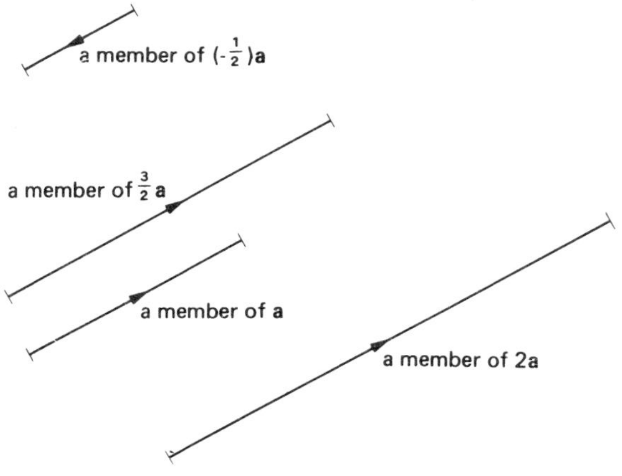


**Fig. 1.11.** To determine scalar multiples of **a**.

A vector **a** whose length is 1, i.e. $|\mathbf{a}| = 1$, is called a *unit vector*, and we use the special notation $\hat{\mathbf{a}}$ (said '*a* hat'). $\hat{\mathbf{r}}$, $\hat{\mathbf{s}}$, and so on will be unit vectors, even if not stated explicitly.

Consider all the vectors in one particular direction. Of these, just two will have unit length—one in each sense. Call one of them $\hat{\mathbf{a}}$, and then the other will be $(-\hat{\mathbf{a}})$. Any other vector in that direction can be written as a scalar multiple of $\hat{\mathbf{a}}$. In particular, the vector **a** with length $a$ may be written as $a\hat{\mathbf{a}}$ if it has the same sense as $\hat{\mathbf{a}}$, or as $-a\hat{\mathbf{a}}$ if its sense is opposite to that of $\hat{\mathbf{a}}$. Thus $+3\hat{\mathbf{a}}$ and $-3\hat{\mathbf{a}}$ have the same direction (namely $\hat{\mathbf{a}}$), the same magnitude (that is, 3), but opposite senses given by the different signs. Notice, too, that the vector $(1/a)\mathbf{a}$ is a unit vector in the direction and sense of **a**, since $a \geqq 0$.

## 1.7 Properties of scalar multiples

In the previous section, we defined the scalar multiple $\alpha\mathbf{a}$ of the vector **a**, where $\alpha$ is a real number. We frequently meet expressions involving such things as $\alpha\mathbf{b}$, where $\mathbf{b} = \mathbf{x} + \mathbf{y}$; or $\beta\mathbf{c}$, where $\beta = \alpha + \delta$. In fact many of the familiar laws of the algebra of real numbers are also true when applied to scalar multiples of vectors. Although these laws are true for scalar multiples of vectors, there are algebraic systems in which they are not necessarily true. It is for this reason that they must be asserted, and their truth demonstrated.

Fig. 1.12 demonstrates the law

$$\alpha(\beta\mathbf{x}) = (\alpha\beta)\mathbf{x} \quad \text{(associative law)} \tag{1}$$

Fig. 1.13 demonstrates the law

$$\alpha(\mathbf{x} + \mathbf{y}) = (\alpha\mathbf{x}) + (\alpha\mathbf{y}) \tag{2}$$
(distributive law, scalar multiplication over vector addition)

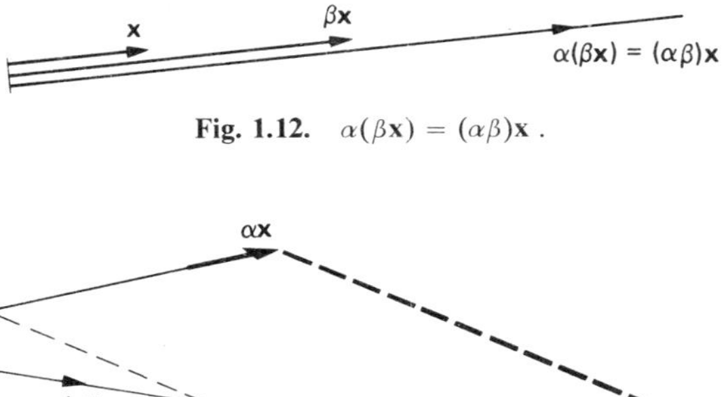


**Fig. 1.12.** $\alpha(\beta\mathbf{x}) = (\alpha\beta)\mathbf{x}$ .

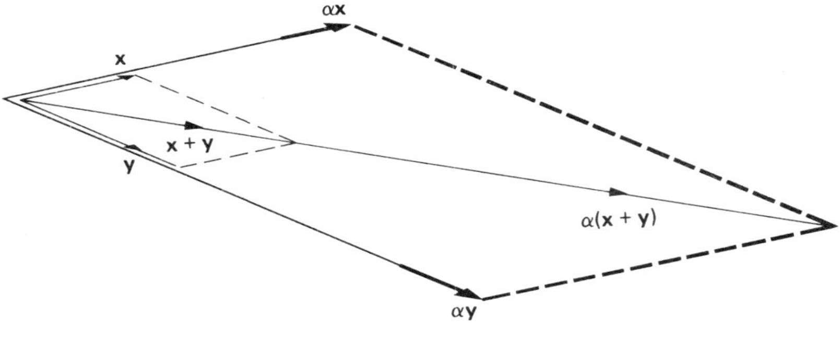


**Fig. 1.13.** $\alpha(\mathbf{x} + \mathbf{y}) = (\alpha\mathbf{x}) + (\alpha\mathbf{y})$.

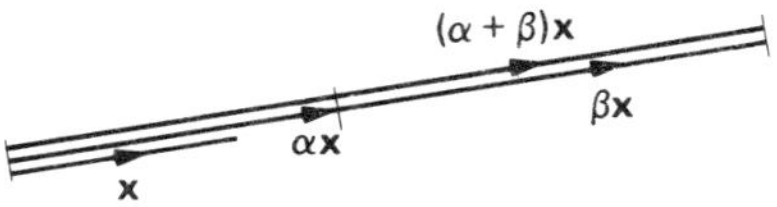


**Fig. 1.14.** $(\alpha\mathbf{x}) + (\beta\mathbf{x}) = (\alpha + \beta)\mathbf{x}$.

Fig. 1.14 demonstrates the law

$$(\alpha + \beta)\mathbf{x} = (\alpha\mathbf{x}) + (\beta\mathbf{x}) \qquad (3)$$

(distributive law, scalar addition over scalar multiplication)

This is a dual law to the law of Fig. 1.13—the roles of the vectors and scalars are reversed. Notice, too, that the addition on the left-hand side is of scalars, and that on the right-hand side is of vectors. The reader is left to draw diagrams to demonstrate two further laws, namely:

the commutative law $\mathbf{a} + \mathbf{b} = \mathbf{b} + \mathbf{a}$ (4)

and

the associative law $(\mathbf{a} + \mathbf{b}) + \mathbf{c} = \mathbf{a} + (\mathbf{b} + \mathbf{c})$ (5)

These five laws enable us to deal with expressions involving vector or scalar sums and scalar multiples. For example, they will show us that it is true to say that

$$(2\mathbf{x} + 3\mathbf{y}) + (5\mathbf{x} + 7\mathbf{y}) = 7\mathbf{x} + 10\mathbf{y}$$

and

$$4(5\mathbf{x} + 6\mathbf{y}) = 20\mathbf{x} + 24\mathbf{y}.$$

Earlier, we defined the negative vector $(-\mathbf{a})$, so that $\mathbf{a} + (-\mathbf{a}) = (-\mathbf{a}) + \mathbf{a} = \mathbf{0}$. We use this, and the above laws, to show how we subtract vectors.

Take law (3), with $\alpha = 1$ and $\beta = -1$. In other words, $0\mathbf{x} = 1\mathbf{x} + (-1)\mathbf{x}$. Now, from our definitions, $0\mathbf{x} = \mathbf{0}$ and $1\mathbf{x} = \mathbf{x}$ (§1.6). Therefore

$$\mathbf{0} = \mathbf{x} + (-1)\mathbf{x}$$

and so

$$(-1)\mathbf{x} = (-\mathbf{x})$$

We now define vector subtraction by the equations

$$\mathbf{x} - \mathbf{y} = \mathbf{x} + (-\mathbf{y}) = \mathbf{x} + (-1)\mathbf{y}$$

In other words, subtracting the vector **y** from the vector **x** is the same as adding the negative vector $(-\mathbf{y}) = (-1)\mathbf{y}$.

## 1.8 Worked example

### Worked Example 1.2

$\overrightarrow{OP}$ is a position vector of length 4 m, and $\overrightarrow{OQ}$ is a position vector of length 5·2 m, at 60° to $\overrightarrow{OP}$. Find the length of the sum of these position vectors.

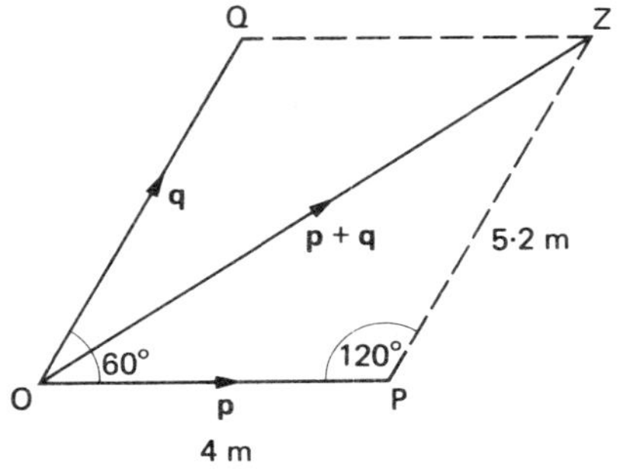


**Fig. 1.15.**

*Solution (i)*

By calculation, using Fig. 1.15. Using the cosine rule,

$$OZ^2 = OP^2 + OQ^2 - 2 \times OP \times OQ \times \cos(\angle OPZ)$$

Therefore

$$\begin{aligned} OZ^2 &= 4^2 + 5{\cdot}2^2 - 2 \times 4 \times 5{\cdot}2 \times \cos 120^\circ \\ &= 16 + 27{\cdot}04 + 20{\cdot}8 \text{ (since } \cos 120^\circ = -\tfrac{1}{2}) \\ &= 63{\cdot}82 \end{aligned}$$

Therefore $OZ = |\mathbf{p} + \mathbf{q}| = \sqrt{63{\cdot}82} = 7{\cdot}988 \approx 7{\cdot}99$ m (3S).

*Solution (ii)*

By scale drawing, based on Fig. 1.15. In order to find the length of the vector $\mathbf{p} + \mathbf{q}$, we draw to scale Fig. 1.15. To obtain reasonable accuracy, we select a scale that gives us a fairly large diagram, such as 20 mm to represent 1 m. Such a scale drawing gives $|\mathbf{p} + \mathbf{q}| = 8{\cdot}0$ m.

**Exercise 1*b***

1. $\overrightarrow{OA}$ is a position vector of length 35 mm, and $\overrightarrow{OB}$ is a position vector at right angles to $\overrightarrow{OA}$, having length 25 mm. Find the length of the sum of these position vectors.

2. $\mathbf{a}$ is a position vector of length 40 mm, and $\mathbf{b}$ is a position vector of length 30 mm. If $\mathbf{a}$ and $\mathbf{b}$ have the same direction, find the two possible lengths of each of $\mathbf{a} + \mathbf{b}$, $\mathbf{a} - \mathbf{b}$, and $2\mathbf{a} + 3\mathbf{b}$.

3. Referred to rectangular axes Ox, Oy, the point A has coordinates (2, 3), B (4, −1) and C (2, 2). $\mathbf{u}$ and $\mathbf{v}$ are free vector families determined by $\overrightarrow{AB}$ and $\overrightarrow{BC}$ respectively. Find the lengths of $\mathbf{u} + \mathbf{v}$, $\mathbf{u} - \mathbf{v}$ and $2\mathbf{u} + 3\mathbf{v}$.

## 1.9 Vector quantities and vectors

We may now return to the problem specified at the beginning of the chapter (see §1.2). This concerned a boat, drifting powerless in an endless ocean, with its movement influenced only by a current flowing due south, and a wind blowing from the east. We now show how our vectors may be used as a mathematical model for this situation, and for similar situations.

The wind and the current may each be represented by free vector families, say **w** and **c** respectively. This is because both the wind and the current have magnitude, direction and sense, the three properties shared by members of free vector families. In particular, **w** will represent the wind in magnitude (the length of **w** representing the speed of the wind), in direction (the north–south great circle), and sense (south rather than north). We then claim that the actual motion of the boat will be represented by the vector sum **w** + **c**, as in Fig. 1.16. This is also called the *resultant velocity*. In this problem, we have used free vectors as a model for velocities. We call anything that may be represented by a vector a *vector quantity*. Thus velocity is a vector quantity, and, in the above example, **w**, **c** and **w** + **c** are vectors representing velocity.

We will now complete the solution of this problem, before discussing other vector quantities. Suppose that the current's speed if $0{\cdot}5\ \text{m s}^{-1}$, and that the wind speed is $3{\cdot}5\ \text{m s}^{-1}$. Using the usual abbreviations,

$$\begin{aligned}|\mathbf{w} + \mathbf{c}|^2 &= w^2 + c^2 \text{ (since } \mathbf{w} \text{ and } \mathbf{c} \text{ are perpendicular)}\\ &= 0{\cdot}5^2 + 3{\cdot}5^2\\ &= 12{\cdot}50\end{aligned}$$

Therefore $|\mathbf{w} + \mathbf{c}| = 3{\cdot}536 \approx 3{\cdot}54\ \text{m s}^{-1}$. Also $\theta = \arctan(0{\cdot}5/3{\cdot}5) = 8{\cdot}1° \approx 8°$. The problem could also be solved by scale drawing.

Among other physical quantities that may be represented by vectors are force, displacement, acceleration and momentum, all of which share the attributes of magnitude, direction and sense with free vectors. It is important, too, that, if **a** and **b** are vectors representing some particular type of vector quantity, then **a** + **b** should represent the same type of vector quantity. This was so in the case of the boat—**w** and **c** both represented the same types of vector quantity, velocity, and we made sure that **w** + **c** would also represent a velocity.

To demonstrate that forces may be represented by vectors, and that combination of two forces may be represented by vector addition we use an experimental example. Take an object and place it on the floor. Attach it to the wall with a spring balance, and pull on it in two different directions with two more spring balances.

The forces pulling on the object may be represented by free vectors $\mathbf{F}_1$ and $\mathbf{F}_2$.

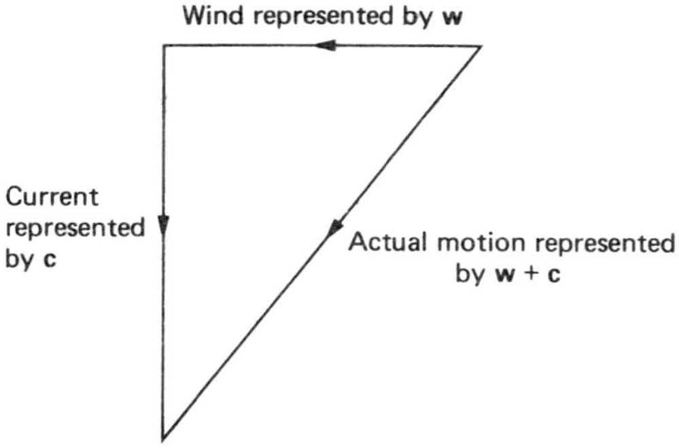


**Fig. 1.16.** A boat drifting in an endless ocean.

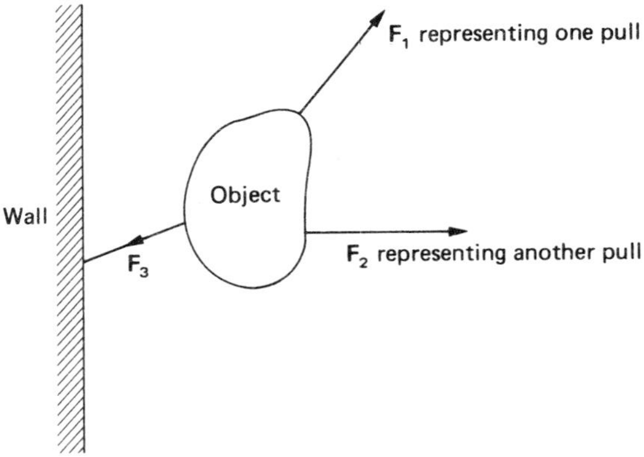


**Fig. 1.17.** An object being pulled by two spring balances against a third.

They will combine to produce a pull on the wall through the third balance. The combined pull is represented by $(-\mathbf{F}_3)$ in Fig. 1.18, with $\mathbf{F}_3$ representing the pull of the wall against the attempts to move the object. Then we claim that $(-\mathbf{F}_3) = \mathbf{F}_1 + \mathbf{F}_2$—the combined pull is represented by the sum of the vectors representing the individual pulls.

These two examples—the boat and the forces—are intended to show that the set $V_3$ of free vectors $\mathbf{v}$ can be used as a mathematical model for *mechanics*—broadly speaking, the mathematics of motion.

## 1.10 Angle

We have already mentioned angles in connection with vectors and vector quantities—the boat in our example drifted on a line 8° south of west, for example. This description fixes the direction of drift exactly, but only relative to some fixed direction (west in this case). This is how we can give a numerical meaning to the direction of a vector.

Suppose we want to describe the direction of the vector $\mathbf{r}$, or its corresponding unit vector $\hat{\mathbf{r}}$. Then we fix some particular direction in space, say by some known free vector family $\mathbf{a}$ with unit vector $\hat{\mathbf{a}}$ (see Fig. 1.19). We then give all other directions relative to $\hat{\mathbf{a}}$. The direction of $\hat{\mathbf{r}}$ is then given by the angle $\theta$ between $\hat{\mathbf{a}}$ and $\hat{\mathbf{r}}$, measured anticlockwise from $\hat{\mathbf{a}}$ to $\hat{\mathbf{r}}$.

In a plane, this angle becomes the polar coordinate angle $\theta$ (measured anti-

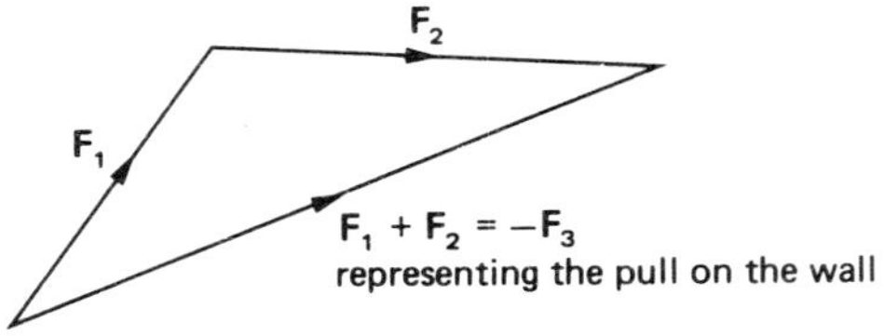


**Fig. 1.18.** Vector representation of Fig. 1.17.

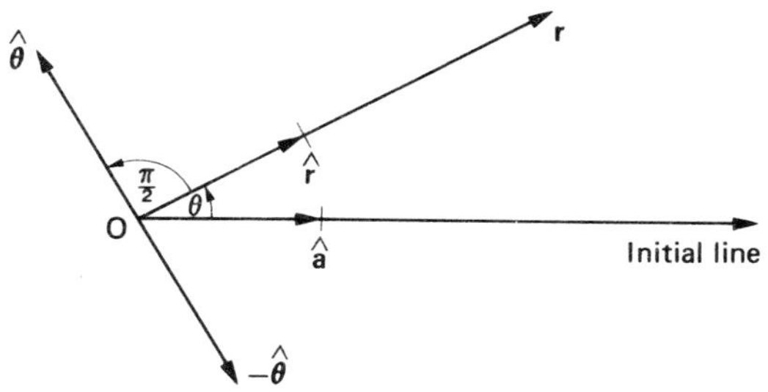


**Fig. 1.19.** The direction of **r**.

clockwise) between the initial line, which is determined by $\hat{\mathbf{a}}$, and the radius vector **r**. The length of **r** is then the other polar coordinate **r**. Sometimes it is useful to define *the* unit vector $\hat{\boldsymbol{\theta}}$ perpendicular to $\hat{\mathbf{r}}$ as that which makes angle $\theta + \frac{1}{2}\pi$ with $\hat{\mathbf{a}}$. This avoids ambiguity with the other perpendicular unit vector $-\hat{\boldsymbol{\theta}}$.

## 1.11 Applications

### Worked Example 1.3

The vector **x** represents a displacement of 3 km on a bearing of 040°, and the vector **y** represents a displacement of 5 km on a bearing of 310°. Find the magnitude and direction of the displacement represented by **x** − 2**y**.

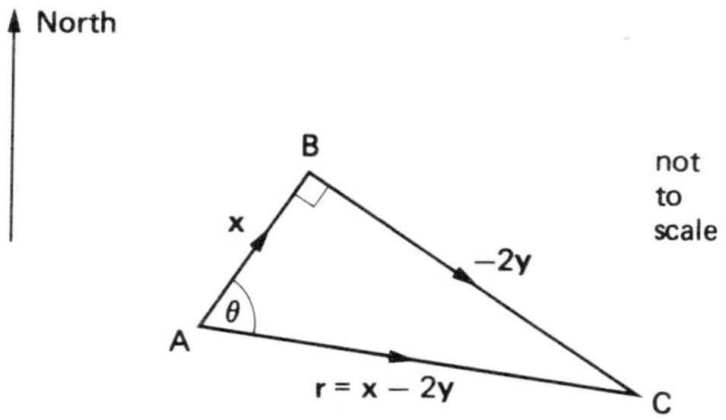


**Fig. 1.20.** The vector sum **r** = **x** − 2**y**.

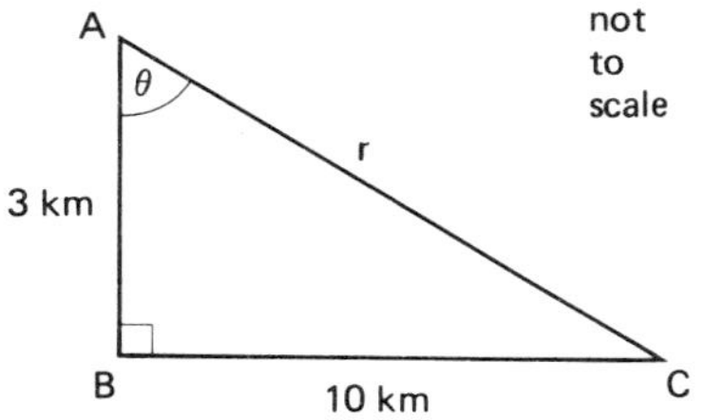


**Fig. 1.21.** The distances represented by **x**, −2**y** and **r** = **x** − 2**y**.

*Solution*

We have drawn two diagrams, one representing the vector sum $\mathbf{x} + (-2\mathbf{y}) = \mathbf{r}$, and the second showing the magnitudes of the displacements represented by the vectors. We have drawn the second diagram with a more convenient orientation—there is no reason why the triangles in the diagrams should be 'the same way up'. Notice that we have used $r$ as the distance represented by $\mathbf{r} = \mathbf{x} - 2\mathbf{y}$, rather than the length of $\mathbf{r}$ itself.

Using Pythagoras' theorem,

$$r^2 = 3^2 + 10^2 = 109$$

and so

$$r = 10{\cdot}4 \text{ km}$$

the negative square root being inadmissible. Also

$$\tan \theta = 10/3$$

and so

$$\theta = 73{\cdot}3°$$

Hence $\mathbf{x} - 2\mathbf{y}$ represents a displacement of 10·4 km on a bearing of 113·3°.

**Worked Example 1.4**

A pilot sets out to fly from London to Manchester and wishes to set a course to combat an easterly wind. The aircraft can fly at 800 km h$^{-1}$ in still air, and the wind speed is 32 km h$^{-1}$. Manchester is 256 km from London on a bearing of 330°. On what course must the aircraft be set?

*Solution*

The speed at which the aircraft can fly in still air is called its *air speed*, which we represent by the vector $\mathbf{v}_a$ in the direction of the *course*, which is the course set by the pilot. The velocity of the wind is represented by the vector $\mathbf{w}$. The speed at which the aircraft actually travels over the ground is called its *ground speed*, and is represented by the vector $\mathbf{v}_g$ in the direction of the actual travel of the aircraft, called its *track*.

We use the property $\mathbf{v}_a + \mathbf{w} = \mathbf{v}_g$. We again draw two diagrams, one representing the vector addition $\mathbf{v}_a + \mathbf{w} = \mathbf{v}_g$ and the second showing the speeds that the three vectors represent (see Fig. 1.22).

Using the sine rule,

$$\frac{\sin(30° - \theta)}{32} = \frac{\sin 60°}{800}$$

Hence

$$30° - \theta = 2{\cdot}0°$$

and so

$$\theta = 28{\cdot}0° \text{ and } 90° + \theta = 118{\cdot}0°$$

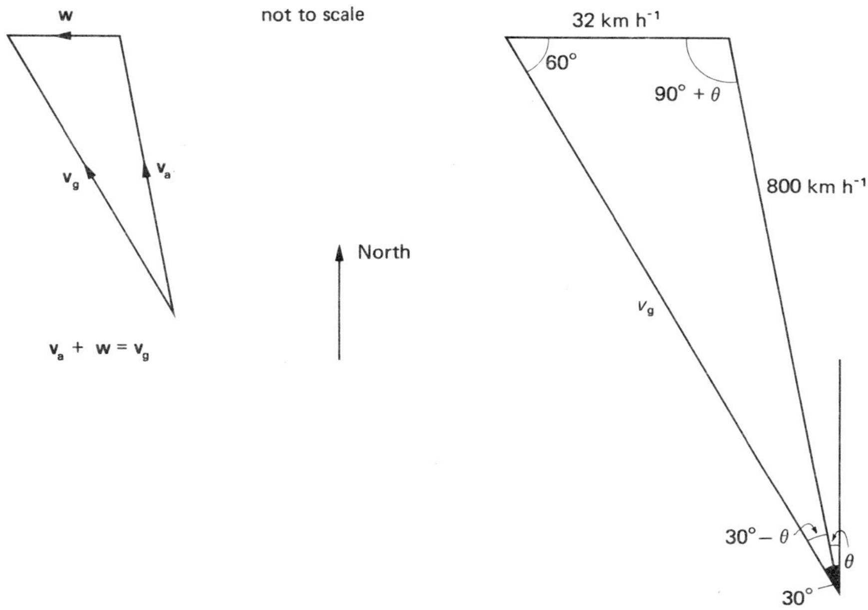


**Fig. 1.22.** An aircraft flying from London to Manchester.

Using the sine rule,

$$\frac{v_g}{\sin 118{\cdot}0^\circ} = \frac{800}{\sin 60^\circ}$$

Hence

$$v_g = \frac{800 \sin 62{\cdot}0^\circ}{\sin 60^\circ} \text{(since } \sin 118{\cdot}0^\circ = \sin 62{\cdot}0^\circ\text{)}$$

and so

$$v_g = 816 \text{ km h}^{-1}$$

Hence the aircraft must set a course of 332·0°, and the speed with which it travels is 816 km h$^{-1}$.

### Worked Example 1.5

A man wishes to swim across a river of width $a$, with straight parallel banks. He can swim at speed $u$ in still water, and there is a current of speed $v$ flowing parallel to the banks.

(i) Find how far downstream he lands if he swims at right angles to the banks.

(ii) Find the direction in which he must swim if he wishes to swim the shortest distance to the opposite bank.

(iii) Find the times taken for the two parts of his journey if he swims at right angles to the bank until he is halfway across, and then turns to swim so that he lands directly opposite his starting point.

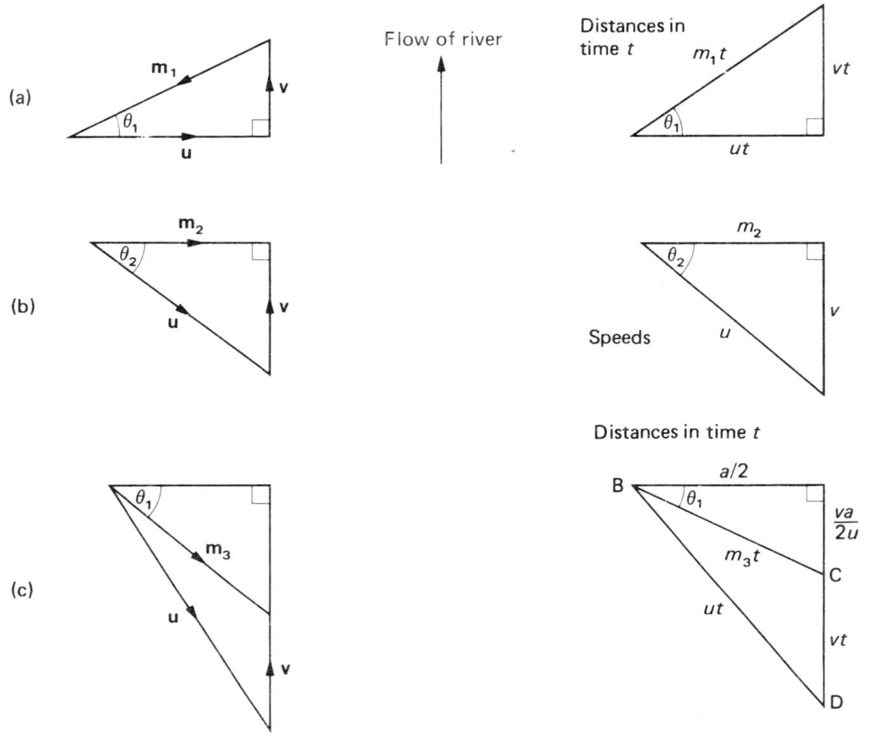


**Fig. 1.23.** Worked example 1.5.

*Solution*

(i) See Fig. 1.23(a). Suppose the velocity of the man is represented by $\mathbf{m}_1$, as shown. In time $t$, the man travels distance $ut$ across and $vt$ down stream. In time $a/u$, he travels distance $u \times a/u = a$ across and $v \times a/u$ downstream. Therefore he lands at a distance $va/u$ downstream.

(ii) See Fig. 1.23(b). Suppose the velocity of the man is represented by $\mathbf{m}_2$, as shown. From the diagram, $\sin \theta_2 = v/u$ and also $v < u$. Therefore the man swims upstream at an angle $\arcsin (v/u)$ to the direction in which he wishes to travel, and faces an impossible task unless $v < u$.

(iii) For the first half-width, the problem is almost as in (i), and we may use Fig. 1.23(a) again. Suppose that the velocity of the man is represented by $\mathbf{m}_1$, as shown. Now, the man will complete a half-width in time $\frac{1}{2}u/a$, after which he will be a distance $\frac{1}{2}va/u$ downstream from his starting point. He will have travelled at an angle $\theta_1 = \arctan (v/u)$ to the shortest crossing.

For the second half-width, see Fig. 1.23(c). Suppose the velocity of the man is represented by $\mathbf{m}_3$, as shown and he takes time $t$ to complete his crossing. Then the distances involved are shown in the second diagram, where he is in the middle of the river at B, wishing to reach C. Since angle BCD is obtuse, it is necessary that $u > v$.

Using Pythagoras' theorem,

$$(ut)^2 = (\tfrac{1}{2}a)^2 + [vt + (va/2u)]^2$$

Therefore

$$0 = \tfrac{1}{4}a^2 + v^2t^2 + 2 \times vt \times \frac{va}{2u} + \frac{v^2a^2}{4u^2} - u^2t^2$$

Hence

$$0 = (v^2 - u^2)t^2 + \frac{v^2a}{u}t + \tfrac{1}{4}a^2 + \tfrac{1}{4}a^2\left(\frac{v^2}{u^2}\right)$$

Therefore

$$(u^2 - v^2)t^2 - \frac{v^2a}{u}t - \frac{a^2}{4u^2}(u^2 + v^2) = 0$$

and so

$$\left((u^2 - v^2)t - \frac{a(u^2 + v^2)}{2u}\right)\left(t + \frac{a}{2u}\right) = 0$$

Hence

$$t = \frac{a(u^2 + v^2)}{2u(u^2 - v^2)}(u > v)$$

since the time $t$ cannot take the negative value $-a/2u$. Hence the time taken for the whole crossing is

$$\frac{a}{2u} + \frac{a(u^2 + v^2)}{2u(u^2 - v^2)} = \frac{2au}{u^2 - v^2} \qquad (13.12)$$

## 1.12 The triangle inequality

Fig. 1.24 shows how two free vectors **a** and **b** are added to give **a** + **b**. Here, as on many diagrams, the notation **a** on the diagram really means 'a representative of the free vector family **a**'. This diagram demonstrates the *triangle inequality*

$$|\mathbf{a} + \mathbf{b}| \leqq |\mathbf{a}| + |\mathbf{b}| \qquad (1)$$

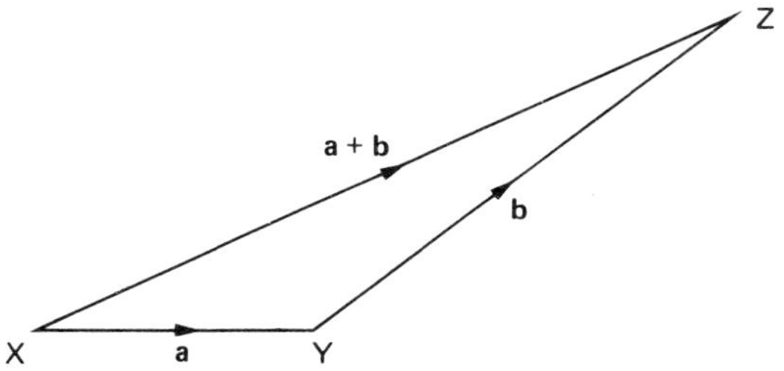


**Fig. 1.24.** The triangle inequality $|\mathbf{a} + \mathbf{b}| \leqq |\mathbf{a}| + |\mathbf{b}|$.

since the length of one side of a triangle (XZ, or $|\mathbf{a} + \mathbf{b}|$) is never greater than the sum of the lengths of the other two sides (XY or $|\mathbf{a}|$, and YZ or $|\mathbf{b}|$).

It is possible for $|\mathbf{a} + \mathbf{b}|$ and $|\mathbf{a}| + |\mathbf{b}|$ to be equal, and this happens when **a** and **b** are in the same direction and sense, or when one of **a** and **b** is the zero vector. In other words, equality occurs if and only if $\lambda\mathbf{a} = \mu\mathbf{b}$ for scalars $\lambda$ and $\mu$. Fig. 1.25 shows one possible case for equality, when neither **a** nor **b** is the zero vector.

If $\mathbf{a} = \mathbf{0}$, then we may take $\mu = 0$, since $\lambda\mathbf{0} = 0\mathbf{b}$. Similarly, if $\mathbf{b} = \mathbf{0}$, then we may take $\lambda = 0$, since $0\mathbf{a} = \mu\mathbf{0}$.

In Equ. (1), suppose that $\mathbf{a} = \mathbf{c} - \mathbf{d}$, and $\mathbf{b} = \mathbf{d}$. Then

$$|\mathbf{a} + \mathbf{b}| = |(\mathbf{c} - \mathbf{d}) + \mathbf{d}| = |\mathbf{c}|$$

and

$$|\mathbf{a}| = |\mathbf{c} - \mathbf{d}|$$

and

$$|\mathbf{b}| = |\mathbf{d}|$$

Therefore Equ. (1) gives

$$|\mathbf{c}| \leqq |\mathbf{c} - \mathbf{d}| + |\mathbf{d}|$$

and so

$$|\mathbf{c} - \mathbf{d}| \geqq |\mathbf{c}| - |\mathbf{d}|$$

Similarly, we may show

$$|\mathbf{d} - \mathbf{c}| \geqq |\mathbf{d}| - |\mathbf{c}|$$

But $|\mathbf{c} - \mathbf{d}| = |\mathbf{d} - \mathbf{c}|$, since $\mathbf{c} - \mathbf{d}$ and $\mathbf{d} - \mathbf{c}$ have the same direction and length. Therefore $|\mathbf{c} - \mathbf{d}|$ is greater than or equal to both of $|\mathbf{c}| - |\mathbf{d}|$ and $-(|\mathbf{c}| - |\mathbf{d}|)$. We may combine these by saying

$$\Big| |\mathbf{c}| - |\mathbf{d}| \Big| \leqq |\mathbf{c} - \mathbf{d}| \tag{2}$$

It must be emphasized that the measurement of length, and the ensuing results such as the inequalities above, are properties *extra* to those of the vector space. There are vector spaces in which length is not measured (and in which the definition of $\alpha\mathbf{v}$ also does not depend on the comparison of lengths). In a given vector space length may be defined in a number of different ways.

**Fig. 1.25.** An exceptional case $|\mathbf{a} + \mathbf{b}| = |\mathbf{a}| + |\mathbf{b}|$

## Exercise 1*c*

Many of these questions can be solved by using scale drawing, but you should answer some of them by calculation. In general, be very careful concerning the accuracy obtainable by scale drawing.

1. If **x** represents a displacement of 3 m due east, and **y** represents a displacement

of 4 m due north, find the magnitude and direction of each of the following, either by calculation or by scale drawing:
(a) $\mathbf{x} + \mathbf{y}$, (b) $\mathbf{x} - \mathbf{y}$, (c) $2\mathbf{x} + 3\mathbf{y}$, (d) $3\mathbf{x} - 4\mathbf{y}$.

2. If $\hat{\mathbf{i}}$ represents a velocity of 1 m $s^{-1}$ due east, and $\hat{\mathbf{j}}$ represents a velocity of 1 m $s^{-1}$ due north, find the magnitude and direction of each of the following:
(a) $\hat{\mathbf{i}} + \hat{\mathbf{j}}$, (b) $2\hat{\mathbf{i}} + 3\hat{\mathbf{j}}$, (c) $3\hat{\mathbf{i}} - 5\hat{\mathbf{j}}$, (d) $2\hat{\mathbf{i}} - 3\hat{\mathbf{j}}$.

3. Find, the terms of $\hat{\mathbf{i}}$ and $\hat{\mathbf{j}}$ (see question 2), position vectors to describe the points with the given polar coordinates $(r, \theta)$:
(a) $(2, 40°)$, (b) $(2, \pi \text{ rad})$, (c) $(4, 2\pi/3 \text{ rad})$.

4. If $\hat{\mathbf{i}}$, $\hat{\mathbf{j}}$ and $\hat{\mathbf{k}}$ represent displacements of 1 m east, north and vertically upwards, respectively, find the magnitude of each of:
(a) $\hat{\mathbf{i}} + \hat{\mathbf{j}} + \hat{\mathbf{k}}$, (b) $3\hat{\mathbf{i}} + 4\hat{\mathbf{j}} + 5\hat{\mathbf{k}}$,
(c) $2\hat{\mathbf{i}} - 3\hat{\mathbf{j}} + 4\hat{\mathbf{k}}$, (d) $\hat{\mathbf{i}} - \hat{\mathbf{j}} + 2\hat{\mathbf{k}}$.

5. If $\mathbf{u}$ represents a momentum of 2 kg m $s^{-1}$ on a bearing 045°, and $\mathbf{v}$ represents a momentum of 3 kg m $s^{-1}$ due east, find the magnitude and direction of each of:
(a) $\mathbf{u} - \mathbf{v}$, (b) $2\mathbf{u} + 3\mathbf{v}$, (c) $-\mathbf{u} + 2\mathbf{v}$.

6. A helicopter whose air speed is 100 km $h^{-1}$ flies from a point A to a point B due west of A. A steady wind of 30 km $h^{-1}$ is blowing from the north west. By drawing or calculation, find the resultant velocity of the helicopter. (C)

The helicopter returns from B to A while the same wind is blowing. Find the resultant velocity of the helicopter for the return journey.

7. A motor-boat is steered due north and has a speed of 12 km $h^{-1}$ through the water, in which there is a tide of 5 km $h^{-1}$ running from east to west. Obtain by calculation the direction in which the boat travels and the time the boat will take to travel 6·5 km in this direction. (MEI)

8. A river with straight parallel banks is $\frac{1}{4}$ km wide. The current is flowing at 3 km $h^{-1}$, and a swimmer can swim at 5 km $h^{-1}$ in still water. Find, by drawing or by calculation:
(a) The least time in which the swimmer can reach the opposite bank.
(b) The time taken to swim from a point on one bank to the nearest point on the opposite bank. (C)

9. A river flows at $1\frac{1}{2}$ km $h^{-1}$. Two swimmers, X and Y, each of whom swims at $2\frac{1}{2}$ km $h^{-1}$ in still water, start from the same point on one bank, where the river is straight and is $\frac{1}{8}$ km wide. X swims in such a direction that he actually moves at right angles to the current, but Y swims in the direction by which he will reach the opposite bank in the shortest possible time. Find: (i) the direction in which X is headed and the direction in which Y actually travels; (ii) how much longer X takes than Y to reach the opposite bank. (MEI)

## 1.13 Bound vectors

We have considered the set $V_3$ of free vectors, and the set $P_3$ of position vectors. We meet, and discuss further, in Chapter 5, the set $R^3$ of component vectors. There are a few other types of vector which we meet in practice, and we will define them in the coming sections.

Take two position vectors $\overrightarrow{OP}$ (or $\mathbf{p}$) and $\overrightarrow{OQ}$ (or $\mathbf{q}$). Then the line segment PQ is called a *bound vector*, which we will denote by **PQ**. In Fig. 1.26, **PQ** and **RS** are two bound vectors. Since these two bound vectors are neither position vectors, nor in this context regarded as representatives of free vector families, we cannot add them by

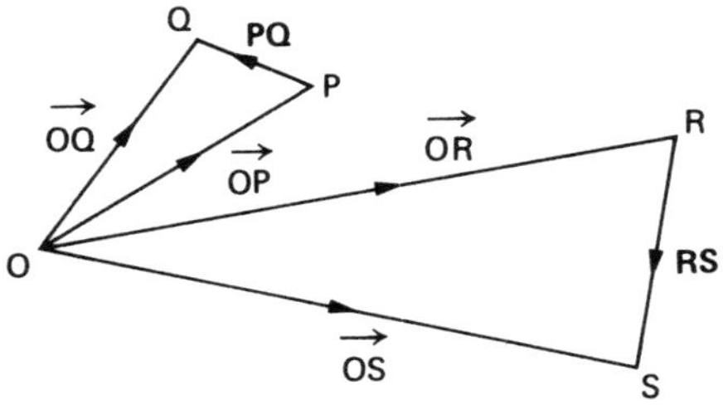


**Fig. 1.26.** Bound vectors **PQ** and **RS**.

any of the laws we have met so far. There are special circumstances under which we are able to add bound vectors. For example, suppose that we have two bound vectors **XY** and **YZ**, as in Fig. 1.27. Then we say that **XY** + **YZ** = **XZ**, which conforms with the definition of the addition of the free vector families defined by $\overrightarrow{XY}$ and $\overrightarrow{YZ}$.

Thus, we can only add the bound vectors **PQ** and **RS** if Q and R are the same point, in which case **PQ** + **QS** = **PS**. In practice, we rarely use bound vectors, but relax the definition to use the more useful localized line vectors (see §1.14).

However, there are circumstances in which we *must* use bound vectors, which are restrictive because their location in space is fixed exactly by their end-points.

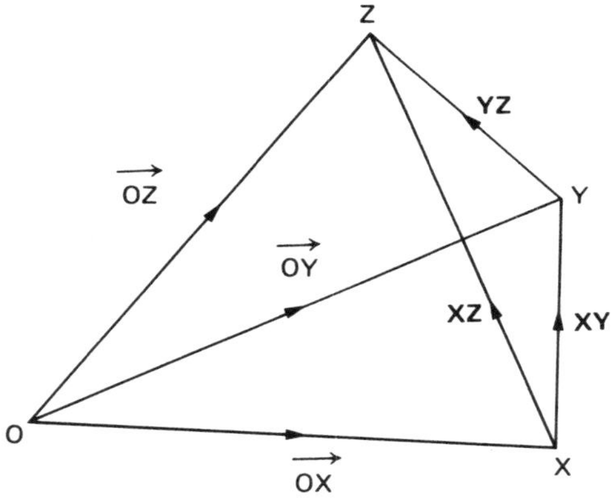


**Fig. 1.27.** **XZ** = **XY** + **YZ**.

## 1.14 Localized line vectors

Take the free vector family **v**, and a bound vector **PQ** such that $\overrightarrow{PQ} \in \mathbf{v}$. Consider the subset of **v** containing all those free vectors lying in the line $\overleftrightarrow{PQ}$ (i.e. the infinite line of which PQ is part). This subset is called a *localized line vector family*, and has a *line of action* $\overleftrightarrow{PQ}$ as well as magnitude, direction and sense. We will denote this family by **PQ**. Then the length |**PQ**| of **PQ** is defined to be the length $|\overrightarrow{PQ}|$ of the free vector $\overrightarrow{PQ}$.

Localized line vectors occur as part of the mechanics we are modelling with

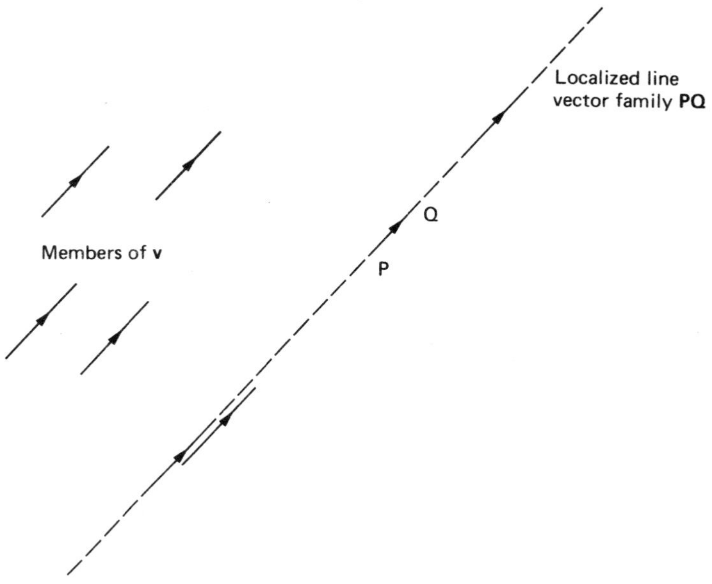


**Fig. 1.28.** The localized line vector family **PQ** defined by **PQ** $\in$ **v**.

vectors. A single force acting on a body will pull it across the floor in a straight line—the force can be represented by a localized line vector, and the line is its line of action. We use this representation to help use define addition of localized line vectors to be analogous to combination of forces on a body.

We consider the addition of localized line vectors in two dimensions only. Imagine we are pulling a sack on level ice with two forces which may be represented by localized line vectors. We want to know the combined effect of the forces we apply. We consider separately the cases when the two forces are: (i) not parallel; and (ii) parallel.

(i) Suppose we apply two forces which are not parallel, and represent them by the localized line vectors **PQ** and **RS**.

In Fig. 1.29, the force represented by **RS** is greater than that represented by **PQ**. Hence we expect the sack to move off in a direction between the directions of **PQ** and **RS**, and nearer to the direction of **RS**. That direction will be given by some line $\overleftrightarrow{TU}$, where T is the point of intersection of the lines $\overleftrightarrow{PQ}$ and $\overleftrightarrow{RS}$. We claim, too, that $\overleftrightarrow{TU}$ will be the line of action of the combined force. To find the magnitude of the combined force, we add the two vectors as if they were free vectors. Thus we take $\overrightarrow{TA}$ equivalent to $\overrightarrow{PQ}$, and $\overrightarrow{AU}$ equivalent to $\overrightarrow{RS}$, and add them by the triangle law to obtain $\overrightarrow{TU}$. We then define the localized line vector family **PQ** + **RS** to be **TU**, determined by the free vector $\overrightarrow{TU}$ just obtained.

To summarize, we add localized line vectors almost as if they were free vectors. We find the line of action of the sum by finding the intersection of the lines of action of the two vectors we are adding.

Many of the applications of localized line vectors that we meet will be described in terms of Cartesian coordinates, and lend themselves to algebraic solution. Such an application is given in the following example.

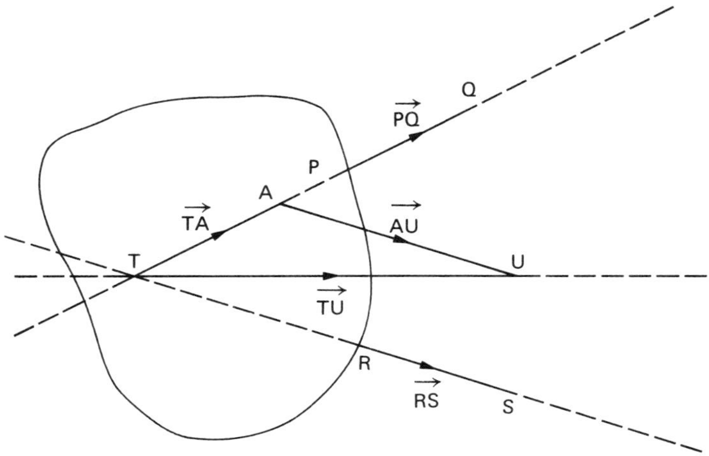


**Fig. 1.29.** **PQ** + **RS** = **TU**.

### Worked Example 1.6

P, Q, R and S are the points with rectangular Cartesian coordinates (3, 4), (5, 5), (4, −1) and (7, −2) respectively. Localized line vectors **PQ** and **RS** are defined by $\overrightarrow{PQ}$ and $\overrightarrow{RS}$. Find their sum.

*Solution*

Suppose, as usual, that $\hat{\mathbf{i}}$ and $\hat{\mathbf{j}}$ are unit vectors in the directions of the $x$ and $y$ axes. Then $\overrightarrow{PQ}$ may be written as $2\hat{\mathbf{i}} + \hat{\mathbf{j}}$. The line of action of **PQ** passes through the point

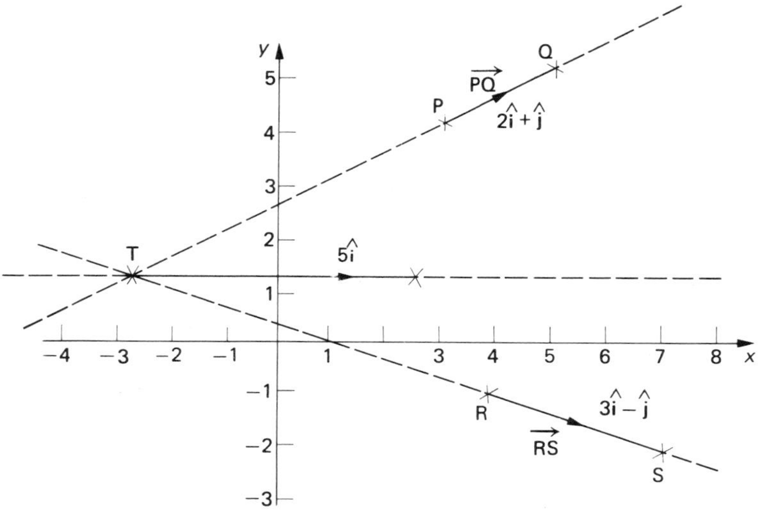


**Fig. 1.30.** Worked example 1.6.

(3, 4). We combine these two, and describe the localized line vector **PQ** as

$$2\hat{\mathbf{i}} + \hat{\mathbf{j}} \text{ acting through } (3, 4)$$

Similarly, **RS** is

$$3\hat{\mathbf{i}} - \hat{\mathbf{j}} \text{ acting through } (4, -1)$$

Adding the free vectors, we obtain $(2\hat{\mathbf{i}} + \hat{\mathbf{j}}) + (3\hat{\mathbf{i}} - \hat{\mathbf{j}}) = 5\hat{\mathbf{i}}$. The lines of action of **PQ** and **RS** have equations

$$y = \tfrac{1}{2}x + 2\tfrac{1}{2} \text{ and } y = -\tfrac{1}{3}x + \tfrac{1}{3}$$

respectively. These meet at the point T with coordinates $(-2{\cdot}6,\ 1{\cdot}2)$. Hence **PQ** + **RS** is $5\hat{\mathbf{i}}$ acting through $(-2{\cdot}6,\ 1{\cdot}2)$.

(ii) Now suppose we wish to add two parallel localized line vectors. Clearly, we cannot use quite the same method as above, since the lines of action do not meet. Suppose we apply two parallel forces, represented by **PQ** and **RS**. We describe them as follows:

$$\left.\begin{array}{l}\text{suppose } \hat{\mathbf{a}} \text{ is a unit position vector;}\\ \text{that } \overrightarrow{PQ} \text{ is equivalent to } \alpha_1\hat{\mathbf{a}}, \text{ and } \mathbf{PQ} \text{ has line of action } \overleftrightarrow{PQ};\\ \text{that } \overrightarrow{RS} \text{ is equivalent to } \alpha_2\hat{\mathbf{a}}, \text{ and } \mathbf{RS} \text{ has line of action } \overleftrightarrow{RS}.\end{array}\right\} \qquad (1)$$

$\alpha_1$ and $\alpha_2$ may be either positive or negative. Fig. 1.31 shows a situation in which both are positive, and Fig. 1.32 one in which $\alpha_1 > 0 > \alpha_2$.

We may assume the results of (i), and add $\overrightarrow{PQ}$ and $\overrightarrow{RS}$ as free vectors to obtain a vector $\overrightarrow{TU}$ equivalent to $\alpha_1\hat{\mathbf{a}} + \alpha_2\hat{\mathbf{a}} = (\alpha_1 + \alpha_2)\hat{\mathbf{a}}$. We now determine the line of action of this sum, and decide whether or not a single force can replace the given forces.

Take any line ABC perpendicular to the lines of action of the three vectors involved, and suppose it meets $\overleftrightarrow{PQ}$ in A, $\overleftrightarrow{RS}$ in B and $\overleftrightarrow{TU}$ in C. Suppose further that $AC/CB = d_1/d_2$, i.e. C divides AB in the ratio $d_1 : d_2$. In Fig. 1.31, C divides AB internally (since it is between A and B), and this ratio will be positive; but in Fig. 1.32 it will be negative since C divides AB externally. We will see below that the value $-1$

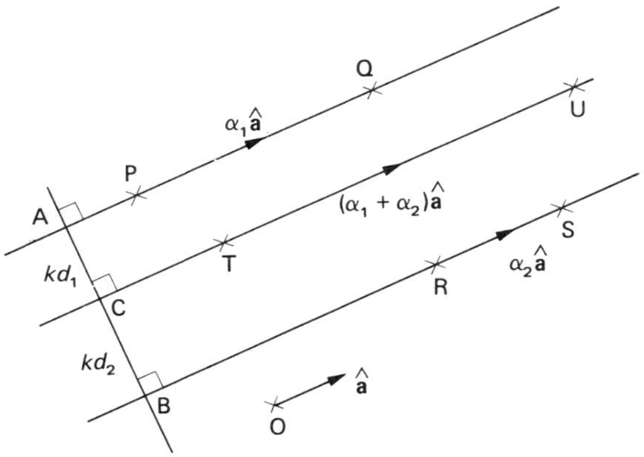


**Fig. 1.31.** Adding parallel localized line vectors $\alpha_1\,\hat{\mathbf{a}}$ and $\alpha_2\,\hat{\mathbf{a}}$ with $\alpha_1$ and $\alpha_2$ both positive.

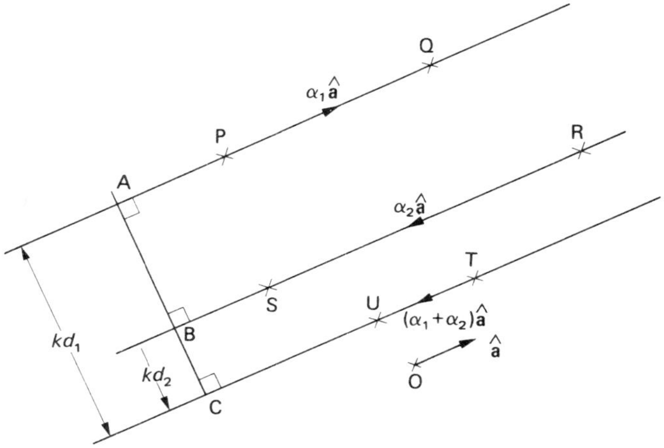


**Fig. 1.32.** Adding parallel localized line vectors $\alpha_1\,\hat{\mathbf{a}}$ and $\alpha_2\,\hat{\mathbf{a}}$ with $\alpha_1 > 0 > \alpha_2$.

of the ratio gives rise to a special case, as there is no finite position of C that gives this ratio.

The moments of the original forces about the point C on $\overleftrightarrow{TU}$ must be equal and opposite, that is to say

$$\alpha_1 d_1 = \alpha_2 d_2 \tag{2}$$

from which we find the ratio $d_1/d_2 = \alpha_2/\alpha_1$, which is indeed positive in the one case ($\alpha_1$ and $\alpha_2$ both positive), and negative in the other ($\alpha_1 > 0 > \alpha_2$). This ratio determines the position of $\overleftrightarrow{TU}$, the line of action of **PQ** + **RS**. The exceptional value of this ratio, namely $-1$, is seen to occur when $\alpha_2/\alpha_1 = -1$, i.e. when $\alpha_2 = -\alpha_1$. In this case, the original forces represented by the localized line vectors are equal and opposite, but differently situated (see Fig. 1.33).

They form what is known as a *couple*; there is no single force equivalent to a couple. The system of forces provides just a rotational effect with no lateral displacement. We meet couples in greater detail in the chapters on forces.

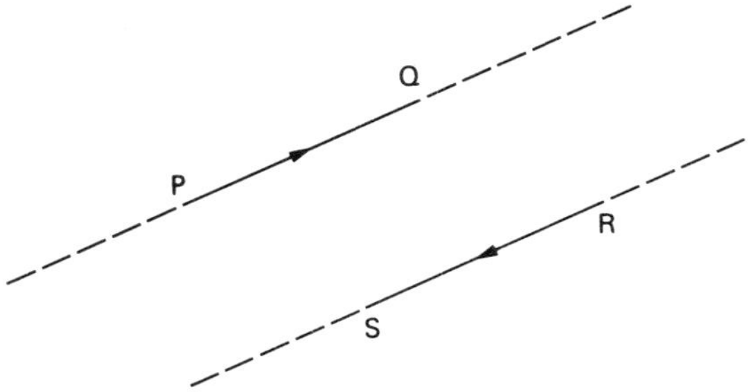


**Fig. 1.33.** Equal and opposite localized line vectors **PQ** and **RS** representing a couple.

**Worked Example 1.7**

Find the sum of the localized line vectors $2\alpha\hat{\mathbf{a}}$ acting through (4, 1) and $(-\alpha)\hat{\mathbf{a}}$ acting through (6, 1), where $\alpha$ is positive and $\hat{\mathbf{a}}$ is a fixed unit vector.

*Solution*

The sum will be $2\alpha\hat{\mathbf{a}} + (-\alpha)\hat{\mathbf{a}} = \alpha\hat{\mathbf{a}}$. Suppose this sum acts through the point T, as shown in Fig. 1.34. Suppose A, B and C are as in the text above, and as shown on the diagram. Then, by considering moments about T, we see that $2\alpha \times AC = (-\alpha) \times BC$, from which we may deduce that A is the mid-point of BC. By the geometrical properties of parallel lines, P is the mid-point of TR, and so T is the point (2, 1).

Thus the required sum is $\alpha\hat{\mathbf{a}}$ acting through (2, 1).

Note that we are unable to say anything about the locations of the points Q, S and U, since, although $\hat{\mathbf{a}}$ is fixed, we do not know its direction.

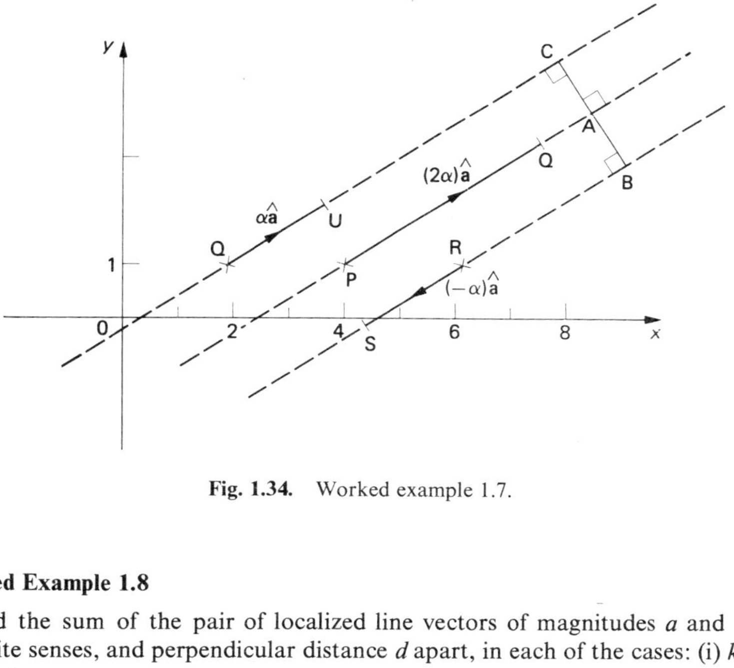


**Fig. 1.34.** Worked example 1.7.

**Worked Example 1.8**

Find the sum of the pair of localized line vectors of magnitudes $a$ and $ka$, in opposite senses, and perpendicular distance $d$ apart, in each of the cases: (i) $k = 3$; (ii) $k = 1$.

*Solution*

(i) See Fig. 1.35. Using the notation of the text, suppose the vector of magnitude $a$ is **PQ**, and the other is **RS**. Then the magnitude of **PQ** + **RS** = TU = $2a - a = a$. **TU** has the direction and sense of **RS**, the longer of the original vectors. Suppose, as in the text, ABC is perpendicular to the lines of action of the vectors **PQ**, **RS** and **TU** and meets them in A, B and C respectively. Let BC = $x$.

Now we know that AC/CB = −3/1, from equation (2).

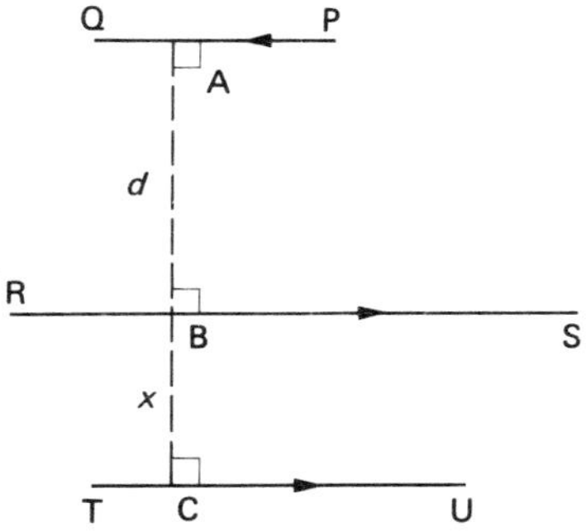


**Fig. 1.35.** Worked example 1.8, part (i).

Therefore

$$\frac{d+x}{-x} = \frac{-3}{1}$$

and so

$$d + x = 3x$$

and so

$$x = \tfrac{1}{2}d$$

which gives the position of $\overleftrightarrow{TU}$ as shown in Fig. 1.35.

(ii) See Fig. 1.36. In this case, the given vectors are equal and opposite—they represent a couple. We do not add them.

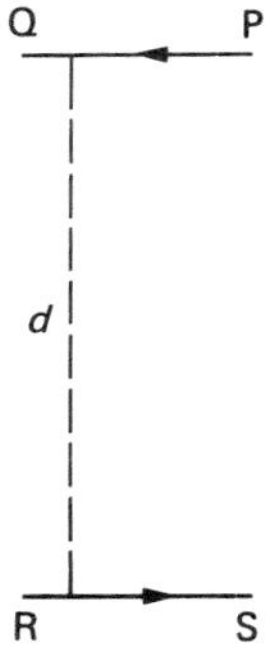


**Fig. 1.36.** Worked example 1.8, part (ii).

**Exercise 1*d***

1. A, B, C and D are the points with rectangular Cartesian coordinates (2, 1), (1, −2), (3, 3) and (2, 0) respectively. Localized line vectors are defined to correspond to free vectors, so that, for example, **AB** is defined by $\overrightarrow{AB}$. Find the follow-

ing sums:

(a) **AB** + **CD**, (b) **AC** + **BD**, (c) **AC** + **AD**.

Give your answers in each of the following forms:

(i) $\alpha\hat{\mathbf{i}} + \beta\hat{\mathbf{j}}$ acting along a line whose equation is given;

(ii) The magnitude of the sum, and the angle between its line of action and the $x$-axis, measured anticlockwise from O$x$.

2. $\hat{\mathbf{a}}$ is a fixed unit vector. **PQ** is equivalent to $2\hat{\mathbf{a}}$ and acts through the point (1, 1); **RS** is equivalent to $3\hat{\mathbf{a}}$ and acts through the point (2, 3); **TU** is equivalent to $4\hat{\mathbf{a}}$ and acts through the point (3, 1). Find the following sums:

(a) **PQ** + **RS**, (b) **RS** + **TU**, (c) **TU** + **PQ**.

3. Find the sums of the following pairs of parallel localized line vectors:

(a) each of magnitude 4, in the same sense, and distance 3 apart;

(b) of magnitude 13 and 5, in the same sense, and distance $d$ apart.

4. Find the sums of the following pairs of localized line vectors:

(a) $\hat{\mathbf{i}} + \hat{\mathbf{j}}$ at (2, 3) and $2\hat{\mathbf{i}} - \hat{\mathbf{j}}$ at (1, 1);

(b) $2\hat{\mathbf{i}} - 3\hat{\mathbf{j}}$ at (1, −1) and $\hat{\mathbf{i}} + 2\hat{\mathbf{j}}$ at (2, 0).

## 1.15 Miscellaneous Exercises 1

1. Referred to rectangular axes O$x$, O$y$, the points A, B and C have coordinates (3, 3), (−2, 5) and (4, −1) respectively. Find the coordinates of the following points:

(i) D, where the position vector **d** is equivalent to the free vector $\overrightarrow{AB}$.

(ii) E, where the free vector $\overrightarrow{AE}$ is equivalent to $\overrightarrow{AB} + \overrightarrow{CB}$.

(iii) F, where the position vector **f** is equivalent to $\overrightarrow{AB} - \overrightarrow{AC}$.

2. (i) Simplify $(2\mathbf{x} + \mathbf{y}) - (\mathbf{x} - 2\mathbf{y})$. (ii) Referred to rectangular axes O$x$, O$y$, the points A and B have coordinates (3, 1) and (1, 2) respectively. Find the length of the vector $(2\,\overrightarrow{OA} + \overrightarrow{OB}) - (\overrightarrow{OA} - 2\overrightarrow{OB})$, and the angle it makes with the $x$- axis.

3. If **a** represents a force of 3 N on a bearing of 040°, and **b** represents a force of 4 N on a bearing of 100°, find the magnitude and direction of each of the forces represented by: (i) **a** − **b**, (ii) **b** − **a**.

4. The velocity of a particle is compounded of two velocities **u** and **v** at an angle $\alpha$. Their resultant is unchanged in *magnitude* if **u** and **v** become $a\mathbf{u}$ and $a^{-1}\mathbf{v}$ without change of direction, where $a > 1$. Show that $a\mathbf{u} = \mathbf{v}$.

Show further that the tangent of the angle between the two resultants in the two cases is

$$\frac{(a - a^{-1})\sin\alpha}{2 + (a + a^{-1})\cos\alpha}$$ (MEI)

5. Using rectangular axes O$x$, O$y$, mark the points A (4, 2) and B (2, −1). Two forces **P**, **Q** are represented in magnitude, direction and line of action by the lines OA, OB, the length of a unit of coordinates representing one newton. Construct the line representing the resultant **R** of the forces **P** and **Q**.

Another force **S** is represented by the line AC, where C is the point (6, 5). State the coordinates of the point where **S** meets **R**. Now construct a line representing in magnitude and direction the resultant of the three forces **P**, **Q** and **S**. State the magnitude of the resultant and the tangent of the angle it makes with the $x$-axis. (MEI)

6. OABCDE is a regular hexagon and $\overrightarrow{OA} = \mathbf{a}$, $\overrightarrow{OB} = \mathbf{b}$. Show that $\overrightarrow{OC} = 2\mathbf{b} - 2\mathbf{a}$ and find $\overrightarrow{OD}$ and $\overrightarrow{OE}$ in terms of **a** and **b**. (L)

7. The angle between the vectors **a** and **b** is 60°. Given that $|\mathbf{a}| = |\mathbf{b}| = 1$, calculate: (i) $|\mathbf{b} - \mathbf{a}|$; (ii) $|\mathbf{b} + \mathbf{a}|$. (C)

8. (i) An aircraft, which can fly at 320 km $h^{-1}$ in still air, sets a course due north. The wind is blowing at 64 km $h^{-1}$ from the south. Find the time taken for the aircraft to fly $x$ km.

The aircraft now turns round and flies back to its starting point. Given that the aircraft initially had sufficient fuel for ten hours flying time, find the greatest possible value of $x$.

(ii) In a wind blowing from the south-east, another aircraft sets a course so that its track is due north. Given that its air speed is ten times the wind speed, calculate the bearing of the course. (C)

# 2
# Linear Combinations and Column Vectors

## Introduction

This chapter like Chapter 1, has its difficult parts, most of which are at the beginning. We therefore recommend that, as in Chapter 1, you read through the whole chapter before you attempt a detailed study of any part. You will then see that the early sections provide fairly abstract arguments and justifications for the definitions which we use in the relatively concrete applications in the later sections. Thus you may like to direct your early energies into a detailed study of column vectors, and return to the arguments of the earlier sections later.

## 2.1 Linear combinations

In Chapter 1, we saw how to add two vectors, and how to form scalar multiples of a vector. We also saw how to evaluate expressions like $(\alpha\mathbf{a} + \beta\mathbf{b}) + (\gamma\mathbf{a} + \delta\mathbf{b})$, where **a** and **b** are both either free vectors or position vectors. Such vector expressions as $\alpha\mathbf{a} + \beta\mathbf{b}$ and $\gamma\mathbf{a} + \delta\mathbf{b}$ are called *linear combinations* of the vectors **a** and **b**. Similarly, the sum $(\alpha + \gamma)\mathbf{a} + (\beta + \delta)\mathbf{b}$ is also a linear combination of **a** and **b**, being a sum of scalar multiples of **a** and **b**.

More formally, suppose that $\{\mathbf{a}, \mathbf{b}, \mathbf{c}, \ldots, \mathbf{k}\}$ is a set of vectors (either free vectors or position vectors) and that $\alpha, \beta, \gamma, \ldots, \kappa$ are real numbers. Then the vector

$$\alpha\mathbf{a} + \beta\mathbf{b} + \gamma\mathbf{c} + \cdots + \kappa\mathbf{k}$$

is called a *linear combination* of the set of vectors $\{\mathbf{a}, \mathbf{b}, \mathbf{c}, \ldots, \mathbf{k}\}$. Thus, for example, $2\mathbf{a} - 3\mathbf{b} + \frac{1}{2}\mathbf{c} = \mathbf{d}$ is a linear combination of the set $\{\mathbf{a}, \mathbf{b}, \mathbf{c}\}$ of position vectors.

Also, if $\hat{\mathbf{i}}$ and $\hat{\mathbf{j}}$ are the directions of the usual coordinate axes $Ox$ and $Oy$ respectively, then $3\hat{\mathbf{i}} - 2\hat{\mathbf{j}}$, $-\frac{1}{2}\hat{\mathbf{i}} + \frac{3}{4}\hat{\mathbf{j}}$ and $-\hat{\mathbf{i}} - 2\hat{\mathbf{j}}$ are linear combinations of the set $\{\hat{\mathbf{i}}, \hat{\mathbf{j}}\}$ of position vectors.

$\hat{\mathbf{i}}$ and $\hat{\mathbf{j}}$ themselves are also linear combinations of the set $\{\hat{\mathbf{i}}, \hat{\mathbf{j}}\}$, since we may write them as $\hat{\mathbf{i}} = 1\hat{\mathbf{i}} + 0\hat{\mathbf{j}}$ and $\hat{\mathbf{j}} = 0\hat{\mathbf{i}} + 1\hat{\mathbf{j}}$.

The zero vector **0** is a linear combination of *any* set of vectors, since it may be obtained by taking the zero scalar multiple of each member of the set.

## 2.2 Spanning sets

Take *any* two position vectors **a** and **b** in $P_3$ that are not in the same direction. We can define the whole plane of **a** and **b** by taking the set $S = \{\alpha\mathbf{a} + \beta\mathbf{b} : \alpha, \beta \in R\}$ of

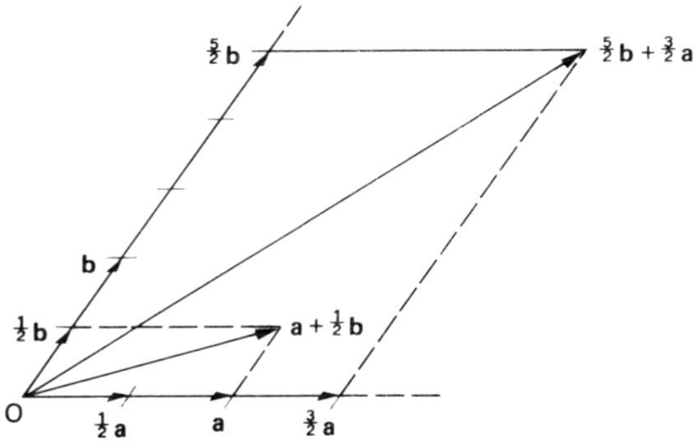


**Fig. 2.1.** Some members of the set $\{\alpha\mathbf{a} + \beta\mathbf{b}\} = S$.

*all* possible linear combinations of $\{\mathbf{a}, \mathbf{b}\}$ (see Fig. 2.1). This set $S$ is called the set *spanned* by $\{\mathbf{a}, \mathbf{b}\}$, and it defines a plane if **a** and **b** are in different directions.

We have just seen one possible case of a spanning set of position vectors—two position vectors **a** and **b** in different directions span a plane. It will be useful to investigate what happens if we start with different sets of position vectors in $P_3$—for example, what will happen if **a** and **b** are in the same direction, or if we take three vectors in our set? Some of the possibilities are listed in Exercise 2*a*, so that the reader may have an opportunity to investigate them for himself. The conclusions are given in the next section.

**Exercise 2*a***

Investigate the sets spanned by the following subsets of the vector space $P_3$ of position vectors (questions 1 to 6):

1. $\{\mathbf{a}, \mathbf{b}\}$, where **a** is any position vector and $\mathbf{b} = -3\mathbf{a}$.
2. $\{\mathbf{a}, \mathbf{0}\}$, where **a** is any position vector.
3. $\{\mathbf{a}, \mathbf{b}, \mathbf{0}\}$, where **a** is any position vector, and: (i) $\mathbf{b} = -3\mathbf{a}$; (ii) **b** is not in the same direction as **a**.
4. $\{\mathbf{a}, \mathbf{b}, \mathbf{c}\}$, where **a** is any position vector, $\mathbf{a} = 2\mathbf{b}$, and: (i) $\mathbf{c} = -2\mathbf{a}$; (ii) **c** is not in the same direction as **a** and **b**.
5. $\{\mathbf{a}, \mathbf{b}, \mathbf{c}\}$, where no two vectors are in the same direction, but: (i) **c** is in the same plane as **a** and **b**; (ii) **c** is not in the same plane as **a** and **b**.
6. $\{\mathbf{a}, \mathbf{b}, \mathbf{c}, \mathbf{d}\}$, where **a**, **b**, **c** and **d** are *any* four position vectors. There are many cases to consider—questions 1 to 5 should help you decide what to consider, and your conclusions from these questions should help you to answer question 6 fairly briefly.

## 2.3 Linear dependence and independence

We now try to generalize the conclusions drawn from the questions of Exercise 2*a*. In each case, we started with a set of position vectors chosen from the vector space $P_3$, but only in some of the cases did our set span the whole vector space $P_3$. Our generalization will tell us in advance whether any given set of position vectors will span the whole of $P_3$, or not.

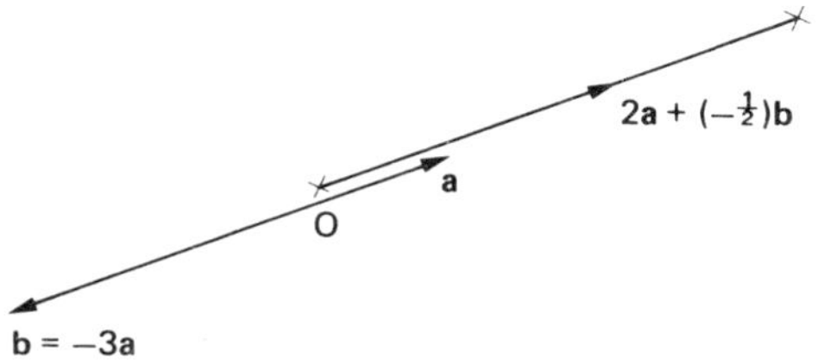


**Fig. 2.2.** An example to show that a linear combination of {**a**, −3**a**} has the direction of **a**.

First, let us consider all the sets of two vectors: those from questions 1 and 2, and the one from Section 2.2. None of these sets spanned the whole of $P_3$. The set {**a**, **b**} in Section 2.2, where **a** and **b** were in different directions, spanned the plane containing **a** and **b**; and the sets in Exercise 2*a* each spanned a line. In particular, from question 1, any linear combination $\alpha\mathbf{a} + \beta\mathbf{b}$ of the given vectors could be simplified by $\alpha\mathbf{a} + \beta\mathbf{b} = \alpha\mathbf{a} + \beta(-3\mathbf{a}) = (\alpha - 3\beta)\mathbf{a}$—in other words, every linear combination of **a** and **b** has the same direction as **a**. We therefore conclude:

(1) A set of two position vectors can span a plane, although it may only span a line.

Now consider all the sets of three vectors: those from questions 3, 4 and 5. Only one of these, that is question 5, part (ii), spanned the whole space $P_3$. The special features of this were that no two of the vectors were in the same direction, and no three were in the same plane, since **c** was not in the plane defined by **a** and **b**. If we now look at all the other cases, we see that, in every one of them, all three vectors were in the same plane, regardless of direction. In some cases, 3(i), for example, the given vectors spanned a line; and in the others, the given vectors spanned a plane. Question 4(ii) is demonstrated in Fig. 2.3.

We will look at more details later; for now, we draw the conclusion:

(2) A set of three position vectors *can* span the whole vector space $P_3$, although it may only span a plane or a line.

Finally, from question 6, we conclude:

(3) A set of four or more position vectors can do no more than a set of three position vectors—in other words, it can span the whole vector space $P_3$, or a plane, or a line.

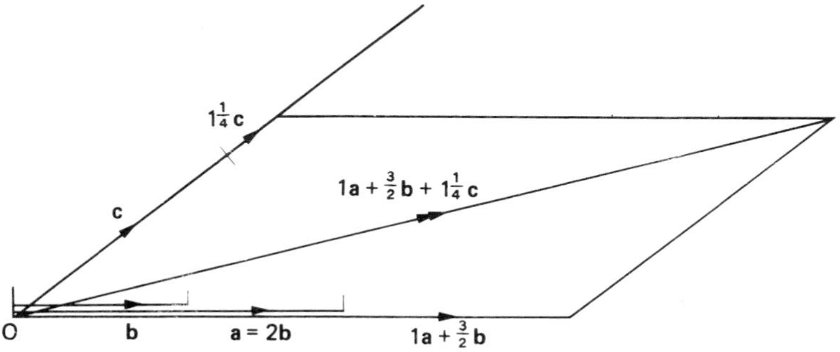


**Fig. 2.3.** $1\mathbf{a} + \frac{3}{2}\mathbf{b} + 1\frac{1}{4}\mathbf{c}$ is in the plane determined by **b** and **c**.

If the zero vector is included in a set, it seems to reduce the effectiveness of that set by one member. For instance, a set of three position vectors, one of which is $\mathbf{0}$, acts as a set of two position vectors, and can span only a plane or a line.

This leaves us with two properties to formalize:

(a) There seems to be something special about the number 3—the smallest number of position vectors capable of spanning the whole vector space.

(b) There might be a connection between the collection of sets of vectors which do not span the whole space.

We will take case (b) first, which refers to the sets of vectors in questions 1, 2, 3(i) and (ii), 4(i) and (ii) and 5(i) of Exercise *2a*. In all these questions, the vectors in the given set somehow depend on each other. In some cases, the dependence is given in the question in the form of an equation; or can be deduced simply:

| | | | |
|---|---|---|---|
| (question 1) | $\mathbf{b} = -3\mathbf{a}$ | or | $3\mathbf{a} + 1\mathbf{b} = \mathbf{0}$ |
| (question 2) | $\mathbf{0} = 0\mathbf{a}$ | or | $0\mathbf{a} + 1\mathbf{0} = \mathbf{0}$ |
| (question 3(i)) | $\mathbf{b} = -3\mathbf{a}$, | or | $3\mathbf{a} + 1\mathbf{b} + 1\mathbf{0} = \mathbf{0}$ |
| (question 3(ii)) | | | $0\mathbf{a} + 0\mathbf{b} + 1\mathbf{0} = \mathbf{0}$ |
| (question 4(i)) | $\mathbf{a} = 2\mathbf{b} = -\frac{1}{2}\mathbf{c}$ | or | $1\mathbf{a} + (-2)\mathbf{b} + 0\mathbf{c} = \mathbf{0}$ |
| (question 4(ii)) | $\mathbf{a} = 2\mathbf{b}$ | or | $1\mathbf{a} + (-2)\mathbf{b} + 0\mathbf{c} = \mathbf{0}$ |
| (question 5(i)) | $\mathbf{c} = \alpha\mathbf{a} + \beta\mathbf{b}$, | since it is in the set spanned by **a** and **b**, | |
| | | or | $\alpha\mathbf{a} + \beta\mathbf{b} + (-1)\mathbf{c} = \mathbf{0}$ |

In all the cases, we have re-written the conditions (on the right-hand side) to give a single equation. This equation always takes the form of a linear combination of the given set of vectors being zero.

In question 5(ii), where **c** is *not* in the plane of **a** and **b**, it is not possible to write **c** as a linear combination of **a** and **b**. So there are *no* real numbers $\alpha$ and $\beta$ such that $\mathbf{c} = \alpha\mathbf{a} + \beta\mathbf{b}$. Hence it is impossible to have a zero linear combination like $\alpha\mathbf{a} + \beta\mathbf{b} - \mathbf{c} = \mathbf{0}$, as we had in the exceptional cases above.

This leads us to the following general definitions, which are the same for free vectors as for position vectors.

$\{\mathbf{a}, \mathbf{b}, \mathbf{c}, \ldots, \mathbf{k}\}$ is *linearly dependent* if there are scalars $\alpha, \beta, \gamma, \ldots, \kappa$, not all zero, such that $\alpha\mathbf{a} + \beta\mathbf{b} + \gamma\mathbf{c} + \cdots + \kappa\mathbf{k} = \mathbf{0}$, i.e. there is a non-trivial zero linear combination.

Thus the sets of vectors in questions 1 to 4 were all linearly dependent.

Alternatively, the given set of vectors is said to be *linearly independent* if no such scalars exist. This may also be stated as:

$\{\mathbf{a}, \mathbf{b}, \mathbf{c}, \ldots, \mathbf{k}\}$ is linearly independent if, for scalars $\alpha, \beta, \gamma, \ldots, \kappa$,

$$\alpha\mathbf{a} + \beta\mathbf{b} + \gamma\mathbf{c} + \cdots + \kappa\mathbf{k} = \mathbf{0} \Rightarrow \alpha = \beta = \gamma = \cdots = \kappa = 0.$$

This is often the more easily used criterion.

The set $\{\mathbf{a}, \mathbf{b}, \mathbf{c}\}$ in question 5(ii) was linearly independent. The set $\{\hat{\mathbf{i}}, \hat{\mathbf{j}}, \hat{\mathbf{k}}\}$ of unit vectors along the coordinate axes in an important example of a linearly independent set of vectors.

Linear dependence and independence are thus the formal ways of describing how the sets of vectors we considered 'depended' or 'did not depend' on each other.

They are complementary properties, in that any set of vectors is either linearly dependent or linearly independent, but cannot be both.

Our conclusion to question 6 can now be re-phrased: any set containing four or more position vectors is linearly dependent.

We now return to our property (a)—the apparently magic number 3. The set of three vectors in question 5(ii) has two properties: it spans the whole vector space $P_3$, and it is linearly independent. We have also seen that any smaller set cannot span the whole space; and that any larger set cannot be linearly independent.

We give a special name to the smallest number of vectors required to span a whole vector space: we call it the *dimension* of the vector space. Thus the vector space $P_3$ has dimension 3, which corresponds to our everyday phrase 'three-dimensional space'.

Any set which contains just three position vectors, and which spans $P_3$ will, it seems, be linearly independent. Such a set is called a *basis* of the vector space. A basis is a linearly independent set which spans the space. Any vector space may have more than one basis, but each basis will have the same number of elements, and that number is the dimension of the vector space.

In $P_3$, the set $\{\hat{\mathbf{i}}, \hat{\mathbf{j}}, \hat{\mathbf{k}}\}$ of unit vectors along the coordinate axes forms a basis, known as the *standard basis* of $P_3$. Similarly, $\{\hat{\mathbf{i}}, \hat{\mathbf{j}}\}$ is called the standard basis of the plane $P_2$. These will be used and discussed extensively.

## 2.4 Linear dependence and independence in $V_3$

The study of linear dependence and independence in the vector space $V_3$ of free vector families follows closely that in $P_3$, since the families of free vectors in $V_3$ can be created from the position vectors in $P_3$.

For example, suppose we have two families **A** and **B** of free vectors, and the position vectors **a** and **b** which are members of **A** and **B** respectively. Then the linear combination $\alpha\mathbf{a} + \beta\mathbf{b}$ determines another family, which we have already defined to be $\alpha\mathbf{A} + \beta\mathbf{B}$. Following this correspondence through, we see that there is a direct connection between a spanning set in $P_3$ and a spanning set in $V_3$; and a linearly independent set in $P_3$ and a linearly independent set in $V_3$.

We deduce further that $V_3$ is also three dimensional, and that any basis $\{\mathbf{a}, \mathbf{b}, \mathbf{c}\}$ of $P_3$ determines a corresponding basis $\{\mathbf{A}, \mathbf{B}, \mathbf{C}\}$ of $V_3$.

What we are really doing, in following this correspondence, is to use the fact that the two vector spaces $V_3$ and $P_3$ have identical structures—a property which we describe by saying that $V_3$ and $P_3$ are *isomorphic.*

**Worked example 2.1**

Show that the set of vectors $\{\mathbf{a} = \hat{\mathbf{i}} + 2\hat{\mathbf{j}}, \mathbf{b} = 2\hat{\mathbf{i}} + \hat{\mathbf{j}}, \mathbf{c} = \hat{\mathbf{i}} - 3\hat{\mathbf{k}}\}$ forms a basis for a three-dimensional space.

*Solution*

This is in two parts—we must show separately that the given set of vectors is linearly independent, and that it spans the space. To show that the set is linearly independent, suppose that

$$\alpha\mathbf{a} + \beta\mathbf{b} + \gamma\mathbf{c} = \mathbf{0}$$

Then

$$\alpha(\hat{\mathbf{i}} + 2\hat{\mathbf{j}}) + \beta(2\hat{\mathbf{i}} + \hat{\mathbf{j}}) + \gamma(\hat{\mathbf{i}} - 3\hat{\mathbf{k}}) = \mathbf{0}$$

Therefore

$$(\alpha + 2\beta + \gamma)\hat{\mathbf{i}} + (2\alpha + \beta)\hat{\mathbf{j}} + (-3\gamma)\hat{\mathbf{k}} = \mathbf{0}$$

Now the set $\{\hat{\mathbf{i}}, \hat{\mathbf{j}}, \hat{\mathbf{k}}\}$ is linearly independent. Therefore

$$\alpha + 2\beta + \gamma = 0, \quad 2\alpha + \beta = 0, \quad \text{and} \quad -3\gamma = 0$$

Hence $\alpha = \beta = \gamma = 0$. Therefore $\{\mathbf{a}, \mathbf{b}, \mathbf{c}\}$ is linearly independent, by our definition of linear independence.

First proof of spanning: by inspecting their definitions in terms of $\hat{\mathbf{i}}$ and $\hat{\mathbf{j}}$, we see that **a** and **b** span the plane of the $x$- and $y$-axes. Also, **c** is not in this plane, and hence the three vectors span the whole space. This argument was used in Section 2.3 in a similar situation.

Alternative proof of spanning: we may see that

$$\hat{\mathbf{i}} = \tfrac{1}{3}(2\mathbf{b} - \mathbf{a}), \quad \hat{\mathbf{j}} = \tfrac{1}{3}(2\mathbf{a} - \mathbf{b}), \quad \hat{\mathbf{k}} = \tfrac{1}{9}(2\mathbf{b} - \mathbf{a} - 3\mathbf{c})$$

Now every vector **v** may be given as a linear combination of $\{\hat{\mathbf{i}}, \hat{\mathbf{j}}, \hat{\mathbf{k}}\}$ and hence as a linear combination of $\{\mathbf{a}, \mathbf{b}, \mathbf{c}\}$.

Thus $\{\mathbf{a}, \mathbf{b}, \mathbf{c}\}$ is linearly independent, and spans the space, and so is a basis for the space.

**Exercise 2*b***

1. In the vector space $P_3$, prove that any set containing the zero vector is linearly dependent.
2. By considering the linear combination $\alpha\mathbf{a} + \beta\mathbf{b} + \gamma\mathbf{c}$ of the vectors $\mathbf{a} = \hat{\mathbf{k}}$, $\mathbf{b} = \hat{\mathbf{j}} + \hat{\mathbf{k}}$ and $\mathbf{c} = \hat{\mathbf{i}} + \hat{\mathbf{j}} + \hat{\mathbf{k}}$, show that the set of vectors $\{\mathbf{a}, \mathbf{b}, \mathbf{c}\}$ is linearly independent.
3. $\mathbf{a} = 2\hat{\mathbf{i}} + 3\hat{\mathbf{j}} + 4\hat{\mathbf{k}}$ and $\mathbf{b} = \hat{\mathbf{i}} + 2\hat{\mathbf{j}} + \hat{\mathbf{k}}$. Give two non-zero vectors **c** and **d** such that: (i) $\{\mathbf{a}, \mathbf{b}, \mathbf{c}\}$ is linearly dependent; (ii) $\{\mathbf{a}, \mathbf{b}, \mathbf{d}\}$ is linearly independent.
4. Show that $\{2\hat{\mathbf{i}}, 3\hat{\mathbf{j}}, \hat{\mathbf{i}} + \hat{\mathbf{j}} + \hat{\mathbf{k}}\}$ is a basis for $P_3$.
5. In the two-dimensional vector space $P_2$, the vectors $\mathbf{a} = 3\hat{\mathbf{i}} + 4\hat{\mathbf{j}}$ and $\mathbf{b} = \alpha\hat{\mathbf{i}} + \beta\hat{\mathbf{j}}$ are linearly dependent. Find an equation connecting $\alpha$ and $\beta$.
6. In the two-dimensional vector space $P_2$, the vectors $\mathbf{a} = a_1\hat{\mathbf{i}} + a_2\hat{\mathbf{j}}$ and $\mathbf{b} = b_1\hat{\mathbf{i}} + b_2\hat{\mathbf{j}}$ are linearly dependent. Prove that $a_1b_2 = b_1a_2$, in other words that the determinant

$$\begin{vmatrix} a_1 & b_1 \\ a_2 & b_2 \end{vmatrix}$$

is zero.

## 2.5 Column vectors

We have said that the standard basis $\{\hat{\mathbf{i}}, \hat{\mathbf{j}}, \hat{\mathbf{k}}\}$ is extensively used, a view that should have been confirmed by the number of exercises which have been conveniently phrased in terms of this basis. We now develop a shorthand notation, which dispenses with the need of writing the vectors $\hat{\mathbf{i}}$, $\hat{\mathbf{j}}$ and $\hat{\mathbf{k}}$ explicitly in each linear combination of them. Consider the following examples of algebra of linear combinations of $\{\hat{\mathbf{i}}, \hat{\mathbf{j}}, \hat{\mathbf{k}}\}$:

(1) $[2\hat{\mathbf{i}} + 3\hat{\mathbf{j}} + (-3)\hat{\mathbf{k}}] + [3\hat{\mathbf{i}} + (-2)\hat{\mathbf{j}}] = 5\hat{\mathbf{i}} + 1\hat{\mathbf{j}} + (-3)\hat{\mathbf{k}}$
(2) $3[2\hat{\mathbf{i}} + 3\hat{\mathbf{j}} + (-3)\hat{\mathbf{k}}] = 6\hat{\mathbf{i}} + 9\hat{\mathbf{j}} + (-9)\hat{\mathbf{k}}$
(3) $2[2\hat{\mathbf{i}} + 3\hat{\mathbf{j}} + (-3)\hat{\mathbf{k}}] + (-1)[3\hat{\mathbf{i}} + (-2)\hat{\mathbf{j}}] = 1\hat{\mathbf{i}} + 8\hat{\mathbf{j}} + (-6)\hat{\mathbf{k}}$

These examples have one thing in common: all the numbers in the linear combinations on the right-hand sides are obtained by calculations on the numbers in the original expressions—the vectors $\hat{\mathbf{i}}$, $\hat{\mathbf{j}}$ and $\hat{\mathbf{k}}$ are only used as 'dummies' to indicate the positions of the numbers. For example, the calculations in (1) are described by

$$2 + 3 = 5$$
$$3 + (-2) = 1$$
$$(-3) + 0 = -3.$$

We can write this as

$$\begin{pmatrix} 2 \\ 3 \\ -3 \end{pmatrix} + \begin{pmatrix} 3 \\ -2 \\ 0 \end{pmatrix} = \begin{pmatrix} 5 \\ 1 \\ -3 \end{pmatrix}$$

where the entities

$$\begin{pmatrix} 2 \\ 3 \\ -3 \end{pmatrix}, \begin{pmatrix} 3 \\ -2 \\ 0 \end{pmatrix}, \text{ and } \begin{pmatrix} 5 \\ 1 \\ -3 \end{pmatrix}$$

are called *column vectors* or column matrices. For the moment, we consider the column vector

$$\begin{pmatrix} a_1 \\ a_2 \\ a_3 \end{pmatrix}$$

to be a shorthand way of writing the position vector $a_1\hat{\mathbf{i}} + a_2\hat{\mathbf{j}} + a_3\hat{\mathbf{k}}$. The set of all such column vectors will be called $R^3$, and it will be a vector space because it is defined to correspond exactly to $P_3$ (i.e. $R^3$ is isomorphic to $P_3$).

The other examples above may be written in terms of column vectors as

(2) $$3\begin{pmatrix} 2 \\ 3 \\ -3 \end{pmatrix} = \begin{pmatrix} 6 \\ 9 \\ -9 \end{pmatrix}$$

(3) $$2\begin{pmatrix} 2 \\ 3 \\ -3 \end{pmatrix} + (-1)\begin{pmatrix} 3 \\ -2 \\ 0 \end{pmatrix} = \begin{pmatrix} 1 \\ 8 \\ -6 \end{pmatrix}$$

More generally, we may use our definitions of addition, scalar multiples, and linear combinations in $P_3$ to give the following, corresponding, definitions for $R^3$:

(1) $$\begin{pmatrix} a_1 \\ a_2 \\ a_3 \end{pmatrix} + \begin{pmatrix} b_1 \\ b_2 \\ b_3 \end{pmatrix} = \begin{pmatrix} a_1 + b_1 \\ a_2 + b_2 \\ a_3 + b_3 \end{pmatrix}$$

(2)
$$\alpha\begin{pmatrix} a_1 \\ b_2 \\ a_3 \end{pmatrix} = \begin{pmatrix} \alpha a_1 \\ \alpha a_2 \\ \alpha a_3 \end{pmatrix}$$

(3)
$$\alpha\begin{pmatrix} a_1 \\ a_2 \\ a_3 \end{pmatrix} + \beta\begin{pmatrix} b_1 \\ b_2 \\ b_3 \end{pmatrix} = \begin{pmatrix} \alpha a_1 + \beta b_1 \\ \alpha a_2 + \beta b_2 \\ \alpha a_3 + \beta b_3 \end{pmatrix}$$

Once again, we use the same notation for our vectors: $\mathbf{a}$ will represent the column vector

$$\begin{pmatrix} a_1 \\ a_2 \\ a_3 \end{pmatrix}$$

except when there might be any ambiguity. Thus the above three laws define $\mathbf{a} + \mathbf{b}$, $\alpha\mathbf{a}$ and $\alpha\mathbf{a} + \beta\mathbf{b}$ for column vectors in a manner exactly corresponding to the definitions of $\mathbf{a} + \mathbf{b}$, $\alpha\mathbf{a}$ and $\alpha\mathbf{a} + \beta\mathbf{b}$ for either position vectors or free vectors.

## 2.6 Properties of column vectors

In the previous section, we defined addition, scalar multiples, and linear combinations in the vector space $R^3$ of column vectors. We now extend these to show the truth in $R^3$ of some of the results and properties we have already established in $P_3$ and $V_3$. First, it will be convenient to have a geometrical interpretation of $R^3$. Remembering that the column vector

$$\mathbf{a} = \begin{pmatrix} a_1 \\ a_2 \\ a_3 \end{pmatrix}$$

corresponds to the position vector $a_1\hat{\mathbf{i}} + a_2\hat{\mathbf{j}} + a_3\hat{\mathbf{k}}$, or $\overrightarrow{OP}$, we see that the point P will have Cartesian coordinates $(a_1, a_2, a_3)$.

Any point P has a position vector $\overrightarrow{OP}$, which may be given as a linear combination $a_1\hat{\mathbf{i}} + a_2\hat{\mathbf{j}} + a_3\hat{\mathbf{k}}$ of the basis $\{\hat{\mathbf{i}}, \hat{\mathbf{j}}, \hat{\mathbf{k}}\}$, and represented by the column vector

$$\mathbf{a} = \begin{pmatrix} a_1 \\ a_2 \\ a_3 \end{pmatrix}$$

*relative to that basis.* We will see the importance of this last phrase elsewhere. Suffice to say at the moment that the column vectors depend on a choice of basis.

We rely on this geometrical interpretation to translate some of our properties of $P_3$ into properties of $R^3$. Firstly, the length of the position vector $\overrightarrow{OP}$ is the length of the line segment OP. Now, using Pythagoras' theorem twice in Fig. 2.4, we have

$$\begin{aligned} OP^2 &= \mathrm{ON}^2 + \mathrm{NP}^2 \\ &= (\mathrm{OA}^2 + \mathrm{AN}^2) + \mathrm{NP}^2 \\ &= a_1^2 + a_2^2 + a_3^2 \end{aligned}$$

and so

$$\mathrm{OP} = \sqrt{a_1^2 + a_2^2 + a_3^2}$$

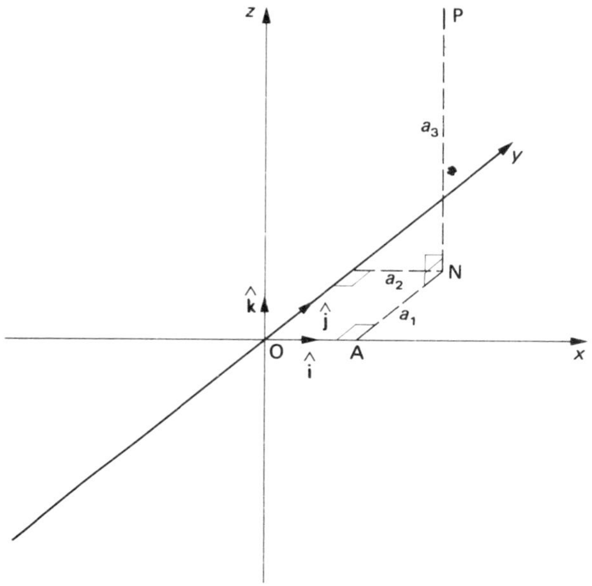


**Fig. 2.4.** The point P $(a_1, a_2, a_3)$ corresponding to the column vector $\mathbf{a} = \begin{pmatrix} a_1 \\ a_2 \\ a_3 \end{pmatrix}$.

We *define* the *modulus* $|\mathbf{a}|$ of the column vector

$$\mathbf{a} = \begin{pmatrix} a_1 \\ a_2 \\ a_3 \end{pmatrix}$$

to be this quantity, namely $\sqrt{a_1^2 + a_2^2 + a_3^2} = |\mathbf{a}|$. Thus, for example,

$$\left|\begin{pmatrix} 4 \\ 3 \\ -12 \end{pmatrix}\right| = \sqrt{4^2 + 3^2 + (-12)^2} = 13.$$

We deduce that the length of the corresponding position vector is also 13.

When we defined scalar multiples of a position vector, we defined them by saying that, among other things, $|\alpha\mathbf{u}| = |\alpha| \times |\mathbf{u}|$ for a scalar $\alpha$ and a position vector $\mathbf{u}$. We must now show that our definition of scalar multiples in $R^3$ satisfies this property.

We defined $\alpha\mathbf{a}$ by

$$\alpha\begin{pmatrix} a_1 \\ a_2 \\ a_3 \end{pmatrix} = \begin{pmatrix} \alpha a_1 \\ \alpha a_2 \\ \alpha a_3 \end{pmatrix}$$

Therefore

$$\begin{aligned}|\alpha\mathbf{a}| &= \sqrt{(\alpha a_1)^2 + (\alpha a_2)^2 + (\alpha a_3)^2}\\ &= \sqrt{\alpha^2(a_1^2 + a_2^2 + a_3^2)}\\ &= \sqrt{\alpha^2}\sqrt{a_1^2 + a_2^2 + a_3^2}\end{aligned}$$

Therefore $|\alpha\mathbf{a}| = |\alpha||\mathbf{a}|$, is required. Thus, for example,

$$\left|\begin{pmatrix}10\\7\cdot5\\-30\end{pmatrix}\right| = \left|2\cdot5\begin{pmatrix}4\\3\\-12\end{pmatrix}\right| = 2\cdot5 \times 13 = 29\cdot5$$

In Chapter 11, we will meet an alternative way of defining length, although, of course, the same result will obtain.

As before, a *unit vector* will be one of unit length—such as

$$\hat{\mathbf{i}} = \begin{pmatrix}1\\0\\0\end{pmatrix}, \hat{\mathbf{k}} = \begin{pmatrix}0\\0\\1\end{pmatrix} \text{ or } \hat{\mathbf{a}} = \begin{pmatrix}4/13\\3/13\\-12/13\end{pmatrix}$$

In Section 1.6, we met some properties of scalar multiples which enabled us to simplify linear combinations of position vectors. These properties also hold in $R^3$, so that, for example, the following simplification is in order:

$$3\begin{pmatrix}3\\-1\\2\end{pmatrix} + 5\begin{pmatrix}2\\5\\-3\end{pmatrix} - 7\begin{pmatrix}1\\-1\\-1\end{pmatrix} = \begin{pmatrix}9\\-3\\6\end{pmatrix} + \begin{pmatrix}10\\25\\-15\end{pmatrix} + \begin{pmatrix}-7\\7\\7\end{pmatrix} = \begin{pmatrix}12\\29\\-2\end{pmatrix}$$

**Exercise 2*c***

For this exercise, you are given the following column vectors:

$$\mathbf{a} = \begin{pmatrix}3\\-1\\-2\end{pmatrix}, \mathbf{b} = \begin{pmatrix}1\\-2\\3\end{pmatrix}, \mathbf{c} = \begin{pmatrix}-6\\2\\4\end{pmatrix}, \mathbf{d} = \begin{pmatrix}5\\0\\-7\end{pmatrix} \text{ and } \mathbf{e} = \begin{pmatrix}5\\-5\\3\end{pmatrix}$$

The points corresponding to these are A, B, C, D and E.

1. Evaluate the following linear combinations as single vectors:
(a) $2\mathbf{a} + 3\mathbf{b}$, (b) $\mathbf{a} - 2\mathbf{b} + \mathbf{c}$, (c) $\mathbf{c} - \mathbf{d} - \mathbf{e}$.

2. Find the lengths of the following vectors:
(a) $\mathbf{a} + \mathbf{b}$, (b) $\mathbf{a} - \mathbf{b}$, (c) $\mathbf{a} + \mathbf{d} + \mathbf{e}$.

3. Is it true or false to say that non-zero numbers $\alpha$, $\beta$ and $\gamma$ exist such that $\alpha\mathbf{a} + \beta\mathbf{b} + \gamma\mathbf{d} = 0$? If such numbers exist, give their values. Is your answer the same if $\mathbf{d}$ is replaced by $\mathbf{e}$?

## 2.7 Linear dependence and independence in $R^3$

The definitions we use are the same as for position vectors (see page 34). We will also only be giving a simplified treatment of linear dependence and independence, in which we consider just three vectors, which we will take as

$$\mathbf{a} = \begin{pmatrix}a_1\\a_2\\a_3\end{pmatrix}, \mathbf{b} = \begin{pmatrix}b_1\\b_2\\b_3\end{pmatrix} \text{ and } \mathbf{c} = \begin{pmatrix}c_1\\c_2\\c_3\end{pmatrix}$$

Suppose that

$$\alpha\mathbf{a} + \beta\mathbf{b} + \gamma\mathbf{c} = \mathbf{0} \tag{1}$$

Then $\{\mathbf{a}, \mathbf{b}, \mathbf{c}\}$ will be linearly independent if $\alpha = \beta = \gamma = 0$ is the only possible set of values for $\alpha$, $\beta$, $\gamma$, and linearly dependent if there are other possible values. We therefore have

$$\alpha\begin{pmatrix} a_1 \\ a_2 \\ a_3 \end{pmatrix} + \beta\begin{pmatrix} b_1 \\ b_2 \\ b_3 \end{pmatrix} + \gamma\begin{pmatrix} c_1 \\ c_2 \\ c_3 \end{pmatrix} = \begin{pmatrix} 0 \\ 0 \\ 0 \end{pmatrix}$$

We may write this as three homogeneous equations in three unknowns $\alpha$, $\beta$ and $\gamma$:

$$\left.\begin{aligned} a_1\alpha + b_1\beta + c_1\gamma = 0 \\ a_2\alpha + b_2\beta + c_2\gamma = 0 \\ a_3\alpha + b_3\beta + c_3\gamma = 0 \end{aligned}\right\} \tag{2}$$

or as the equivalent matrix equation

$$M\boldsymbol{\alpha} = \mathbf{0} \tag{3}$$

where

$$M = \begin{pmatrix} a_1 & b_1 & c_1 \\ a_2 & b_2 & c_2 \\ a_3 & b_3 & c_3 \end{pmatrix} \text{ and } \boldsymbol{\alpha} = \begin{pmatrix} \alpha \\ \beta \\ \gamma \end{pmatrix}$$

Now, it can be shown that the matrix equation (3) has a solution other than $\boldsymbol{\alpha} = \mathbf{0}$ if and only if the determinant $\det M$ is zero. For those not familiar with matrices and determinants, this condition may be expressed by a definition of $\det M$:

$$\det M = a_1(b_2c_3 - b_3c_2) - b_1(a_2c_3 - a_3c_2) + c_1(a_2b_3 - a_3b_2)$$

Details will be found in texts on determinants and matrices.

Then $\det M = 0$ is the necessary and sufficient condition for each of:

(1) the vectors $\{\mathbf{a}, \mathbf{b}, \mathbf{c}\}$ to be linearly dependent;
(2) the equations (2) to have solutions other than $\alpha = \beta = \gamma = 0$;
(3) the equation (3) to have a solution other than $\boldsymbol{\alpha} = \mathbf{0}$.

**Worked Example 2.2**

Show that the set of vectors

$$\left\{\mathbf{a} = \begin{pmatrix} 2 \\ 3 \\ 4 \end{pmatrix}, \mathbf{b} = \begin{pmatrix} 3 \\ -2 \\ -1 \end{pmatrix}, \mathbf{c} = \begin{pmatrix} 1 \\ 8 \\ 9 \end{pmatrix}\right\}$$

is linearly dependent.

*Solution*

This example shows that the evaluation of a determinant is not always necessary. By observation, we see that $\mathbf{c} = 2\mathbf{a} - \mathbf{b}$, or $2\mathbf{a} - \mathbf{b} - \mathbf{c} = \mathbf{0}$. Thus there is a nontrivial zero linear combination of the given vectors, and the set is linearly dependent.

**Worked Example 2.3**

Find the value of $\beta$ for which the set of vectors

$$\left\{ \mathbf{a} = \begin{pmatrix} 2 \\ 3 \\ 4 \end{pmatrix}, \mathbf{b} = \begin{pmatrix} 3 \\ -2 \\ -1 \end{pmatrix}, \text{ and } \mathbf{c} = \begin{pmatrix} 1 \\ \beta \\ 3 \end{pmatrix} \right\}$$

is linearly dependent.

*Solution*

If the set of vectors is linearly dependent, then the determinant with these vectors as columns must be zero.
Thus

$$\begin{vmatrix} 2 & 3 & 1 \\ 3 & -2 & \beta \\ 4 & -1 & 3 \end{vmatrix} = 0$$

Expanding along the centre row, we obtain

$$(-3)(9 + 1) + (-2)(6 - 4) + [-\beta(-2 - 12)] = 0$$

Hence

$$-30 - 4 + 14\beta = 0$$

Hence the given set of vectors is linearly dependent only for $\beta = +34/14 = +17/7$.

**Exercise 2*d***

1. You are given the following vectors in $R^3$:

$$\mathbf{a} = \begin{pmatrix} 3 \\ -1 \\ -2 \end{pmatrix}, \mathbf{b} = \begin{pmatrix} 1 \\ -2 \\ 3 \end{pmatrix}, \mathbf{c} = \begin{pmatrix} -6 \\ 2 \\ 4 \end{pmatrix}, \mathbf{d} = \begin{pmatrix} 5 \\ 0 \\ -7 \end{pmatrix}, \mathbf{e} = \begin{pmatrix} 5 \\ -5 \\ 3 \end{pmatrix}$$

(i) Prove that $\{\mathbf{a}, \mathbf{c}\}$ is linearly dependent, and that $\{\mathbf{a}, \mathbf{b}\}$ is linearly independent.
(ii) Prove that $\{\mathbf{a}, \mathbf{b}, \mathbf{d}\}$ is linearly dependent, and that $\{\mathbf{a}, \mathbf{b}, \mathbf{e}\}$ is linearly independent.
(iii) Express $\mathbf{c}$ and $\mathbf{d}$ as linear combinations of $\{\mathbf{a}, \mathbf{b}, \mathbf{e}\}$.

2. Show that the set

$$\left\{ \begin{pmatrix} 1 \\ 1 \\ 1 \end{pmatrix}, \begin{pmatrix} 0 \\ 1 \\ 1 \end{pmatrix}, \begin{pmatrix} 0 \\ 0 \\ -1 \end{pmatrix} \right\}$$

is a basis of $R^3$, and express the vector

$$\begin{pmatrix} x_1 \\ x_2 \\ x_3 \end{pmatrix}$$

as a linear combination of the members of this basis.

## 2.8 The subspace $R^2$

So far we have been considering only column vectors from the vector space $R^3$. All that we have said may be applied directly to the vector space $R^2$ of column vectors with two entries. This is because there is an isomorphism between the set

$$R^2 = \left\{ \begin{pmatrix} x_1 \\ x_2 \end{pmatrix} : x_1, x_2 \in R \right\}$$

and the subset

$$\left\{ \begin{pmatrix} x_1 \\ x_2 \\ 0 \end{pmatrix} : x_1, x_2 \in R \right\}$$

of $R^3$. This subset, and consequently $R^2$, forms a vector space in itself, and is called a *vector subspace* of the vector space $R^3$. We allow the isomorphism to influence our language a little, and say also that $R^2$ is a subspace of $R^3$, where, strictly, it is isomorphic to a subspace of $R^3$.

Thus the following results are true for $R^2$, by direct application of those established for $R^3$ in Sections 2.5 and 2.7.

We define addition, scalar multiples and linear combinations in $R^2$ as follows:

(1) $$\begin{pmatrix} x_1 \\ y_1 \end{pmatrix} + \begin{pmatrix} x_2 \\ y_2 \end{pmatrix} = \begin{pmatrix} x_1 + x_2 \\ y_1 + y_2 \end{pmatrix}$$

(2) $$\alpha \begin{pmatrix} x_1 \\ y_1 \end{pmatrix} = \begin{pmatrix} \alpha x_1 \\ \alpha y_1 \end{pmatrix}$$

(3) $$\alpha \begin{pmatrix} x_1 \\ y_1 \end{pmatrix} + \beta \begin{pmatrix} x_2 \\ y_2 \end{pmatrix} = \begin{pmatrix} \alpha x_1 + \beta x_2 \\ \alpha y_1 + \beta y_2 \end{pmatrix}$$

The column vector

$$\begin{pmatrix} x_1 \\ y_1 \end{pmatrix} = \mathbf{x}$$

corresponds to the position vector $x_1\hat{\mathbf{i}} + y_1\hat{\mathbf{i}}$, or $\overrightarrow{\mathrm{OP}}$, and to the point P in the plane with Cartesian coordinates $(x_1, y_1)$.

We define the modulus of the column vector

$$\mathbf{x} = \begin{pmatrix} x_1 \\ y_1 \end{pmatrix}$$

to be the length of the corresponding position vector $\overrightarrow{\mathrm{OP}}$, which, using Pythagoras' theorem, is $|\mathbf{x}| = \sqrt{x_1^2 + y_1^2}$. Thus, for example,

$$\left| \begin{pmatrix} 5 \\ -6 \end{pmatrix} \right| = \sqrt{5^2 + (-6)^2} = \sqrt{61} \approx 7{\cdot}81$$

We will again give a simplified treatment of linear dependence and independence, in which we consider just two vectors, which we will take as

$$\mathbf{a} = \begin{pmatrix} a_1 \\ a_2 \end{pmatrix} \text{ and } \mathbf{b} = \begin{pmatrix} b_1 \\ b_2 \end{pmatrix}$$

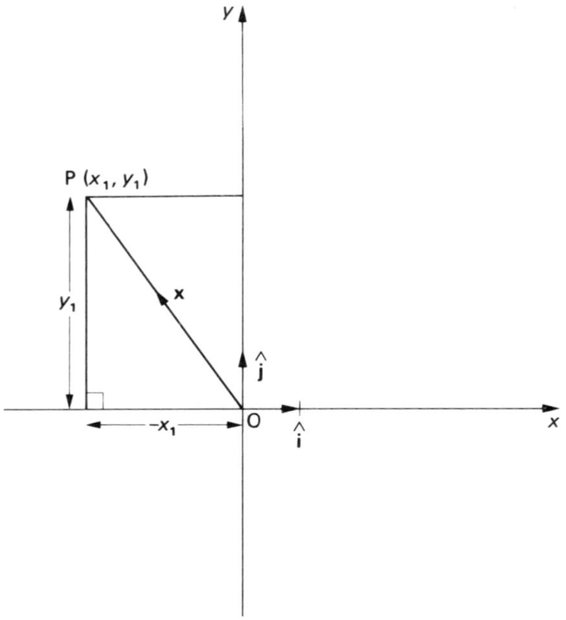


**Fig. 2.5.** The point $P(x_1, y_1)$ corresponding to the column vector $\mathbf{x} = \begin{pmatrix} x_1 \\ y_1 \end{pmatrix}$, with $x_1 < 0$.

Suppose that

$$\alpha \mathbf{a} + \beta \mathbf{b} = \mathbf{0} \tag{1}$$

Then $\{\mathbf{a}, \mathbf{b}\}$ will be linearly independent if $\alpha = \beta = 0$ is the only possible pair of values for $\alpha$ and $\beta$, and linearly dependent if there are other possible values. We therefore have

$$\alpha \begin{pmatrix} a_1 \\ a_2 \end{pmatrix} + \beta \begin{pmatrix} b_1 \\ b_2 \end{pmatrix} = \begin{pmatrix} 0 \\ 0 \end{pmatrix}$$

We may write this as two equations in the two unknowns $\alpha$ and $\beta$:

$$\left.\begin{aligned} a_1\alpha + b_1\beta = 0 \\ a_2\alpha + b_2\beta = 0 \end{aligned}\right\} \tag{2}$$

or as the equivalent matrix equation

$$\mathbf{M}\gamma = \mathbf{0} \tag{3}$$

where

$$\mathbf{M} = \begin{pmatrix} a_1 & b_1 \\ a_2 & b_2 \end{pmatrix} \text{ and } \gamma = \begin{pmatrix} \alpha \\ \beta \end{pmatrix}$$

Now, it can be shown that the matrix equation (2) has a solution other than

$\boldsymbol{\gamma} = \mathbf{0}$ if and only if the determinant det $\mathbf{M} = a_1b_2 - b_1a_2$ is zero. Thus det $\mathbf{M} = a_1b_2 - b_1a_2 = 0$ is the necessary and sufficient condition for each of:

(1) the vectors $\{\mathbf{a}, \mathbf{b}\}$ to be linearly dependent;

(2) the equations (2) to have solutions other than $\alpha = \beta = 0$;

(3) the equation (3) to have a solution other than $\boldsymbol{\gamma} = \mathbf{0}$.

**Worked example 2.4**

To find the value of $\alpha$ for which

$$\mathbf{a} = \begin{pmatrix} \alpha \\ 2 \end{pmatrix} \text{ and } \mathbf{b} = \begin{pmatrix} 3 \\ 4 \end{pmatrix}$$

are linearly dependent.

*Solution*

The vectors are linearly dependent if and only if

$$\begin{vmatrix} \alpha & 3 \\ 2 & 4 \end{vmatrix} = 0$$

i.e. $4\alpha - 6 = 0$, or $\alpha = 3/2$. Thus

$$\mathbf{a} = \begin{pmatrix} 3/2 \\ 2 \end{pmatrix} = \tfrac{1}{2}\mathbf{b}$$

This suggests the possibility that the condition for linear dependence of vectors in $R^2$ may be expressed more simply and conveniently. We return to the determinant condition:

$$\mathbf{a} = \begin{pmatrix} a_1 \\ a_2 \end{pmatrix} \text{ and } \mathbf{b} = \begin{pmatrix} b_1 \\ b_2 \end{pmatrix}$$

are linearly dependent if and only if $a_1b_2 - b_1a_2 = 0$, in other words $b_1/a_1 = b_2/a_2 (a_1a_2 \neq 0)$, which we see is the condition for $\mathbf{b}$ to be a scalar multiple of $\mathbf{a}$ with $\mathbf{a} \neq \mathbf{0}$. Thus two vectors in $R^2$ are linearly dependent if and only if one is a non-zero scalar multiple of the other. Thus $\{\mathbf{0}, \mathbf{a}\}$ is linearly dependent, because $\mathbf{a} = \alpha\mathbf{0}$ for any non-zero $\alpha$, even though there is no non-zero scalar $\beta$ such that $\mathbf{0} = \beta\mathbf{a}$.

**Exercise 2*e***

For this exercise, you are given the following vectors in $R^2$:

$$\hat{\mathbf{i}} = \begin{pmatrix} 1 \\ 0 \end{pmatrix}, \hat{\mathbf{j}} = \begin{pmatrix} 0 \\ 1 \end{pmatrix}, \mathbf{a} = \begin{pmatrix} 2 \\ -3 \end{pmatrix}, \mathbf{b} = \begin{pmatrix} 3 \\ \beta \end{pmatrix} \text{ and } \mathbf{c} = \begin{pmatrix} \alpha \\ 0{\cdot}4 \end{pmatrix}$$

1. Find the modulus of each of the following vectors:
   (a) $\mathbf{a}$, (b) $2\mathbf{a} - 3\hat{\mathbf{j}}$, (c) $\hat{\mathbf{i}} + \hat{\mathbf{j}} + \mathbf{a}$.
2. If $\tfrac{1}{6}\mathbf{b}$ and $\tfrac{1}{2}\mathbf{c}$ are both unit vectors, find $\alpha$ and $\beta$.
3. Find the value $\beta_0$ of $\beta$ such that $\{\mathbf{a}, \mathbf{b}\}$ is linearly dependent. Express each of $\hat{\mathbf{i}}$, $\hat{\mathbf{j}}$ and $\mathbf{c}$ as linear combinations of $\{\mathbf{a}, \mathbf{b}\}$ in the case $\beta = \beta_0 + \tfrac{1}{2}$, $\alpha = -2\beta_0$.

## 2.9 Miscellaneous exercises 2

1. $\hat{\imath}$, $\hat{\jmath}$ and $\hat{k}$ are the usual unit vectors. What are the spaces spanned by the following sets of vectors?
(a) $\{\hat{\imath}, \hat{\jmath}\}$, (b) $\{\hat{\imath} + \hat{\jmath}, \hat{\imath} - \hat{\jmath}, 2\hat{\imath} - 3\hat{\jmath}\}$
(c) $\{\hat{\imath} + \hat{\jmath}, \hat{\imath} - \hat{\jmath} - \hat{k}, 2\hat{\imath} - \hat{k}\}$
(d) $\{\hat{\imath} + \hat{\jmath}, \hat{\imath} - \hat{\jmath} - \hat{k}, \hat{\imath} - 2\hat{\jmath} + 3\hat{k}\}$

2. Show that the vectors $\mathbf{a} = \hat{\imath} - \hat{\jmath}$, $\mathbf{b} = \hat{\imath} - \hat{k}$ and $\mathbf{c} = \hat{\imath} + \hat{\jmath} + \hat{k}$ form a basis for three-dimensional space, and express each of $\hat{\imath}$, $\hat{\jmath}$ and $\hat{k}$ as linear combinations of these base vectors.

3.
$$\mathbf{a} = \begin{pmatrix} 2 \\ -3 \\ -1 \end{pmatrix} \text{ and } \mathbf{b} = \begin{pmatrix} -2 \\ 1 \\ 4 \end{pmatrix}$$

Find the modulus of each of the following column vectors: (a) $\mathbf{b}$, (b) $3\mathbf{a} - 4\mathbf{b}$.

4.
$$\mathbf{a} = \begin{pmatrix} 2 \\ -3 \\ -1 \end{pmatrix} \text{ and } \mathbf{b} = \begin{pmatrix} -2 \\ 1 \\ 4 \end{pmatrix}$$

Find the value of $\alpha$ for which the set $\{\mathbf{a}, \mathbf{b}, \mathbf{e}\}$ is linearly dependent, where

$$\mathbf{e} = \begin{pmatrix} \alpha \\ \alpha \\ 2 \end{pmatrix}$$

5. $\mathbf{a} = \begin{pmatrix} 2 \\ -3 \end{pmatrix}$, $\mathbf{b} = \begin{pmatrix} 4 \\ 3 \end{pmatrix}$ and $\mathbf{c} = \begin{pmatrix} \alpha \\ \beta \end{pmatrix}$

(a) Show that $\{\mathbf{a}, \mathbf{b}\}$ is linearly independent. Is it a basis for $R^2$?
(b) Is it possible to find non-zero $\alpha$ and $\beta$ such that $\{\mathbf{a}, \mathbf{c}\}$ and $\{\mathbf{b}, \mathbf{c}\}$ are both linearly dependent?
(c) Find $\alpha$ and $\beta$ such that $\{\mathbf{a}, \mathbf{c}\}$ is linearly dependent and $\mathbf{c}$ is a unit vector.

6. Show that the set of vectors

$$\mathbf{x}_1 = \begin{pmatrix} -1 \\ 2 \\ 1 \end{pmatrix}, \mathbf{x}_2 = \begin{pmatrix} 1 \\ 1 \\ 2 \end{pmatrix} \text{ and } \mathbf{x}_3 = \begin{pmatrix} -1 \\ 8 \\ 7 \end{pmatrix}$$

spans the same space as the set of vectors

$$\mathbf{y}_1 = \begin{pmatrix} -5 \\ 4 \\ -1 \end{pmatrix}, \mathbf{y}_2 = \begin{pmatrix} 1 \\ 7 \\ 8 \end{pmatrix} \text{ and } \mathbf{y}_3 = \begin{pmatrix} -11 \\ 1 \\ -10 \end{pmatrix}$$ (JMB)

7. Show that there is one and only one real value of $k$ for which the vectors

$$\mathbf{a} = \begin{pmatrix} k+1 \\ -3 \\ k \end{pmatrix}, \mathbf{b} = \begin{pmatrix} k \\ k+1 \\ -3 \end{pmatrix}, \mathbf{c} = \begin{pmatrix} -3 \\ k \\ k+1 \end{pmatrix}$$

are linearly dependent. (JMB)

# 3
# Introduction to Dynamics

## 3.1 Scalar displacement, velocity and acceleration

We presume that the reader is familiar with the relationship between distance, speed and acceleration in the case of straight line motion, but we will nevertheless summarize the results and give some proofs, for later comparison with the corresponding vector results.

Suppose a particle P moves in a straight line and that $x$ is its displacement from a fixed point O at time $t$. Then if the particle has displacements $x_1$ and $x_2$ at times $t_1$ and $t_2$ respectively, the *average velocity* of the particle between these times is defined as

$$\frac{\text{change in displacement}}{\text{change in time}} = \frac{x_2 - x_1}{t_2 - t_1}$$

In Fig. 3.1, the particle is at $P_1$ at time $t = 3$ s, and at $P_2$ at time $t = 5{\cdot}5$ s. If we take $\overrightarrow{OP_1}$ to determine the positive sense, then the displacement of $P_1$ is $3{\cdot}5$ m, and the displacement of $P_2$ is $-2$ m. Thus

$$\text{the average velocity} = \frac{[(-2) - (3{\cdot}5)]\text{ m}}{(5{\cdot}5 - 3)\text{ s}} = -2{\cdot}2 \text{ m s}^{-1}$$

i.e. of magnitude $2{\cdot}2$ m s$^{-1}$ in the direction and sense of $\overrightarrow{P_1O}$.

If, further, the particle has velocities $v_1$ and $v_2$ at times $t_1$ and $t_2$ respectively, then the *average acceleration* of the particle between times $t_1$ and $t_2$ is defined as

$$\frac{\text{change in velocity}}{\text{change in time}} = \frac{v_2 - v_1}{t_2 - t_1}$$

In Fig. 3.1, suppose the particle is moving in the direction and sense of $\overrightarrow{OP_2}$, and that its speed as it passes through $P_1$ is 4 m s$^{-1}$, and its speed as it passes through

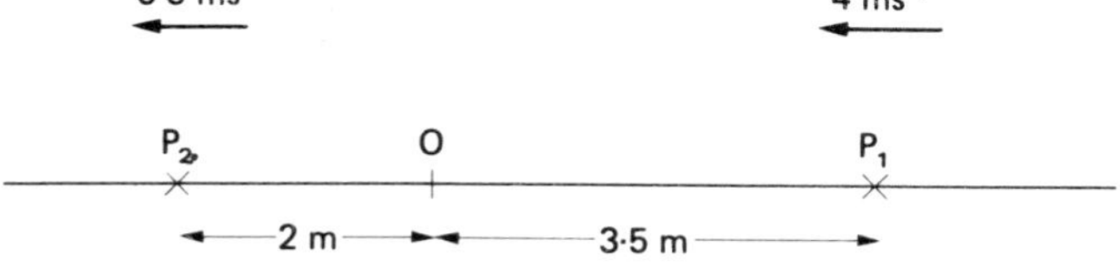


Fig. 3.1.

$P_2$ is $0\cdot5 \text{ m s}^{-1}$. Then its average acceleration is

$$\frac{[(-0\cdot5) - (-4)] \text{ ms}^{-1}}{(5\cdot5 - 3)\text{s}} = 1\cdot4 \text{ ms}^{-2}$$

In this diagram we have used the convention that velocities are shown with blocked-in arrows e.g. ⟶. Accelerations are usually marked ⟶».

In many instances, we wish to know the velocity or acceleration of the particle at a given instant of time, $t_0$ say. If we suppose that $x = x(t)$ is a differentiable function of time $t$, then the *instantaneous velocity* $v$ at time $t_0$ is given by

$$v = \lim_{t_1 \to t_0} \frac{x(t_1) - x(t_0)}{t_1 - t_0} = \left(\frac{\mathrm{d}x}{\mathrm{d}t}\right)_{t=t_0}$$

$= x'(t_0)$, where the prime denotes differentiation with respect to $t$

$= \dot{x}(t_0)$, where the dot denotes differentiation with respect to $t$.

We now have $v = v(t)$, say. The *instantaneous acceleration* $a$ at time $t_0$ is given by

$$\begin{aligned} a = \lim_{t_1 \to t_0} \frac{v(t_1) - v(t_0)}{t_1 - t_0} &= \left(\frac{\mathrm{d}v}{\mathrm{d}t}\right)_{t=t_0} \\ &= v'(t_0) \\ &= x''(t_0) \\ &= \dot{v}(t_0) \\ &= \ddot{x}(t_0) \\ &= \left(\frac{\mathrm{d}^2x}{\mathrm{d}t^2}\right)_{t=t_0} \\ &= \left(v\frac{\mathrm{d}v}{\mathrm{d}x}\right)_{\substack{v=v_0 \\ x=x_0}} \end{aligned}$$

where $x = x_0$, $v = v_0$ when $t = t_0$. (Since

$$\left.\frac{\mathrm{d}v}{\mathrm{d}t} = \frac{\mathrm{d}v}{\mathrm{d}x}\frac{\mathrm{d}x}{\mathrm{d}t} = v\frac{\mathrm{d}v}{\mathrm{d}x}\right)$$

We now have $a = a(t)$, say.

The reader will notice the large choice of methods of expression of these results, all of which are in current use.

By regarding integration as anti-differentiation, we may see that many of these results can be reversed. Thus

$$a(t) = \mathrm{d}v/\mathrm{d}t \quad \Rightarrow \quad \int_{t_1}^{t_2} a(t)\mathrm{d}t = \int_{v_1}^{v_2} \mathrm{d}v$$

Thus

$$v_2 - v_1 = \int_{t_1}^{t_2} a(t)\mathrm{d}t$$

where $v_1$ and $v_2$ are the velocities at times $t_1$ and $t_2$ respectively. More generally, if $v(t)$ is the velocity at time $t$, then we may obtain

$$v(t) - v_1 = \int_{t_1}^{t} a(t)\,\mathrm{d}t$$

Similarly,

$$v(t) = \mathrm{d}x/\mathrm{d}t$$

$$\Rightarrow \qquad \int_{t_1}^{t_2} v(t)\,\mathrm{d}t = \int_{x_1}^{x_2} \mathrm{d}x$$

and so

$$x_2 - x_1 = \int_{t_1}^{t_2} v(t)\,\mathrm{d}t,$$

where $x_1$ and $x_2$ are the displacements at times $t_1$ and $t_2$ respectively. More generally, if $x(t)$ is the displacement at time $t$, when we may obtain

$$x(t) - x_1 = \int_{t_1}^{t} v(t)\,\mathrm{d}t$$

## 3.2 Worked examples

**Worked Example 3.1**

If $x(t) = 2t^3 + 2t - 3$, then $v(t) = 6t^2 + 2$ and $a(t) = 12t$. Thus, in particular, the velocity $v$ is never zero in this case.

**Worked Example 3.2**

If $x(t) = t^2 - 5t + 4$, then $v(t) = 2t - 5$ and $a(t) = 2$. Then $x(4) = x(1) = 0$, so that the particle is at the origin at times $t = 1$ s and $t = 4$ s.

Also, $v(2{\cdot}5) = 0$, so that at time $t = 2{\cdot}5$ s the particle is momentarily at rest, and after that time it travels in the opposite sense to its earlier motion.

Since $a(t)$ is constant and positive $v(t)$ increases steadily with time.

**Worked Example 3.3**

Suppose that $v(t) = t^2 - 5t + 4 = (t - 4)(t - 1)$, and that $x(0) = 0$. Then

$$x(t) - x(0) = \int_{0}^{t} (t^2 - 5t + 4)\,\mathrm{d}t \qquad (1)$$

$$= \left[\tfrac{1}{3}t^3 - \tfrac{5}{2}t^2 + 4t\right]_0^t$$

and so

$$x(t) = \tfrac{1}{3}t^3 - \tfrac{5}{2}t^2 + 4t$$

A special problem arises in this case if we wish to find the total distance travelled between, say, $t = 0$ s and $t = 2$ s, rather than the change in displacement between these times. The problem arises because the integrand in equation (1) changes sign in the range concerned, namely at $t = 1$ s.

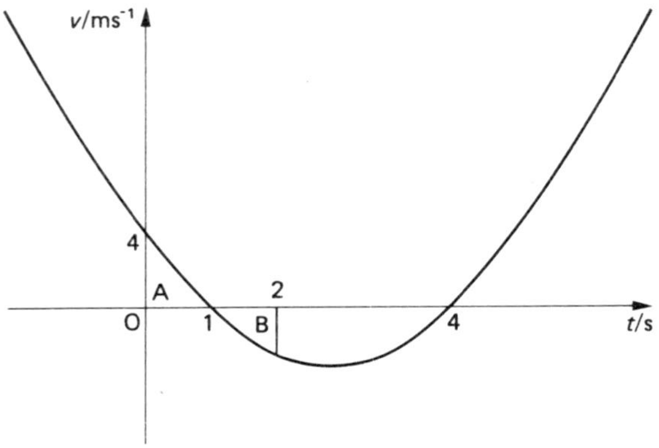


**Fig. 3.2.** Worked example 3.3.

This is perhaps best demonstrated by drawing a sketch of the graph of $v(t)$ against $t$ (see Fig. 3.2). The change in *displacement* is given by the integral $\int_0^2 v(t)\,dt$, which gives the value of the area beneath the curve, which will be $A - B$, where $A$ and $B$ are the magnitudes of the areas shown in the diagram. The total *distance* travelled is given by $A + B$, i.e. by

$$\begin{aligned}\int_0^1 v(t)\,dt - \int_1^2 v(t)\,dt &= x(1) - x(0) - [x(2) - x(1)] \\ &= 2x(1) - x(2) \quad (\text{since } x(0) = 0) \\ &= [2(\tfrac{1}{3} - \tfrac{5}{2} + 4) - (\tfrac{8}{3} - 10 + 8)]\ \text{m} \\ &= 3\ \text{m}\end{aligned}$$

More generally, we may say that the distance travelled between times $t_1$ and $t_2$ can be written as

$$\text{distance travelled} = \int_{t_1}^{t_2} |v(t)|\,dt = d(t_2) - d(t_1),$$

say, thus defining the distance function

$$d(t) = d(t_1) + \int_{t_1}^{t} |v(t)|\,dt$$

In the above example, $d(0) = 0$, and we may write

$$d(t) = \begin{cases} \tfrac{1}{3}t^3 - \tfrac{5}{2}t^2 + 4t & (0 \leqq t \leqq 1) \\ \tfrac{11}{3} - (\tfrac{1}{3}t^3 - \tfrac{5}{2}t^2 + 4t) & (1 \leqq t \leqq 4) \\ 9 + (\tfrac{1}{3}t^3 - \tfrac{5}{2}t^2 + 4t) & (4 \leqq t) \end{cases}$$

**Exercise 3*a***

These questions all involve a particle travelling in a straight line, so that at time $t$ (in s), its displacement from the origin O is $x(t)$ (in m), its velocity is $v(t)$ (in m s$^{-1}$), and its acceleration is $a(t)$ (in m s$^{-2}$).

1. $x(t) = 2t^3 - 21t^2 + 72t + 45$. Find $x$ and $a$ when $v$ is zero.
2. Discuss the motion of a particle obeying $x(t) = \sin t$.
3. $v(t) = t^2 - 9$. Find the distance travelled between the two times when $v$ is zero.
4. $v(t) = t^2 + 3t - 4$. Find the distance travelled: (a) in the first second; (b) in the first two seconds.
5. $v(t) = t^2 - 4t + 3$. Find $a(2)$, $a(3)$, and the acceleration when $v$ is zero.
6. $v(t) = \sin t + \cos t$. Find the distance travelled before the particle returns to its starting place.
7. $v(t) = \sin 3t \cos 4t$, $x(0) = 0$. Find $x(t)$ and $a(t)$.
8. $v(t) = t^{-2}$, $x(1) = 1$. Find $a(t)$ and $x(t)$.
9. $a(t) = kt$, $k$ constant, $v(0) = u$, $x(0) = b$. Find $v(t)$ and $x(t)$.
10. $x(t) = 2^t$. Discuss the motion.
11. $x(t) = 2t^2 - 3t + 4$. Find the least distance from the origin.
12. $v(x) = 3x$. Find $a(x)$. Does it matter what $x$ is?
13. $v(x) = x^2$. Find $x(t)$, $a(x)$ and $a(t)$, given that $x(0) = 1$ m and $t < 1$ s.

## 3.3 Vector functions

In the previous sections, $x$, $v$ and $a$ have all been scalar functions of the time $t$. Similarly, our common quadratics, like $y = 3x^2 - 4x$, are scalar functions of $x$. It is natural to wish to be able to deal in a similar fashion with vector functions of a scalar variable. Such functions may represent vector quantities like velocity or force. In other words, we do not wish to be confined to motion in a straight line, or even in a plane.

The simplest form a vector function of a scalar variable can take is $\mathbf{r}(u) = \mathbf{a}$, where $\mathbf{r}(u)$ is our vector function, which we may abbreviate as $\mathbf{r}$, $u$ is the scalar variable, and $\mathbf{a}$ is some fixed vector. In other words, $\mathbf{r}(u) = \mathbf{a}$ does not actually depend on $u$ at all, in this case.

We could equally well have $\mathbf{r}(u) = u^2\hat{\mathbf{a}}$, for example, which is a vector constant in direction, but varying in magnitude according to the law $|\mathbf{r}| = u^2$.

If $\mathbf{r}$ is a position vector, then it determines a point P at its head, i.e. $\overrightarrow{OP} = \mathbf{r}$. As the scalar variable $u$ varies, so P will describe some path (perhaps a curve) called its *locus*. We shall often be interested in the locus of P. In the case $\mathbf{r}(u) = u^2\hat{\mathbf{a}}$, the locus of P is a straight line.

Now consider $\mathbf{r}(u) = 2u\,\hat{\mathbf{i}} + u^2\hat{\mathbf{j}}$, where $\hat{\mathbf{i}}$ and $\hat{\mathbf{j}}$ are the usual unit vectors along the axis O$x$ and O$y$. We may draw the locus of P as follows: The locus of P consists of the set of points $\{(2u, u^2)\}$, i.e. it is the curve $x^2 = 4y$, a parabola. Fig. 3.3 shows this locus, with some particular positions of P marked.

We could use vector functions of a scalar variable to describe the position in a plane, or in space, of a particle at time $t$. For example, if the scalar variable $t$ represents time, then the vector function $\mathbf{r}(t) = 3t^2\hat{\mathbf{i}} + 4\hat{\mathbf{j}} + 6t\hat{\mathbf{k}}$ may be taken to represent the position $\mathbf{r}$ of a particle at time $t$.

In particular, if we take $t = 2$ s, we see that the position of the particle after two seconds is $\mathbf{r}(2) = 12\hat{\mathbf{i}} + 4\hat{\mathbf{j}} + 12\hat{\mathbf{k}}$, i.e. the particle is at the point (12, 4, 12). The next section will show how to find the velocity and acceleration of this particle at any given instant.

If we have a particle moving in a plane, then we can express its position vector $\mathbf{r}(t)$ in the form $\mathbf{r}(t) = r(t)\,\hat{\mathbf{r}}$, where $\hat{\mathbf{r}}$ is the unit vector in the direction $\mathbf{r}$, i.e. its

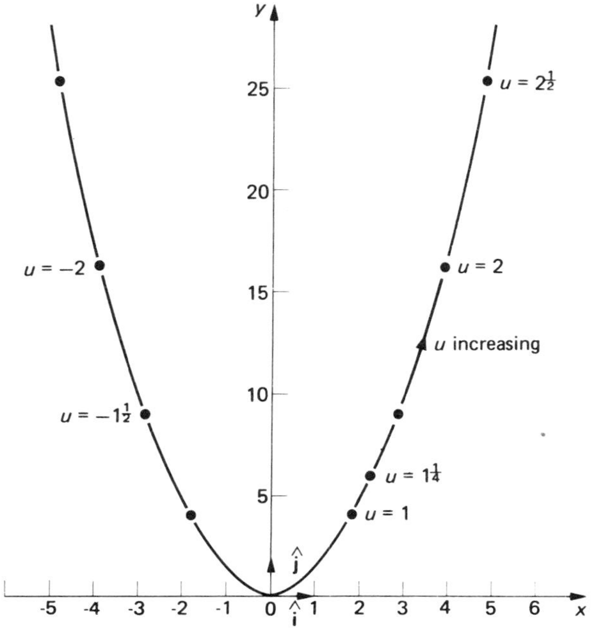


**Fig. 3.3.** The locus of the point with position vector $2u\hat{\mathbf{i}} + u^2\hat{\mathbf{j}}$.

direction changes with the motion of the particle. We will see later that we need also the unit vector $\hat{\theta}$ at right angles to $\hat{\mathbf{r}}$ to describe the velocity of the particle. These unit vectors were defined in Chapter 1.

## 3.4 Differentiation of vector functions

We shall now attempt to differentiate vector functions of a single scalar variable. Note that the variable will not necessarily be taken to be time, although we are particularly interested in that possibility. Although it is not possible at this stage to deal with the differentiation of vector functions with great rigour, the results we shall deduce are all valid.

One possible motive for the differentiation of vector functions is that we hope that $\mathrm{d}\mathbf{r}/\mathrm{d}t$ might give the velocity of a particle whose position at time $t$ is given by $\mathbf{r}$. This would then be in line with the scalar result that $\mathrm{d}x/\mathrm{d}t$ is the velocity of a particle moving in a straight line such that its displacement from the origin O at time $t$ is $x(t)$.

Suppose, then, that a vector $\mathbf{r}$ is a continuous function of a single scalar variable $u$. We may write $\mathbf{r} = \mathbf{r}(u)$. Choose an origin O, and suppose that $\mathbf{r}$ is the position vector of a point P corresponding to the value $u$ of the scalar variable.

An increment $\delta u$ in $u$ will produce an increment $\delta\mathbf{r}$ in $\mathbf{r}$. Let P′ be the point corresponding to the value $u + \delta u$ of the scalar variable. P′ is, of course, a point on the locus of P.

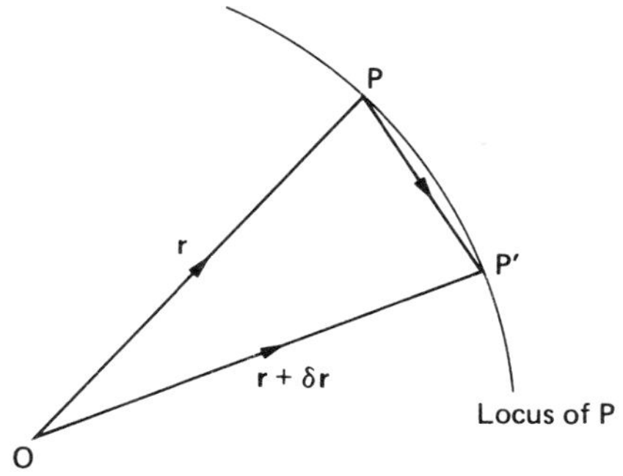


**Fig. 3.4.** The points given by $\mathbf{r}$ and $\mathbf{r} + \delta\mathbf{r}$.

From the diagram, we have

$$\mathbf{r} + \overrightarrow{PP'} = \mathbf{r} + \delta\mathbf{r}$$

thus

$$\overrightarrow{PP'} = \delta\mathbf{r}$$

Now consider $\delta\mathbf{r}/\delta u$. This is a vector, and is a scalar multiple of $\delta\mathbf{r}$. Now, as $\delta u$ tends to zero, then P′ approaches P along the curve, and the chord PP′ approaches the tangent to the curve at P. This argument is analogous to that used in an elementary treatment of differentiation of scalar functions. Hence the limit as $\delta u$ tends to zero of $\delta\mathbf{r}/\delta u$, i.e.

$$\lim_{\delta u \to 0} \frac{\delta\mathbf{r}}{\delta u}$$

is a vector with direction that of the tangent at P. The sense of this vector is that of increasing $u$. If this limit exists, it is called the derivative of $\mathbf{r}(u)$ with respect to $u$, and we write

$$\frac{d\mathbf{r}}{du} = \lim_{\delta u \to 0} \frac{\delta\mathbf{r}}{\delta u}$$

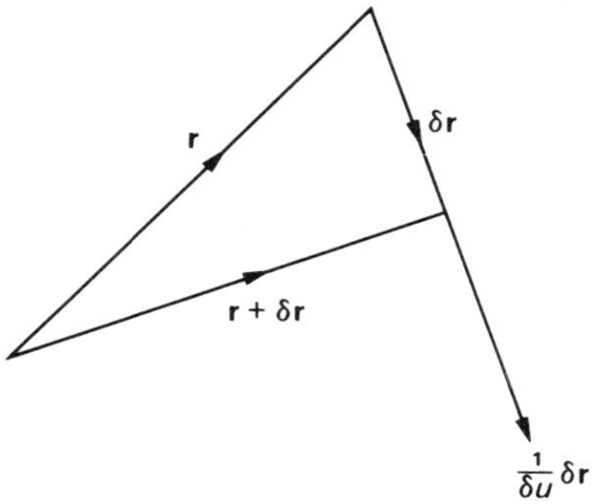


**Fig. 3.5.** $\delta\mathbf{r}/\delta u$ as a scalar multiple of $\delta\mathbf{r}$.

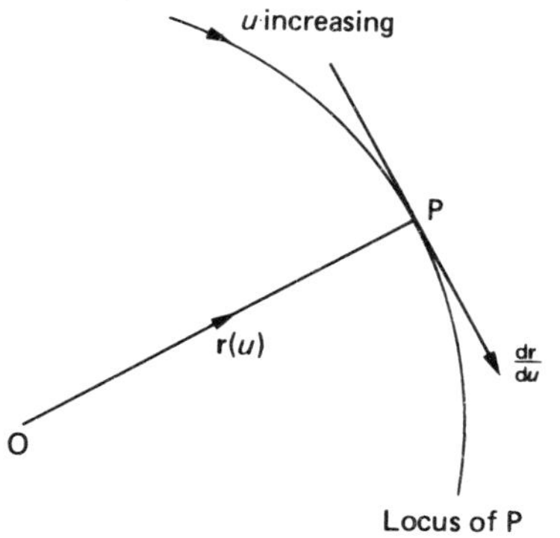


**Fig. 3.6.** The tangent vector $\mathrm{d}\mathbf{r}/\mathrm{d}u$.

This process is called differentiation of the vector function $\mathbf{r}(u)$. Higher-order derivatives, e.g.

$$\frac{\mathrm{d}^2\mathbf{r}}{\mathrm{d}u^2} = \frac{\mathrm{d}}{\mathrm{d}u}\left(\frac{\mathrm{d}\mathbf{r}}{\mathrm{d}u}\right)$$

may also exist.

The process may also be expressed entirely algebraically, as follows. Let the vector $\mathbf{r}$ be a function of the scalar $u$:

$$\mathbf{r} = \mathbf{r}(u)$$

Evaluate $\mathbf{r}$ for the value $u + \delta u$:

$$\mathbf{r} + \delta\mathbf{r} = \mathbf{r}(u + \delta u)$$

Subtract to find the change in $\mathbf{r}$:

$$\delta\mathbf{r} = \mathbf{r}(u + \delta u) - \mathbf{r}(u)$$

Divide by $\delta u$ to find the rate of increase:

$$\frac{\delta\mathbf{r}}{\delta u} = \frac{\mathbf{r}(u + \delta u) - \mathbf{r}(u)}{\delta u}$$

Take the limit as $\delta u$ tends to zero:

$$\frac{\mathrm{d}\mathbf{r}}{\mathrm{d}u} = \lim_{\delta u \to 0} \frac{\delta\mathbf{r}}{\delta u} = \lim_{\delta u \to 0} \frac{\mathbf{r}(u + \delta u) - \mathbf{r}(u)}{\delta u}$$

## 3.5 Differentiation of vector functions of time

Let us now consider the case where the scalar variable is time. In Fig. 3.4, we now see that $\delta\mathbf{r}$ represents the displacement of particle P in time $\delta t$ (where $t$ is written instead of $u$). Hence $\delta\mathbf{r}/\delta t$ is the average velocity for the time interval $\delta t$. By analogy with scalar functions, we see that

$$\frac{\mathrm{d}\mathbf{r}}{\mathrm{d}t} = \lim_{\delta t \to 0} \frac{\delta\mathbf{r}}{\delta t}$$

is the instantaneous velocity $\mathbf{v}(t)$ of the particle at time $t$.

Similarly, the instantaneous acceleration $\mathbf{a}(t)$ of the particle at time $t$ is given by

$$\mathbf{a}(t) = \frac{d\mathbf{v}}{dt} = \frac{d^2\mathbf{r}}{dt^2}$$

as in the scalar case. We have not yet done enough to enable us to actually *find* these quantities—we so far only know where to look.

## 3.6 Differentiation of linear combinations

As we said above, we are not yet actually in the position to find velocities and accelerations. To do this, we will require to be able to differentiate functions like

$$\mathbf{r}(t) = 3t^2\hat{\mathbf{i}} + 4\hat{\mathbf{j}} + 6t\hat{\mathbf{k}},$$

and

$$\mathbf{r}(t) = 5t^3\hat{\mathbf{r}}$$

and

$$\mathbf{v}(t) = 2t\hat{\mathbf{r}} + (t^2 - t - 1)\hat{\boldsymbol{\theta}}$$

These are all linear combinations of unit vectors, which may themselves vary with time.

The following results are all true:

(1) For a constant vector $\mathbf{a}$, $d\mathbf{a}/du = 0$.

(2) For $\mathbf{x} = \mathbf{x}(u)$ and $\mathbf{y} = \mathbf{y}(u)$, we have

$$\frac{d}{du}(\mathbf{x} + \mathbf{y}) = \frac{d\mathbf{x}}{du} + \frac{d\mathbf{y}}{du}$$

(3) For a vector function $\mathbf{x} = \mathbf{x}(u)$ and a scalar function $f = f(u)$, then

$$\frac{d}{du}(f\mathbf{x}) = f\frac{d\mathbf{x}}{du} + \mathbf{x}\frac{df}{du}$$

We will prove (3), and leave the other two proofs to the reader.

$$\begin{aligned}
\frac{d}{du}(f\mathbf{x}) &= \lim_{\delta u \to 0} \frac{(f\mathbf{x})(u + \delta u) - (f\mathbf{x})(u)}{\delta u} \quad \text{by definition} \\
&= \lim_{\delta u \to 0} \frac{f(u + \delta u)\mathbf{x}(u + \delta u) - f(u)\mathbf{x}(u)}{\delta u} \\
&= \lim_{\delta u \to 0} \frac{f(u + \delta u)\mathbf{x}(u + \delta u) - f(u + \delta u)\mathbf{x}(u) + f(u + \delta u)\mathbf{x}(u) - f(u)\mathbf{x}(u)}{\delta u} \\
&= \lim_{\delta u \to 0} f(u + \delta u)\frac{\mathbf{x}(u + \delta u) - \mathbf{x}(u)}{\delta u} + \lim_{\delta u \to 0} \mathbf{x}(u)\frac{f(u + \delta u) - f(u)}{\delta u}
\end{aligned}$$

by limit theory

Thus

$$\frac{d}{du}(f\mathbf{x}) = f(u)\frac{d\mathbf{x}}{du} + \mathbf{x}(u)\frac{df}{du}$$

by limit theory and by our definition of derivative.

We may combine these three results to give a particularly useful result:

$$\frac{d}{du}(p_1(u)\hat{\mathbf{i}} + p_2(u)\hat{\mathbf{j}} + p_3(u)\hat{\mathbf{k}})$$

$$= \frac{d}{du}(p_1(u)\hat{\mathbf{i}}) + \frac{d}{du}(p_2(u)\hat{\mathbf{j}}) + \frac{d}{du}(p_3(u)\hat{\mathbf{k}}) \qquad \text{by (2)}$$

$$= p_1\frac{d\hat{\mathbf{i}}}{du} + \hat{\mathbf{i}}\frac{dp_1}{du} + p_2\frac{d\hat{\mathbf{j}}}{du} + \hat{\mathbf{j}}\frac{dp_2}{du} + p_3\frac{d\hat{\mathbf{k}}}{du} + \hat{\mathbf{k}}\frac{dp_3}{du} \qquad \text{by (3)}$$

$$= \frac{dp_1}{du}\hat{\mathbf{i}} + \frac{dp_2}{du}\hat{\mathbf{j}} + \frac{dp_3}{du}\hat{\mathbf{k}} \qquad \text{by (1)}$$

In other words, the components of a vector expressed in Cartesian form may be differentiated separately to give the components of the derivative.

Thus, in our original example, we have

$$\mathbf{r}(t) = 3t^2\hat{\mathbf{i}} + 4\hat{\mathbf{j}} + 6t\,\hat{\mathbf{k}}$$

thus

$$\mathbf{v}(t) = \frac{d\mathbf{r}}{dt} = 6t\,\hat{\mathbf{i}} + 0\hat{\mathbf{j}} + 6\hat{\mathbf{k}}$$

and

$$\mathbf{a}(t) = \frac{d\mathbf{v}}{dt} = 6\hat{\mathbf{i}},$$

which is a constant—the particle is subjected to a constant acceleration of 6 m s$^{-2}$ in the direction and sense of $\hat{\mathbf{i}}$.

Note that at this stage we still cannot differentiate fully the function

$$\mathbf{r}(t) = 5t^3\hat{\mathbf{r}}$$

since

$$\frac{d\mathbf{r}}{dt} = 15t^2\hat{\mathbf{r}} + 5t^3\frac{d\hat{\mathbf{r}}}{dt}$$

and $d\hat{\mathbf{r}}/dt$ is *not* zero, as its direction is variable. This will be dealt with in a later chapter.

**Exercise 3*b***

1. Differentiate $\mathbf{a}/u$ and $\mathbf{a}\sin u + \mathbf{b}$ with respect to $u$, where $\mathbf{a}$ and $\mathbf{b}$ are constant vectors.

2. Find $d\mathbf{r}/dt$ and $d^2\mathbf{r}/dt^2$, if $\mathbf{r} = \mathbf{a}\cos nt + \mathbf{b}\sin nt$ and $\mathbf{a}$ and $\mathbf{b}$ are constant vectors. Hence find a differential equation not involving $\mathbf{a}$ and $\mathbf{b}$.

3. Differentiate the following with respect to $u$, where $\mathbf{a}$ and $\mathbf{b}$ are constant vectors:

(a) $\dfrac{\mathbf{a} + \mathbf{b}u^2}{u^3}$, (b) $e^u\mathbf{a} - e^{-u}\mathbf{b}$, (c) $\sin(u^2)\mathbf{a} + \arctan u\mathbf{b}$

4. Find $d\mathbf{r}/dt$ and its magnitude for

(a) $\mathbf{r} = 3t^2\hat{\mathbf{i}} - t^2\hat{\mathbf{j}}$, (b) $\mathbf{r} = \sin t\,\hat{\mathbf{i}} + \cos t\,\hat{\mathbf{j}} + \tan t\,\hat{\mathbf{k}}$

## 3.7 Integration of vector functions

We shall, for the time being, regard the process of integration as that of anti-differentiation. As in the case of differentiation, we shall not concern ourselves with extensive rigour, but shall state some useful results, which will be proved at a later stage.

Suppose, then, that $\mathbf{F}(u)$ is a differentiable vector function, and that $\mathbf{F}'(u) = \mathbf{f}(u)$. Then we define the *definite integral* $\int_a^b \mathbf{f}(u)\mathrm{d}u$ by

$$\int_a^b \mathbf{f}(u)\mathrm{d}u = \mathbf{F}(b) - \mathbf{F}(a) \tag{1}$$

and the *indefinite integral* $\int \mathbf{f}(u)\mathrm{d}u$ by

$$\int \mathbf{f}(u)\mathrm{d}u = \mathbf{F}(u) + \mathbf{c}$$

where $\mathbf{c}$ is an arbitrary constant vector.

In the particular case when the scalar variable $u$ is time $t$, then we have results corresponding to those of Section 3.1, page 48. Thus

$$\mathbf{a}(t) = \mathrm{d}\mathbf{v}/\mathrm{d}t \quad \Rightarrow \quad \int_{t_1}^{t_2} \mathbf{a}(t)\mathrm{d}t = \mathbf{v}(t_2) - \mathbf{v}(t_1)$$

and

$$\int_{t_1}^{t} \mathbf{a}(t)\mathrm{d}t = \mathbf{v}(t) - \mathbf{v}(t_1)$$

Similarly,

$$\mathbf{v}(t) = \mathrm{d}\mathbf{r}/\mathrm{d}t \quad \Rightarrow \quad \int_{t_1}^{t_2} \mathbf{v}(t)\mathrm{d}t = \mathbf{r}(t_2) - \mathbf{r}(t_1)$$

and

$$\int_{t_1}^{t} \mathbf{v}(t)\mathrm{d}t = \mathbf{r}(t) - \mathbf{r}(t_1)$$

We may also establish results for the integration of scalar multiples and linear combinations, corresponding to those of Section 3.6 for differentiation. Again, proof will be avoided at this stage.

The following are all true:

(1) For a constant vector $\mathbf{a}$, $\int \mathbf{a}\,\mathrm{d}u = \mathbf{a}u + \mathbf{b}$, where $\mathbf{b}$ is a constant vector.

(2) For $\mathbf{x} = \mathbf{x}(u)$ and $\mathbf{y} = \mathbf{y}(u)$, we have $\int (\mathbf{x} + \mathbf{y})\mathrm{d}u = \int \mathbf{x}\,\mathrm{d}u + \int \mathbf{y}\,\mathrm{d}u$.

(3) For a vector function $\mathbf{x} = \mathbf{x}(u)$ and a scalar function $f' = f'(u)$, then

$$\int \mathbf{x}f'\mathrm{d}u = \mathbf{x}f - \int f\mathbf{x}'\mathrm{d}u$$

i.e. integration by parts is possible.

(4) For a vector function $\mathbf{x}' = \mathbf{x}'(u)$ and a scalar function $f = f(u)$, then

$$\int \mathbf{x}'f\,\mathrm{d}u = \mathbf{x}f - \int \mathbf{x}f'\,\mathrm{d}u$$

This may, of course, be deduced directly from Equ. 3 instead of being quoted in its own right.

We may combine these results to give a particularly useful result:

$$\int (p_1(u)\hat{\mathbf{i}} + p_2(u)\hat{\mathbf{j}} + p_3(u)\hat{\mathbf{k}})\mathrm{d}u$$
$$= \hat{\mathbf{i}}\int p_1(u)\mathrm{d}u + \hat{\mathbf{j}}\int p_2(u)\mathrm{d}u + \hat{\mathbf{k}}\int p_3(u)\mathrm{d}u$$

In other words, the components of a vector expressed in Cartesian form may be integrated separately to give the components of the integrated vector.

## 3.8 Worked examples

These worked examples are intended to demonstrate the processes of differentiation and integration of vectors, although they will be expressed in terms of the motion of a particle.

### Worked example 3.4

The velocity of a particle at time $t$ is given by the vector function $\mathbf{v}(t) = (t^2 - 4)\hat{\mathbf{i}} + 5t\hat{\mathbf{j}}$. Find the displacement $\mathbf{x}(t)$ and the acceleration $\mathbf{a}(t)$ at time $t$, if it is given that $\mathbf{x}(1) = \hat{\mathbf{j}}$.

*Solution*

$$\mathbf{a}(t) = \mathbf{v}'(t) = 2t\hat{\mathbf{i}} + 5\hat{\mathbf{j}}$$

$$\mathbf{x}(t) - \mathbf{x}(1) = \int_1^t \mathbf{v}(t)\mathrm{d}t$$

thus

$$\mathbf{x}(t) - \hat{\mathbf{j}} = \int_1^t \left[(t^2 - 4)\hat{\mathbf{i}} + 5t\hat{\mathbf{j}}\right]\mathrm{d}t$$

and so

$$\mathbf{x}(t) = \left[(\tfrac{1}{3}t^3 - 4t)\hat{\mathbf{i}} + \tfrac{5}{2}t^2\hat{\mathbf{j}}\right]_1^t + \hat{\mathbf{j}}$$
$$= (\tfrac{1}{3}t^3 - 4t)\hat{\mathbf{i}} + \tfrac{5}{2}t^2\hat{\mathbf{j}} - (-\tfrac{11}{3}\hat{\mathbf{i}} + \tfrac{5}{2}\hat{\mathbf{j}}) + \hat{\mathbf{j}}$$

thus

$$\mathbf{x}(t) = (\tfrac{1}{3}t^3 - 4t + \tfrac{11}{3})\hat{\mathbf{i}} + (\tfrac{5}{2}t^2 - \tfrac{3}{2})\hat{\mathbf{j}}$$

### Worked example 3.5

A particle moves with acceleration $\mathbf{a}(t) = t\hat{\mathbf{i}} + t\hat{\mathbf{j}}$, and is at rest at the origin at time $t = 0$ s. Investigate its subsequent motion.

*Solution*

This problem shows that there is a need for careful thought before proceeding with a solution using the formulae automatically. For we have

$$\mathbf{a}(t) = t\hat{\mathbf{i}} + t\hat{\mathbf{j}}$$
$$= t(\hat{\mathbf{i}} + \hat{\mathbf{j}})$$
$$= t\mathbf{b} \text{ say}$$

where $\mathbf{b} = \hat{\mathbf{i}} + \hat{\mathbf{j}}$ and is constant. Thus

$$\mathbf{v}(t) - \mathbf{v}(0) = \int_0^t t\mathbf{b}\,\mathrm{d}t$$

and so

$$\mathbf{v}(t) = \tfrac{1}{2}t^2\mathbf{b}$$

Similarly,

$$\mathbf{x}(t) = \tfrac{1}{6}t^3\mathbf{b}$$

and we see that the particle is moving in the straight line $y = x$, which is the direction given by the constant vector $\mathbf{b} = \hat{\mathbf{i}} + \hat{\mathbf{j}}$. Its distance from the origin at time $t$ is

$$|\mathbf{x}(t)| = |\tfrac{1}{6}t^3| \times |\mathbf{b}| = \tfrac{1}{6}t^3\sqrt{2} \quad \text{since } t \geqq 0$$

Note, however, that this problem is changed if we change the initial conditions in certain ways, as, for example, in worked example 3.6.

**Worked example 3.6**

A particle moves with acceleration $\mathbf{a}(t) = t\hat{\mathbf{i}} + t\hat{\mathbf{j}}$, and has velocity $\mathbf{v}(t)$ and displacement $\mathbf{x}(t)$ at time $t$. Investigate the subsequent motion of the particle if $\mathbf{x}(0) = -\hat{\mathbf{i}}$ and $\mathbf{v}(0) = -\hat{\mathbf{j}}$.

*Solution*

This problem is different from the previous worked example, in that the acceleration and the initial velocity are not now in the same direction. The acceleration will therefore cause a change in direction of the velocity, and the particle will not in this case move in a straight line.

We have

$$\mathbf{a}(t) = t\hat{\mathbf{i}} + t\hat{\mathbf{j}}$$

Therefore

$$\mathbf{v}(t) - \mathbf{v}(0) = \int_0^t (t\hat{\mathbf{i}} + t\hat{\mathbf{j}})\mathrm{d}t$$

and so

$$\mathbf{v}(t) + \hat{\mathbf{j}} = \left[\tfrac{1}{2}t^2\hat{\mathbf{i}} + \tfrac{1}{2}t^2\hat{\mathbf{j}}\right]_0^t$$

Therefore

$$\mathbf{v}(t) = \tfrac{1}{2}t^2\hat{\mathbf{i}} + (\tfrac{1}{2}t^2 - 1)\hat{\mathbf{j}}$$

Therefore

$$\mathbf{x}(t) - \mathbf{x}(0) = \int_0^t \left[\tfrac{1}{2}t^2\hat{\mathbf{i}} + (\tfrac{1}{2}t^2 - 1)\hat{\mathbf{j}}\right]\mathrm{d}t$$

and so

$$\mathbf{x}(t) + \hat{\mathbf{i}} = \left[\tfrac{1}{6}t^3\hat{\mathbf{i}} + (\tfrac{1}{6}t^3 - t)\hat{\mathbf{j}}\right]_0^t$$

Therefore

$$\mathbf{x}(t) = (\tfrac{1}{6}t^3 - 1)\hat{\mathbf{i}} + (\tfrac{1}{6}t^3 - t)\hat{\mathbf{j}}$$
$$= x(t)\hat{\mathbf{i}} + y(t)\hat{\mathbf{j}} \text{ say}$$

By eliminating $t$, we obtain $6(x + 1) = (x - y + 1)^3$ as the equation of the curve along which the particle moves. If we tabulate the vector $\mathbf{x}(t)$ for $t = 0{\cdot}0(0{\cdot}5)4{\cdot}0$, we obtain the graph shown in Fig. 3.7 as the path of the particle.

We thus see that, initially, the particle moves on a curve, but eventually its motion is nearly linear and in approximately the same direction and sense at the acceleration $\mathbf{a}(t)$.

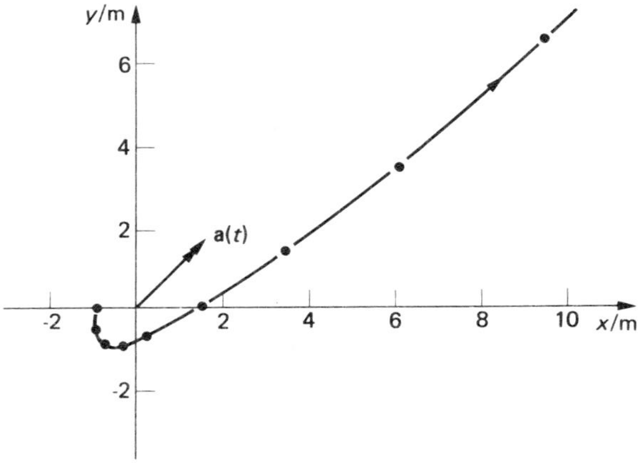


**Fig. 3.7.** Worked example 3.6.

## Exercise 3*c*

1. Integrate the following with respect to $u$, where $\mathbf{a}$ and $\mathbf{b}$ are constant vectors:

(a) $\dfrac{\mathbf{a} + \mathbf{b}u^2}{u^3}$, (b) $e^u\mathbf{a} - e^{-u}\mathbf{b}$, (c) $\sin^2 u\,\mathbf{a} + \tan u\,\mathbf{b}$

2. Integrate the following with respect to $t$:

(a) $2t\hat{\mathbf{i}} + t^3\hat{\mathbf{j}}$, (b) $\sin 2t\,\hat{\mathbf{i}} - \cos 3t\,\hat{\mathbf{j}}$, (c) $\cos^3 t\,\hat{\mathbf{i}} + \sin^3 t\,\hat{\mathbf{j}}$

3. Find (i) $\int_0^t |\mathbf{r}(t)|\mathrm{d}t$ and (ii) $|\int_0^t \mathbf{r}(t)\mathrm{d}t|$ if

(a) $\mathbf{r} = 2t\hat{\mathbf{i}} + 3t\hat{\mathbf{j}}$
(b) $\mathbf{r} = 2t\hat{\mathbf{i}} + 3\hat{\mathbf{j}}$

4. Evaluate the definite integrals

(a) $\displaystyle\int_{-1}^{1}(t^2\hat{\mathbf{i}} - 2t^3\hat{\mathbf{j}} + \hat{\mathbf{k}})\mathrm{d}t$, (b) $\displaystyle\int_1^2\left(\frac{\hat{\mathbf{i}} + \hat{\mathbf{j}}}{2t} + t\hat{\mathbf{k}}\right)\mathrm{d}t$

5. The velocity of a particle at time $t$ is given by the vector function $\mathbf{v}(t) = (2t + 1)\hat{\mathbf{i}} + (1 - t)\hat{\mathbf{j}}$. Find the displacement $\mathbf{x}(t)$ and the acceleration $\mathbf{a}(t)$ at time $t$ if it is given that $\mathbf{x}(1) = \hat{\mathbf{i}} - \hat{\mathbf{j}}$.

6. A particle moves with acceleration $t^2\hat{\mathbf{i}} + (t^2 - \alpha)\hat{\mathbf{j}}$, and is at rest at the origin at time $t = 0$ s. Investigate its subsequent motion in the cases: (a) $\alpha = -1$; (b) $\alpha = 0$; and (c) $\alpha = +1$.

## 3.9 Miscellaneous exercises 3

1. A particle travels in a straight line so that at time $t$ its displacement from the origin O is $x$, its velocity is $v$ and its acceleration $a$.
(i) If $a(t) = t^3 - 5t^2 - 7$ and $v(1) = 0$, find $v(t)$.
(ii) If, further, $x(0) = 1$, find $x(t)$.
(iii) Find the time at which the acceleration is least.

2. Differentiate the following with respect to $u$, where $\mathbf{a}$ and $\mathbf{b}$ are constant vectors:

(a) $(\sin 3u - 3\sin u)\mathbf{a} + (\cos 3u - \cos^3 u)\mathbf{b}$, (b) $\dfrac{u^2\mathbf{a} + 2u\,\mathbf{b}}{u^2 + 2u}$

3. Find $d\mathbf{r}/dt$ and its magnitude for the following vectors:
(a) $\hat{\mathbf{i}} - \tan t\,\hat{\mathbf{j}} + \sec t\,\hat{\mathbf{k}}$, (b) $(1 - t)\hat{\mathbf{i}} + (1 + t)\hat{\mathbf{j}} + (1 - t)(1 + t)\hat{\mathbf{k}}$

4. Find $\mathbf{r}'(t)$ and $\int_t^{2t}\mathbf{r}(t)dt$ for each of the following functions:
(a) $\mathbf{r}(t) = (t - 2)(t - 3)\hat{\mathbf{i}} + \frac{1}{4}e^t\hat{\mathbf{j}}$
(b) $\mathbf{r}(t) = 3\sin t\hat{\mathbf{i}} + (\cos t - \cos 2t)\hat{\mathbf{j}}$

5. Integrate the following with respect to $u$, where $\mathbf{a}$ and $\mathbf{b}$ are constant vectors:

(a) $3u\mathbf{a} - (5u^2 - 2u + 3)\mathbf{b}$, (b) $\dfrac{u^2\mathbf{a} + 2u\mathbf{b}}{u^2 + 2u}$

6. Find $\int_0^t\mathbf{r}(t)dt$ and its magnitude if
(a) $\mathbf{r} = \hat{\mathbf{i}} - \tan t\hat{\mathbf{j}} + \sec t\hat{\mathbf{k}}$
(b) $\mathbf{r} = (1 - t)\hat{\mathbf{i}} + (1 + t)\hat{\mathbf{j}} + (1 - t)(1 + t)\hat{\mathbf{k}}$

7. The velocity of a particle at time $t$ is given by the vector function $\mathbf{v}(t) = (1 - 3t)\hat{\mathbf{i}} + t^2\hat{\mathbf{j}}$. Find the displacement $\mathbf{x}(t)$ and the acceleration $\mathbf{a}(t)$ at time $t$, if it is given that $\mathbf{x}(1) = \hat{\mathbf{i}} - \hat{\mathbf{j}}$.

8. A body moves in a straight line OA, and at time $t$ seconds after it leaves O, its displacement from O is $x$ m and its velocity is $v$ m s$^{-1}$, where $dv/dt = 4 - 2t$. Initially the body leaves O with a velocity of 5 m s$^{-1}$.
(i) Find formulae for $v$ and $x$ in terms of $t$, and hence prove that the distance moved by the body in reaching its maximum velocity is $15\frac{1}{3}$ m.
(ii) Find the time at which the body is momentarily at rest, and its displacement from O at that time.
(iii) Find the velocity and acceleration of the body when $t = 6$. State the direction of motion of the body at that time, and also state whether its *speed* is increasing or decreasing, giving your reasons clearly. (MME)

9. A body moves along a straight line OA in such a way that at time $t$ seconds after it leaves O its displacement from O is $s$ metre, where $s = t(t - 3)^2$. Find:
(i) the initial velocity of the body;
(ii) the times at which it is momentarily at rest;
(iii) the time at which the acceleration is zero. (MME)

10. A particle moving initially due north with a velocity of 25 cm s$^{-1}$ is subjected to an acceleration of 5 cm s$^{-2}$ in a direction of 240° (S 60° W). Find, graphically, or otherwise, the velocity of the particle three seconds later. After what further period of time will the particle be moving instantaneously due west? (MEI)

# 4
# Vector Geometry (i)

## 4.1 The bound vector PQ

In much of geometry, we are greatly concerned with line segments that are equal and parallel. It will therefore be useful if we first clarify how we can use vectors in geometry to prove that two particular line segments are equal and parallel.

Any line segment PQ will be specified by the bound vector **PQ**, which in turn is defined by the position vectors **p** and **q** of its end-points, referred to some origin O. We observe that the bound vector **PQ** is equivalent to the position vector **q** − **p**, that is they have the same magnitude, direction and sense. They are therefore both members of the same free vector family, which we will also call **q** − **p**. Thus we may be able to show that two bound vectors **PQ** and **RS** are equal and parallel by showing that they belong to the same free vector family **q** − **p**.

There is one possible difficulty about this: we have ignored the sense of the bound vector. For example, in Fig. 4.1, the line segments PQ and RS are equal and parallel, although the bound vectors **PQ** and **RS** do not both belong to the free vector family **q** − **p**. In this case, **PQ** and **SR** both belong to **q** − **p**.

Thus we can assert that the line segment RS is parallel to the line segment PQ if *either* **RS** *or* **SR** belongs to the free vector family **q** − **p**.

We will economize on notation by writing **PQ** = **q** − **p** to mean that the bound vector **PQ** is a member of the free vector family **q** − **p** which contains as a member the position vector **q** − **p**.

We will demonstrate this principle by proving a simple geometrical theorem.

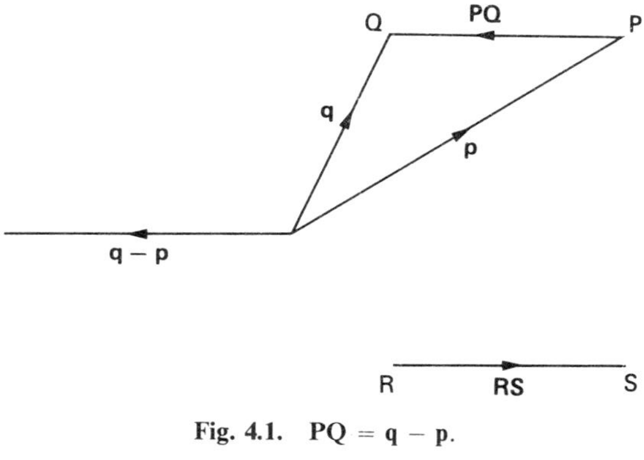


**Fig. 4.1.** PQ = q − p.

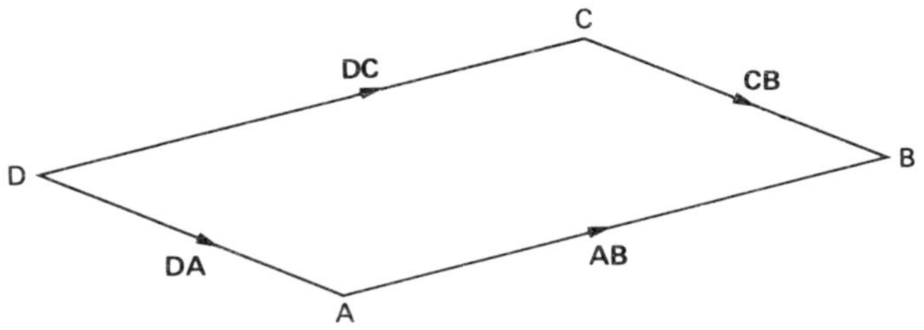


Fig. 4.2.

**Theorem**

If ABCD is a quadrilateral in which AB is equal and parallel to CD, then AD and BC are also equal and parallel.

*Proof*

We are given that AB and CD are equal and parallel. Thus we see that

$$\mathbf{AB} = \mathbf{DC}$$

and therefore

$$\mathbf{b} - \mathbf{a} = \mathbf{c} - \mathbf{d}$$

Therefore

$$\mathbf{b} - \mathbf{c} = \mathbf{a} - \mathbf{d}$$

and so

$$\mathbf{CB} = \mathbf{DA}$$

Hence AD and BC are equal and parallel, as required.

Notice that in this question, we have assumed the existence of an origin O. Since the origin is an arbitrary point, we could have chosen one of the given points as origin. This is not usually a good idea, since it often robs a solution of a symmetry which might be useful in detecting results.

## 4.2 The section formula

Suppose we are given a line segment AB, and a point C and $\overleftrightarrow{AB}$. The point C is then said to divide the line segment AB in the ratio $\pm |\mathbf{AC}|/|\mathbf{CB}|$, the ratio being positive if and only if C is in the line segment AB. Alternatively, we may say that the ratio is positive if and only if **AC** and **CB** have the same sense.

For example, in Fig. 4.3, we show the line segment AB, the line $\overleftrightarrow{AB}$, and four points:

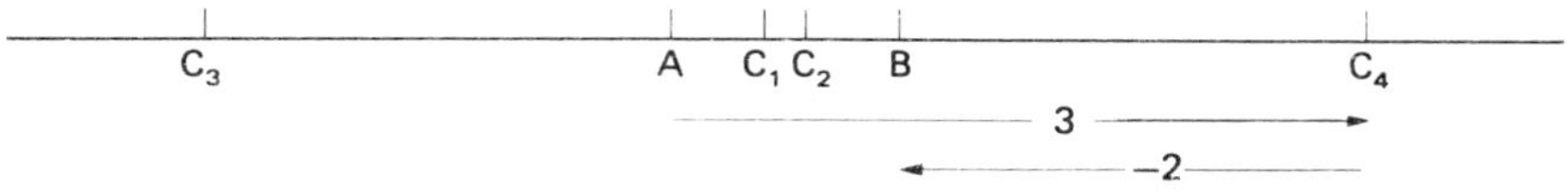


**Fig. 4.3.** Some ratios on the line $\overleftrightarrow{AB}$.

$C_1$, dividing AB in the ratio 2 : 3 or $-2 : -3$

$C_2$, dividing AB in the ratio 3 : 2 or $-3 : -2$

$C_3$, dividing AB in the ratio $-2 : 3$ or $2 : -3$

and

$C_4$, dividing AB in the ratio $3 : -2$ or $-3 : 2$

We also say that $C_3$ and $C_4$ divide AB *externally*, in the respective ratios 2 : 3 and 3 : 2. Similarly, $C_1$ and $C_2$ are said to divide AB *internally*.

The diagram also shows how we may determine negative signs in ratios, by imagining a journey from A to B *via* $C_4$ as being made up of three units in the sense $\overrightarrow{AC_4}$ and two in the opposite sense $\overrightarrow{C_4B}$. The signs are the same if both journeys are in the same sense; e.g. $-2 : -3$ for $AC_1 : C_1B$.

We will now establish a general result for locating any point P on the line $\overleftrightarrow{AB}$.

Suppose that A, B and P have position vectors **a**, **b** and **p**.

Suppose that P divides AB in the ratio $\alpha : \beta$, where, of course, one of $\alpha$ and $\beta$ is negative if P divides AB externally, and where $\alpha$ and $\beta$ are not both zero.

Then $\beta\mathbf{AP} = \alpha\mathbf{PB}$, which takes due count of internal and external division. Therefore

$$\beta(\mathbf{p} - \mathbf{a}) = \alpha(\mathbf{b} - \mathbf{p})$$

Therefore

$$(\alpha + \beta)\mathbf{p} = \beta\mathbf{a} + \alpha\mathbf{b} \tag{1a}$$

and so

$$\mathbf{p} = \frac{\beta\mathbf{a} + \alpha\mathbf{b}}{\alpha + \beta} \tag{1b}$$

is the position vector of the point P which divides AB and in the ratio $\alpha : \beta$. Either form of this result is known as the *section formula*.

This result may be re-written in two particularly common different ways. Firstly, we have

$$\mathbf{p} = \frac{\beta}{\alpha + \beta}\mathbf{a} + \frac{\alpha}{\alpha + \beta}\mathbf{b}$$

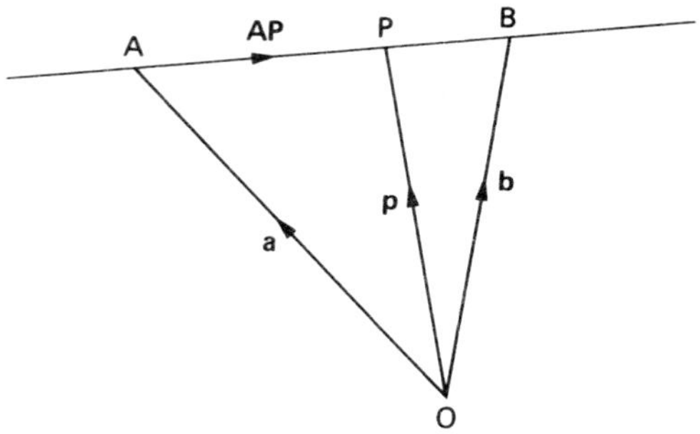


**Fig. 4.4.** The point P dividing the line AB in the ratio $\alpha : B$.

that is

$$\mathbf{p} = \lambda\mathbf{a} + \mu\mathbf{b} \text{ with } \lambda + \mu = 1 \tag{2}$$

We see that $\lambda$ and $\mu$ are, respectively, the ratios of the lengths of BP and AP to the length of AB, with appropriate signs.

Alternatively, if we assume that $\beta$ rather than $\alpha$ is non-zero, we may re-write equations 1 as

$$\mathbf{p} = \frac{\mathbf{a} + (\alpha/\beta)\mathbf{b}}{1 + (\alpha/\beta)} \quad (\beta \neq 0)$$

that is

$$\mathbf{p} = \frac{\mathbf{a} + \gamma\mathbf{b}}{1 + \gamma} \tag{3}$$

In this case, we have re-written the section formula to give the position vector of the point P which divides the line AB in the ratio $\gamma:1$, or $\alpha/\beta:1$.

Let us consider this third form, and the position of P for various values of $\gamma$ in the ratio $\gamma:1$. In particular, if $\gamma = 0$, Eq. 3 gives $\mathbf{p} = \mathbf{a}$, and the point P is at A.

If $\gamma > 0$, P divides AB internally, and as $\gamma$ increases indefinitely, the point P approaches closer and closer to B.

If $-1 < \gamma < 0$, then P is to the left of A in the diagram, and if $\gamma < -1$, then P is to the right of A.

We may show all this information in the form of a graph, where the line $\overleftrightarrow{AB}$ replaces the $x$-axis, and the $y$-axis shows values of $\gamma$, as in Fig. 4.5. For example, the point Q in the diagram corresponds to the value $\gamma = 1$, i.e. Q is the mid-point of the line segment AB.

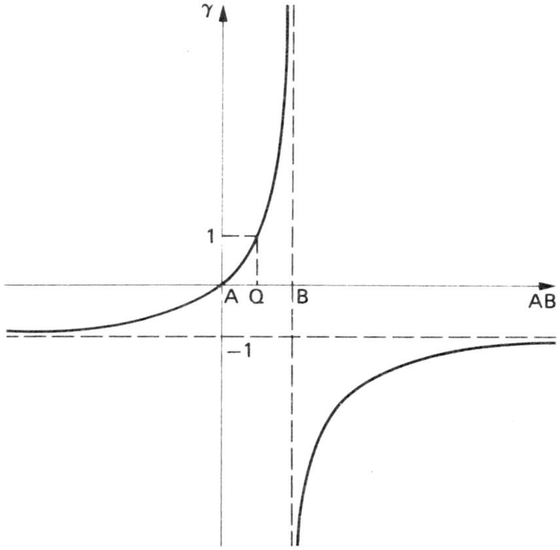


**Fig. 4.5.** The line AB divided in the ratio $\gamma:1$.

From Eq. 3, we see that the position vector $\mathbf{q}$ of the mid-point Q of AB is given by $\mathbf{q} = \frac{1}{2}(\mathbf{a} + \mathbf{b})$. This is an important result which is worth remembering in its own right.

As a further example, the point C which divides AB in the ratio $-2:5$ has position vector

$$\mathbf{c} = \frac{5\mathbf{a} + (-2)\mathbf{b}}{5 + (-2)}$$

from Equ. 1b. Therefore

$$\mathbf{c} = (5\mathbf{a} - 2\mathbf{b})/3$$

Similarly, the two points of trisection of AB are given by the position vectors $(2\mathbf{a} + \mathbf{b})/3$ and $(\mathbf{a} + 2\mathbf{b})/3$.

**Worked Example 4.1**

The points A, B and C have position vectors **a**, **b** and **c** respectively referred to some origin O.

(i) If C divides AB in the ratio $2:3$, give **c** in terms of **a** and **b**
(ii) If $\mathbf{c} = 3\mathbf{a} - 2\mathbf{b}$, give the ratio in which C divides AB
(iii) If C divides AB in the ratio $1:-4$, give **a** in terms of **b** and **c**
(iv) If $\mathbf{a} = k(2\mathbf{b} + 3\mathbf{c})$, and it is known that A, B and C lie on the same straight line, find the numerical value of $k$.

*Solution*

(i) By the section formula,

$$\mathbf{c} = \frac{3\mathbf{a} + 2\mathbf{b}}{3 + 2} = \tfrac{3}{5}\mathbf{a} + \tfrac{2}{5}\mathbf{b}$$

(ii) We are given $\mathbf{c} = (3\mathbf{a} - 2\mathbf{b})/[3 + (-2)]$, which, by comparison with the section formula, shows that C divides AB in the ratio $-2:3$.

(iii) By the section formula,

$$\mathbf{c} = \frac{(-4)\mathbf{a} + \mathbf{b}}{(-4) + 1} = \tfrac{4}{3}\mathbf{a} - \tfrac{1}{3}\mathbf{b}$$

Hence $\mathbf{a} = \frac{3}{4}\mathbf{c} + \frac{1}{4}\mathbf{b}$.

(iv) By comparison with the section formula, $k = \frac{1}{5}$, and A divides BC in the ratio $3:2$.

**Exercise 4*a***

1. The points A and B have position vectors **a** and **b** referred to some origin O. Find, in terms of **a** and **b**, the position vectors for the following points:
(i) The point C dividing AB in the ratio $2:3$.
(ii) The point D dividing AC in the ratio $3:2$.
(iii) The point E dividing BC in the ratio $2:3$.
(iv) The mid-point F of DE.

2. The points P and Q have position vectors **p** and **q** referred to some origin O.

Find, in terms of **p** and **q**, the position vectors for the following points:

(i) The point R dividing PQ in the ratio $-1:3$.

(ii) The point S such that P divides QS in the ratio $-1:3$.

(iii) The point T such that R divides ST in the ratio $-1:3$.

3. The points L, M and N have position vectors **l**, **m** and **n** referred to some origin O. Find, in terms of **l**, **m** and **n**, the position vectors for the following points:

(i) The mid-point P of LM.

(ii) The point of trisection G of NP that is nearer P.

(iii) The mid-point Q of MN.

(iv) The point of trisection H of LQ that is nearer Q.

Comment on your results, with reference to the triangle LMN.

4. The points A, B and C have position vectors **a**, **b** and **c** referred to some origin O.

(i) If $2\mathbf{a} + 3\mathbf{b} = 4\mathbf{c}$, are A, B and C in the same straight line?

(ii) If $2\mathbf{a} + 3\mathbf{b} = 5\mathbf{c}$, are A, B and C in the same straight line?

## 4.3 Conditions for collinearity

We will now extend the section formula to give an important general result. We are concerned with three points, and in establishing whether or not they lie on the same straight line. Suppose, then, that the points A, B and C have position vectors **a**, **b** and **c** referred to some origin O. Suppose, to begin with, that they are *collinear*, i.e. they lie in a straight line. Then C will divide AB in some ratio, say $\alpha:\beta$. Therefore, by the section formula,

$$\mathbf{c} = \frac{\alpha\mathbf{b} + \beta\mathbf{a}}{\alpha + \beta}$$

that is

$$\mathbf{c} = \lambda\mathbf{a} + \mu\mathbf{b} \text{ where } \lambda + \mu = 1 \text{ (and } \lambda = \alpha/(\alpha + \beta))$$

Now, conversely, suppose that some point D, say, has position vector $\mathbf{d} = \theta\mathbf{a} + \phi\mathbf{b}$, where $\theta + \phi = 1$. Then we may write

$$\theta = \frac{\gamma}{\gamma + \delta} \text{ and so } \phi = \frac{\delta}{\gamma + \delta}$$

Therefore

$$\mathbf{d} = \frac{\gamma\mathbf{a} + \delta\mathbf{b}}{\gamma + \delta}$$

which is the section formula and shows that D divides AB in the ratio $\delta:\gamma$.

We have thus proved that A, B and C are collinear if and only if we may write **c** as $\lambda\mathbf{a} + \mu\mathbf{b}$, where $\lambda + \mu = 1$. This condition may be re-written as

$$\lambda\mathbf{a} + \mu\mathbf{b} - \mathbf{c} = \mathbf{0} \quad (\lambda + \mu = 1)$$

and thus as

$$\alpha\mathbf{a} + \beta\mathbf{b} + \gamma\mathbf{c} = \mathbf{0} \; (\alpha + \beta = -\gamma),$$

if we multiply both sides by $-\gamma$ and write $\alpha = -\gamma\lambda$, $\beta = -\gamma\mu$.

Thus the condition may be symmetrically written as

$$\alpha\mathbf{a} + \beta\mathbf{b} + \gamma\mathbf{c} = \mathbf{0} \text{ (where } \alpha + \beta + \gamma = 0)$$

This is the necessary and sufficient condition for the points A, B and C to be collinear. It is also necessary that the numbers $\alpha$, $\beta$ and $\gamma$ be all non-zero, or else the ratio used in the original application of the section formula would not have been finite.

Thus A, B and C are collinear if and only if there exist numbers $\alpha$, $\beta$ and $\gamma$, not all zero, such that

$$\alpha\mathbf{a} + \beta\mathbf{b} + \gamma\mathbf{c} = \mathbf{0} \quad \text{and} \quad \alpha + \beta + \gamma = 0.$$

**Worked Example 4.2**

The points A and B have position vectors **a** and **b** respectively, relative to some origin 0. Show that the points with position vectors **a**, **b** and $-2\mathbf{a} + 3\mathbf{b}$ are collinear.

*Solution*

We see that

$$(-2)\mathbf{a} + 3\mathbf{b} + (-1)(-2\mathbf{a} + 3\mathbf{b}) = \mathbf{0}$$

and

$$(-2) + 3 + (-1) = 0.$$

Hence, by the result established above, the three points are collinear.

**Worked Example 4.3**

ABCD is a trapezium, with $\mathbf{AB} = 2\mathbf{DC}$. P is the mid-point of AD; Q is the point of trisection of BC nearer to B; and R divides AB in the ratio $5:-3$. Prove that the points P, Q and R are collinear.

*Solution*

$\mathbf{AB} = 2\mathbf{DC}$, thus

$$\mathbf{b} - \mathbf{a} = 2\mathbf{c} - 2\mathbf{d}$$

and so

$$\mathbf{d} = \tfrac{1}{2}\mathbf{a} - \tfrac{1}{2}\mathbf{b} + \mathbf{c}$$

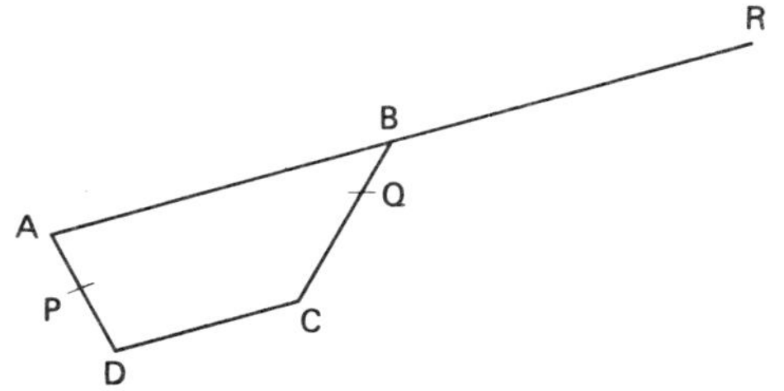


**Fig. 4.6.** Worked example 4.3.

By the section formula,

$$\mathbf{p} = \tfrac{1}{2}\mathbf{a} + \tfrac{1}{2}\mathbf{d} = \tfrac{3}{4}\mathbf{a} - \tfrac{1}{4}\mathbf{b} + \tfrac{1}{2}\mathbf{c}$$

$$\mathbf{q} = \frac{2\mathbf{b} + \mathbf{c}}{3}$$

$$\mathbf{r} = \frac{5\mathbf{b} - 3\mathbf{a}}{2} = -\tfrac{3}{2}\mathbf{a} + \tfrac{5}{2}\mathbf{b}$$

Consider

$$\alpha\mathbf{p} + \beta\mathbf{q} + \gamma\mathbf{r} = (\tfrac{3}{4}\alpha - \tfrac{3}{2}\gamma)\mathbf{a} + (-\tfrac{1}{4}\alpha + \tfrac{2}{3}\beta + \tfrac{5}{2}\gamma)\mathbf{b} + (\tfrac{1}{2}\alpha + \tfrac{1}{3}\beta)\mathbf{c}$$

Now A, B and C are *not* collinear (i.e. **a**, **b** and **c** are linearly independent). Therefore this expression can be the zero vector only if

$$\tfrac{3}{4}\alpha - \tfrac{3}{2}\gamma = -\tfrac{1}{4}\alpha + \tfrac{2}{3}\beta + \tfrac{5}{2}\gamma = \tfrac{1}{2}\alpha + \tfrac{1}{3}\beta = 0$$

Therefore

$$\beta = -\tfrac{3}{2}\alpha \quad \text{and} \quad \gamma = \tfrac{1}{2}\alpha$$

Therefore

$$\alpha\mathbf{p} - \tfrac{3}{2}\alpha\mathbf{q} + \tfrac{1}{2}\alpha\mathbf{r} = \mathbf{0}$$

Also

$$\alpha - \tfrac{3}{2}\alpha + \tfrac{1}{2}\alpha = 0$$

Therefore the points P, Q and R are collinear, as required.

## 4.4 Applications to Euclidean geometry

We have already seen some examples of geometrical results which may be proved using vector methods. We will here give some further examples, to demonstrate the type of approach that might be useful when faced with such a problem. We will invariably need to use the result given at the beginning of the chapter, namely $\mathbf{PQ} = \mathbf{q} - \mathbf{p}$, and results directly derived from it.

**Worked Example 4.4 (the mid-point theorem)**

The line joining the mid-points of two sides of a triangle is parallel to the third side, and equal in length to half the third side.

*Proof*

Suppose the triangle is ABC, and that M and N are the respective mid-points of CA and AB. Suppose also that all position vectors are referred to some origin 0. Then

$$\mathbf{m} = \tfrac{1}{2}\mathbf{c} + \tfrac{1}{2}\mathbf{a} \quad \text{and} \quad \mathbf{n} = \tfrac{1}{2}\mathbf{a} + \tfrac{1}{2}\mathbf{b}$$

Therefore

$$\begin{aligned}\mathbf{MN} = \mathbf{n} - \mathbf{m} &= \tfrac{1}{2}\mathbf{b} - \tfrac{1}{2}\mathbf{c} \\ &= \tfrac{1}{2}(\mathbf{b} - \mathbf{c})\end{aligned}$$

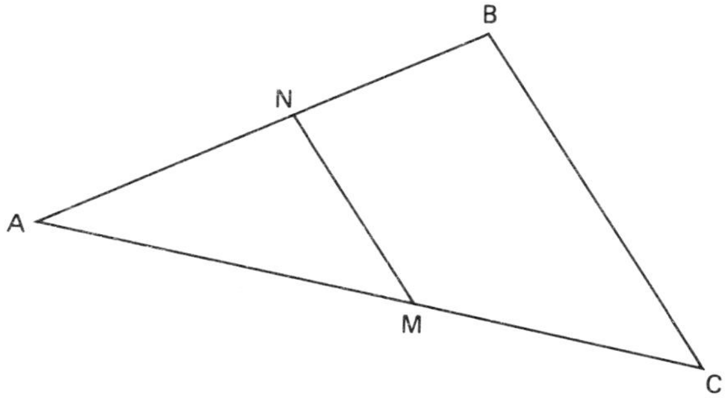


**Fig. 4.7.** The mid-point theorem.

that is

$$\mathbf{MN} = \tfrac{1}{2}\mathbf{CB}$$

Therefore MN is parallel to CB, and half its length; and the theorem is proved.

**Worked Example 4.5**

In the pentagon ABCDE, it is given that $\mathbf{BE} = 3\mathbf{CD}$ and $2\mathbf{AE} = 3\mathbf{BC}$. Prove that $2\mathbf{AB} = 3\mathbf{ED}$. Find the location of the point F on EA such that CF is parallel to BA.

*Solution*

$\mathbf{BE} = 3\mathbf{CD}$, thus

$$\mathbf{e} - \mathbf{b} = 3\mathbf{d} - 3\mathbf{c}$$

$2\mathbf{AE} = 3\mathbf{BC}$, thus

$$2\mathbf{e} - 2\mathbf{a} = 3\mathbf{c} - 3\mathbf{b}$$

Add:

$$3\mathbf{e} - \mathbf{b} - 2\mathbf{a} = 3\mathbf{d} - 3\mathbf{b}$$

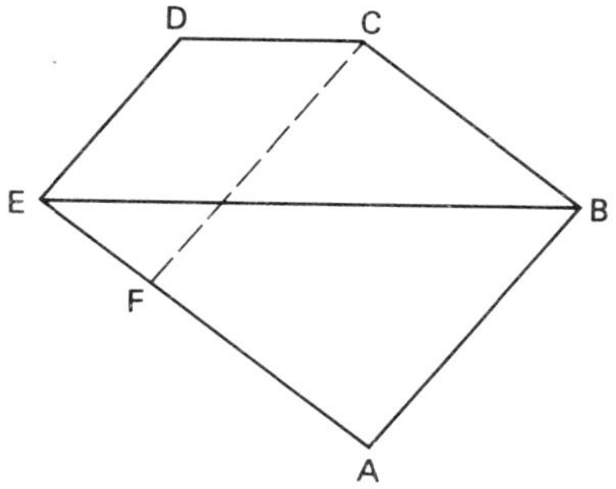


**Fig. 4.8.** Worked example 4.5.

Therefore

$$2\mathbf{b} - 2\mathbf{a} = 3\mathbf{d} - 3\mathbf{e}$$

and so

$$2\mathbf{AB} = 3\mathbf{ED}$$

as required.

Now, AE is parallel to CB (given), and so CFAB is a parallelogram. Therefore

$$\mathbf{CF} = \mathbf{BA}.$$

Therefore

$$\mathbf{f} - \mathbf{c} = \mathbf{a} - \mathbf{b}$$

Therefore

$$\mathbf{f} = \mathbf{a} - \mathbf{b} + \mathbf{c}$$

Suppose also F divides EA in the ratio $\alpha:\beta$. Then, by the section formula,

$$\mathbf{f} = \frac{\alpha\mathbf{a} + \beta\mathbf{e}}{\alpha + \beta}$$

$$= \frac{\alpha\mathbf{a} + \frac{1}{3}\beta(2\mathbf{a} - 3\mathbf{b} + 3\mathbf{c})}{\alpha + \beta}$$

that is,

$$\mathbf{f} = \frac{(\alpha + \beta)\mathbf{a} - \frac{3}{2}\beta\mathbf{b} + \frac{3}{2}\beta\mathbf{c}}{\alpha + \beta}$$

But

$$\mathbf{f} = \mathbf{a} - \mathbf{b} + \mathbf{c}$$

Therefore

$$\frac{\frac{3}{2}\beta}{\alpha + \beta} = 1$$

Hence $\alpha = \frac{1}{2}\beta$, and so $\alpha:\beta = 1:2$. Therefore F is the point of trisection of EA nearer to E.

## 4.5 The centroid of a triangle

In question 4 of Exercise 4*a*, an important result concerning triangles was suggested, involving the medians of a triangle. We will approach the problem slightly differently at first, and later give a shorter proof based on the question from Exercise 4*a*.

Before doing so, though, we will give a definition which will be needed. Suppose we have $n$ points $A_1, A_2, \ldots, A_n$, with respective position vectors $\mathbf{a}_1, \mathbf{a}_2, \ldots, \mathbf{a}_n$, referred to some origin 0. Then the *centroid of these n points* is defined to be the point with position vector

$$\frac{1}{n}\sum_{i=1}^{n}\mathbf{a}_i = \frac{(\mathbf{a}_1 + \mathbf{a}_2 + \cdots + \mathbf{a}_n)}{n}$$

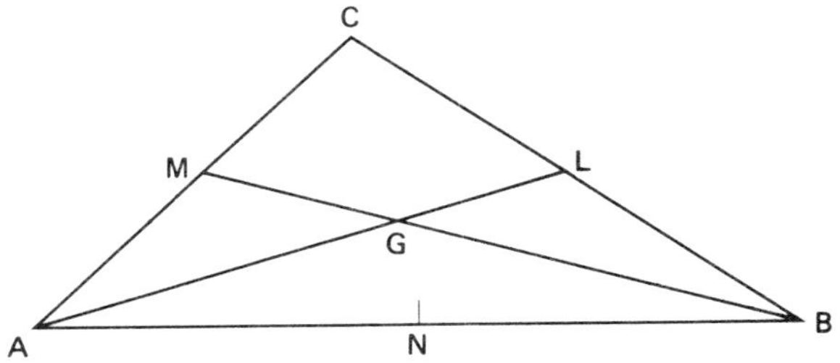


**Fig. 4.9.** AG/GL = $\alpha/\beta$, BG/GM = $\lambda/\mu$.

Now suppose that we have a triangle ABC, and that the vertices have position vectors **a**, **b** and **c** referred to some origin 0. Suppose that L, M and N are the mid-points of BC, CA and AB respectively. Then the line segments AL, BM and CN are called the *medians* of the triangle. We shall prove that these three medians all pass through a single point, which is also the centroid of the three points A, B and C.

First, we shall find an expression for the position vector of the point G where AL meets BM.

The position vectors for the mid-points L and M are

$$\mathbf{l} = \tfrac{1}{2}\mathbf{b} + \tfrac{1}{2}\mathbf{c} \quad \text{and} \quad \mathbf{m} = \tfrac{1}{2}\mathbf{c} + \tfrac{1}{2}\mathbf{a}$$

Suppose that G divides AL in the ratio $\alpha:\beta$, and BM in the ratio $\lambda:\mu$. Then, by the section formula,

$$\mathbf{g} = \frac{\beta\mathbf{a} + \alpha\mathbf{l}}{\beta + \alpha} = \frac{\beta\mathbf{a} + \frac{1}{2}\alpha\mathbf{b} + \frac{1}{2}\alpha\mathbf{c}}{\alpha + \beta}$$

and

$$\mathbf{g} = \frac{\mu\mathbf{b} + \lambda\mathbf{m}}{\mu + \lambda} = \frac{\mu\mathbf{b} + \frac{1}{2}\lambda\mathbf{c} + \frac{1}{2}\lambda\mathbf{a}}{\lambda + \mu}$$

But these two position vectors represent the same point G. Therefore

$$\frac{\beta\mathbf{a} + \frac{1}{2}\alpha\mathbf{b} + \frac{1}{2}\alpha\mathbf{c}}{\alpha + \beta} = \frac{\mu\mathbf{b} + \frac{1}{2}\lambda\mathbf{c} + \frac{1}{2}\lambda\mathbf{a}}{\lambda + \mu}$$

Multiply both sides by $(\alpha + \beta)(\lambda + \mu)$, and re-arrange:

$$[\beta(\lambda + \mu) - \tfrac{1}{2}\lambda(\alpha + \beta)]\mathbf{a} + [\tfrac{1}{2}\alpha(\lambda + \mu) - \mu(\alpha + \beta)]\mathbf{b} + \\ + [\tfrac{1}{2}\alpha(\lambda + \mu) - \tfrac{1}{2}\lambda(\alpha + \beta)]\mathbf{c} = \mathbf{0}$$

Therefore

$$[\beta(\tfrac{1}{2}\lambda + \mu) - \tfrac{1}{2}\lambda\alpha]\mathbf{a} + [\tfrac{1}{2}\alpha(\lambda - \mu) - \mu\beta]\mathbf{b} + (\alpha\mu - \beta\lambda)\mathbf{c} = \mathbf{0}$$

Now $\{\mathbf{a}, \mathbf{b}, \mathbf{c}\}$ is linearly independent, and so

$$\beta(\tfrac{1}{2}\lambda + \mu) - \tfrac{1}{2}\lambda\alpha = \tfrac{1}{2}\alpha(\lambda - \mu) - \mu\beta = \alpha\mu - \beta\lambda = \mathbf{0}$$

Hence $\alpha:\beta = \lambda:\mu$, i.e. G divides AL and BM in the same ratio. Also

$$\frac{\alpha}{\beta} = \frac{\frac{1}{2}\lambda + \mu}{\frac{1}{2}\lambda} = \frac{\mu}{\frac{1}{2}(\lambda - \mu)}$$

shows that

$$\frac{\lambda}{\mu} = \frac{\alpha}{\beta} = \frac{2}{1}$$

and that G is the point of trisection of each median farthest away from the vertex of the triangle. Thus $\mathbf{g} = \frac{1}{3}(\mathbf{a} + \mathbf{b} + \mathbf{c})$, the centroid of the three points A, B and C. From the symmetry of this expression, we argue that we would obtain the same result if we start with another pair of medians. We thus claim the following theorem.

**Theorem**

The medians of a triangle are concurrent, and the point where they meet is a point of trisection of each median. That point is also the centroid of the three vertices of the triangle, and will also be called the *centroid G of the triangle.*

We now give a shorter proof of this theorem, noting that this relies on knowing the answer, whereas the proof above actually established the theorem without knowing the answer in advance.

Using the notation above, the position vector $\mathbf{l}$ of the mid-point L of BC is $\mathbf{l} = \frac{1}{2}\mathbf{a} + \frac{1}{2}\mathbf{b}$. Therefore the position vector $\mathbf{g}$ of the point G dividing AL in the ratio 2:1 is

$$\mathbf{g} = \frac{2\mathbf{l} + \mathbf{a}}{3} = \frac{1}{3}\mathbf{a} + \frac{1}{3}\mathbf{b} + \frac{1}{3}\mathbf{c}$$

By symmetry, this is also the position vector of points of trisection of the other two medians. Thus the theorem is proved.

**Worked example 4.6**

L, M and N are the mid-points of the sides of the triangle ABC. Prove that the triangles ABC and LMN have the same centroid.

*Solution*

The position vector of the centroid of ABC is $\frac{1}{3}\mathbf{a} + \frac{1}{3}\mathbf{b} + \frac{1}{3}\mathbf{c}$. The position vectors of L, M and N are $\frac{1}{2}\mathbf{a} + \frac{1}{2}\mathbf{b}$, $\frac{1}{2}\mathbf{b} + \frac{1}{2}\mathbf{c}$ and $\frac{1}{2}\mathbf{c} + \frac{1}{2}\mathbf{a}$. The position vector of the centroid of the triangle LMN is

$$\tfrac{1}{3}(\tfrac{1}{2}\mathbf{a} + \tfrac{1}{2}\mathbf{b}) + \tfrac{1}{3}(\tfrac{1}{2}\mathbf{b} + \tfrac{1}{2}\mathbf{c}) + \tfrac{1}{3}(\tfrac{1}{2}\mathbf{c} + \tfrac{1}{2}\mathbf{a}) = \tfrac{1}{3}\mathbf{a} + \tfrac{1}{3}\mathbf{b} + \tfrac{1}{3}\mathbf{c}$$

Thus the two triangles have the same centroid.

Notice that untold confusion would have arisen if we had chosen a vertex as origin in any part of the above, as then the symmetry of the expressions would not have been evident.

**Worked example 4.7**

ABCD is a tetrahedron. G is the centroid of the face BCD. The line AG is called a *median* of the tetrahedron. Find position vectors for G, and for points dividing AG in the ratios 1:1, 2:1 and 3:1. Comment on your results.

*Solution*

We will refer all position vectors to some origin O, and use the usual notation. Then $\mathbf{g} = \frac{1}{3}(\mathbf{b} + \mathbf{c} + \mathbf{d})$. Suppose the point H divides AG in the ratio 1:1 (i.e. H is the mid-point of AG). Then

$$\mathbf{h} = \tfrac{1}{2}\mathbf{a} + \tfrac{1}{2}\mathbf{g} = \tfrac{1}{2}\mathbf{a} + \tfrac{1}{6}(\mathbf{b} + \mathbf{c} + \mathbf{d})$$

Suppose the point L divides AG in the ratio 2:1. Then

$$\mathbf{l} = \frac{2\mathbf{g} + \mathbf{a}}{3} = \frac{1}{3}\mathbf{a} + \frac{2}{9}(\mathbf{b} + \mathbf{c} + \mathbf{d})$$

Suppose the point M divides AG in the ratio 3:1. Then

$$\mathbf{m} = \frac{3\mathbf{g} + \mathbf{a}}{4} = \frac{1}{4}(\mathbf{a} + \mathbf{b} + \mathbf{c} + \mathbf{d})$$

and M is the centroid of the four points A, B, C, D.

Also, the symmetry of this last expression proves that the medians of a tetrahedron are concurrent at a point which divides each median in the ratio 3:1. This point will be called the *centroid of the tetrahedron.*

The centroid of a tetrahedron ABCD has position vector $\frac{1}{4}(\mathbf{a} + \mathbf{b} + \mathbf{c} + \mathbf{d})$.

**Exercise 4*b***

1. OABC is a parallelogram. Find the position vectors, referred to 0 as origin, of the centroids of the triangles OAC, OAB and ABC in terms of the position vectors **a** and **b** of the points A and B.
2. ABCD is any quadrilateral. Show, using vectors, that the mid-points of the sides of ABCD form a parallelogram.
3. ABC is a triangle. D lies on BC produced, and C is the mid-point of BD; similarly A is the mid-point of CF and B is the mid-point of AH. Prove that the triangles ABC and DFH have the same centroid.
4. E is a point of trisection of the straight line PQ such that PE:EQ = 1:2. The position vectors of P, Q and E are **p**, **q** and **e** respectively relative to an origin O. Express **e** in terms of **p** and **q**.

The point R, not on the straight line PQ, has position vector **r** relative to the same origin O. The point F divides QR internally so that QF:FR = 2:1. Find the position vector of F.

Use vector methods to show that EF is parallel to PR and to find the ratio of their lengths. (L)

5. B, R, C are the mid-points of the sides AP, PQ, QA of triangle APQ. If **a**, **b**, **c** are the position vectors of the points A, B, C, find the position vectors of P, Q, R in terms of **a**, **b**, **c**. (SMP)

6. Points X, Y, Z have position vectors denoted by $\mathbf{x}$, $\mathbf{y}$, $\mathbf{z}$ relative to an origin O. Write the expression $\mathbf{p} = \frac{1}{2}\mathbf{x} + (2/5)\mathbf{y} + (1/10)\mathbf{z}$ in the form $a\mathbf{x} + b(c\mathbf{y} + d\mathbf{z})$, where $a + b = 1$. Hence describe how the point P, with position vector $\mathbf{p}$, is related to the points X, Y, Z. By writing $\mathbf{p}$ in terms of $\mathbf{x}$, $\mathbf{y}$, $\mathbf{z}$ in another way, give a different description of the relation of P to X, Y, Z. (SMP)

## 4.6 The equation of a straight line

We wish to find a method of describing the position of any point R on a given straight line, using vector notation. First of all, let us consider just what determines a straight line. There are two relevant possible ways of giving a unique description of a straight line:

(1) we could give two fixed points A and B on the line; or
(2) we could give one point A on the line, and a position vector $\mathbf{c}$ parallel to the line, i.e. one point and the direction of the line.

We will deal firstly with the line through the points A and B.

Suppose that A and B have position vectors $\mathbf{a}$ and $\mathbf{b}$ relative to some origin O. Suppose that R, with position vector $\mathbf{r}$, is *any* point on the line. We may fix its position by giving the ratio of lengths $AR/AB = t/1$, say. Therefore

$$\mathbf{AR} = t\mathbf{AB}$$

and so

$$\mathbf{r} - \mathbf{a} = t(\mathbf{b} - \mathbf{a})$$

Therefore

$$\mathbf{r} = (1 - t)\mathbf{a} + t\mathbf{b} \tag{1}$$

Equ. 1 is one version of the equation of the straight line $\overleftrightarrow{AB}$—it gives the position vector for the (variable) point $\mathbf{r}$ in terms of the fixed position vectors $\mathbf{a}$ and $\mathbf{b}$ and the (variable) parameter $t$.

Now let us consider the second case. In this case, we have the straight line through A, in the direction given by $\mathbf{c}$. Suppose again that R, with position vector $\mathbf{r}$, is *any* point on the line. We may fix its position by giving the ratio of lengths $AR/|\mathbf{c}| = t/1$, say. Therefore

$$\mathbf{AR} = t\mathbf{c}$$

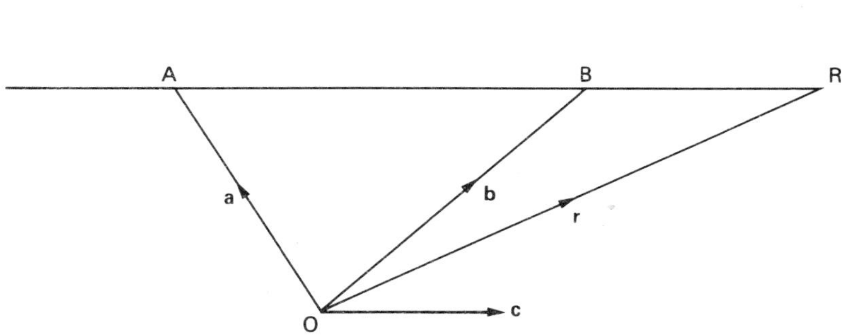


**Fig. 4.10.** The straight line through A and B in the direction of $\mathbf{c}$.

and so

$$\mathbf{r} - \mathbf{a} = t\mathbf{c}$$

Therefore

$$\mathbf{r} = \mathbf{a} + t\mathbf{c} \qquad (2)$$

Equ. 2 is the second version of the vector equation of a straight line—it gives the position vector of the (variable) point $\mathbf{r}$ in terms of the fixed position vectors $\mathbf{a}$ and $\mathbf{c}$ and the variable parameter $t$.

The two cases may be related by taking $\mathbf{c} = \mathbf{AB} = \mathbf{b} - \mathbf{a}$, in which case equations 1 and 2 become identical.

## 4.7 The equation of a plane

We will give here just two forms of the vector equation of a plane. A third, more useful, form will be found in Chapter 13, but the ones here correspond to the equation of the line that we have just given.

As with the line, we first of all consider what information can be used to describe a plane uniquely. We consider two relevant possibilities:

(1). we could give one point A in the plane, and two fixed vectors $\mathbf{d}$ and $\mathbf{e}$ parallel to the plane and in different directions; or

(2) we could give three fixed points A, B and C in the plane

In the first case, consider *any* point R in the plane, with position vector $\mathbf{r}$. Then the vectors $\mathbf{d}$ and $\mathbf{e}$ span the plane, and so we may write $\mathbf{AR} = \alpha\mathbf{d} + \beta\mathbf{e}$ for some scalars $\alpha$ and $\beta$. Therefore

$$\mathbf{r} = \mathbf{a} + \mathbf{AR}$$

and so

$$\mathbf{r} = \mathbf{a} + \alpha\mathbf{d} + \beta\mathbf{e} \qquad (1)$$

for fixed vectors $\mathbf{a}$, $\mathbf{d}$ and $\mathbf{e}$ and parameters $\alpha$ and $\beta$. This is one form of the equation of the plane determined by the point A and the vectors $\mathbf{d}$ and $\mathbf{e}$.

For the second case, we may use the same diagram, with the justifiable assumption that $\mathbf{AB} = \mathbf{d}$ and $\mathbf{AC} = \mathbf{e}$. In other words, $\mathbf{d} = \mathbf{b} - \mathbf{a}$ and $\mathbf{e} = \mathbf{c} - \mathbf{a}$. Therefore the

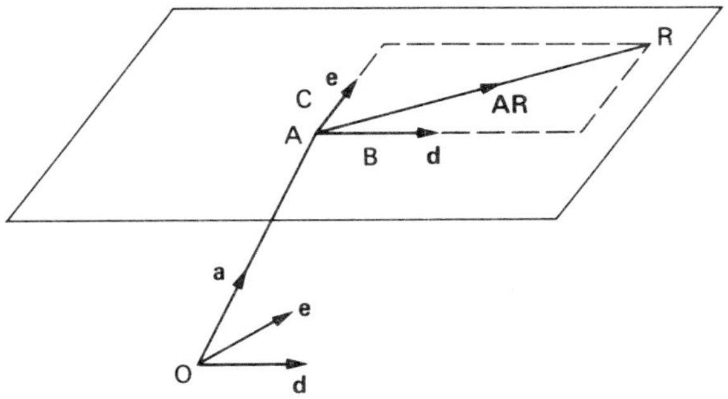


**Fig. 4.11.** The equation of a plane.

equation of the plane becomes

$$\mathbf{r} = \mathbf{a} + \alpha(\mathbf{b} - \mathbf{a}) + \beta(\mathbf{c} - \mathbf{a}) \tag{2a}$$

or

$$\mathbf{r} = (1 - \alpha - \beta)\mathbf{a} + \alpha\mathbf{b} + \beta\mathbf{c} \tag{2b}$$

We may use the second of these equations, namely Equ. $2b$, to establish a condition for four points to lie in the same plane. We have, for the four coplanar points A, B, C and R,

$$(1 - \alpha - \beta)\mathbf{a} + \alpha\mathbf{b} + \beta\mathbf{c} + (-1)\mathbf{r} = 0$$

and we notice that

$$(1 - \alpha - \beta) + \alpha + \beta + (-1) = 0$$

Thus, if we put

$$\kappa = 1 - \alpha - \beta,\ \lambda = \alpha,\ \mu = \beta \quad \text{and} \quad \gamma = (-1),$$

we see that, if the four points are coplanar, then

$$\left.\begin{aligned} \kappa\mathbf{a} + \lambda\mathbf{b} + \mu\mathbf{c} + \gamma\mathbf{r} &= \mathbf{0} \\ \text{and} \qquad & \\ \kappa + \lambda + \mu + \gamma &= 0 \end{aligned}\right\} \tag{3}$$

This condition corresponds to the condition we obtained for three points to be collinear.

Suppose, conversely, that condition 3 is given. Then, if we write $\alpha = \lambda$, $\beta = \mu$, and set $v = -1$, we obtain

$$(1 - \alpha - \beta)\mathbf{a} + \alpha\mathbf{b} + \beta\mathbf{c} + (-1)\mathbf{r} = \mathbf{0}$$

and so

$$\mathbf{r} = (1 - \alpha - \beta)a + \alpha\mathbf{b} + \beta\mathbf{c}$$

which is the equation of the plane ABC and shows that R lies in this plane.

Hence we have proved that four points, A, B, C and D, say are coplanar if and only if there exist numbers $\kappa$, $\lambda$, $\mu$ and $v$, not all zero, such that

$$\kappa\mathbf{a} + \lambda\mathbf{b} + \mu\mathbf{c} + v\mathbf{d} = \mathbf{0}$$

and

$$\kappa + \lambda + \mu + v = 0$$

## 4.8 Worked examples

### Worked Example 4.8

The points A and B have position vectors $\mathbf{a} = \hat{\mathbf{i}} + \hat{\mathbf{j}} + \hat{\mathbf{k}}$ and $\mathbf{b} = 2\hat{\mathbf{i}} - 3\hat{\mathbf{j}} + \hat{\mathbf{k}}$, in the usual notation.

(i) Find, in vector form, the equation of the line $\overleftrightarrow{AB}$.

(ii) Find $\alpha$ if the point C with position vector $\mathbf{c} = 2\hat{\mathbf{i}} + \alpha\hat{\mathbf{j}} + \hat{\mathbf{k}}$ lies on $\overleftrightarrow{AB}$.

(iii) The point S with position vector $\mathbf{s} = (3u - 1)\hat{\mathbf{i}} + (9 - 5u)\hat{\mathbf{j}} + (1 - 2u)\hat{\mathbf{k}}$ lies on a line which meets $\overleftrightarrow{AB}$ at D. Find the value of $u$ for which S is on $\overleftrightarrow{AB}$, and hence find the position vector $\mathbf{d}$ of D.

*Solution*

(i) The direction of the line is given by $\mathbf{b} - \mathbf{a} = \hat{\mathbf{i}} - 4\hat{\mathbf{j}}$. Thus the line has equation

$$\mathbf{r} = (\hat{\mathbf{i}} + \hat{\mathbf{j}} + \hat{\mathbf{k}}) + t(\hat{\mathbf{i}} - 4\hat{\mathbf{j}})$$

or

$$\mathbf{r} = (1 + t)\hat{\mathbf{i}} + (1 - 4t)\hat{\mathbf{j}} + \hat{\mathbf{k}}$$

(ii) We see that $t = 1$ gives $\mathbf{r} = \mathbf{c}$, and so $\alpha = 1 - 4 \times 1 = -3$.

(iii) S is on $\overleftrightarrow{AB}$ if

$$3u - 1 = 1 + t$$

$$9 - 5u = 1 - 4t$$

and

$$1 - 2u = 1$$

for some values of $t$ and $u$. These three equations are simultaneously satisfied by $u = 0$ and $t = -2$. Thus $\mathbf{d}$ may be obtained by setting $u = 0$ in the expression for $\mathbf{s}$, or by setting $t = -2$ in the expression for $\mathbf{r}$. Therefore $\mathbf{d} = -\hat{\mathbf{i}} + 9\hat{\mathbf{j}} + \hat{\mathbf{k}}$.

**Worked Example 4.9**

The points A, B and C have position vectors $\mathbf{a} = \hat{\mathbf{i}} + \hat{\mathbf{j}} + 2\hat{\mathbf{k}}$, $\mathbf{b} = 4\hat{\mathbf{i}} - 3\hat{\mathbf{j}} + \hat{\mathbf{k}}$ and $\mathbf{c} = 5\hat{\mathbf{i}} + 2\hat{\mathbf{j}} - 2\hat{\mathbf{k}}$.

(i) Find, in vector form, the equation of the plane ABC.

(ii) Find the value of $\alpha$ if the point D with position vector $\mathbf{d} = 2\hat{\mathbf{i}} + 6\hat{\mathbf{j}} + \alpha\hat{\mathbf{k}}$ lies in the plane ABC.

*Solution*

(i) Two fixed vectors in the plane are given by

$$\mathbf{b} - \mathbf{a} = 3\hat{\mathbf{i}} - 4\hat{\mathbf{j}} - \hat{\mathbf{k}} \quad \text{and} \quad \mathbf{c} - \mathbf{a} = 4\hat{\mathbf{i}} + \hat{\mathbf{j}} - 4\hat{\mathbf{k}}$$

The plane therefore has equation

$$\mathbf{r} = (\hat{\mathbf{i}} + \hat{\mathbf{j}} + 2\hat{\mathbf{k}}) + t(3\hat{\mathbf{i}} - 4\hat{\mathbf{j}} - \hat{\mathbf{k}}) + u(4\hat{\mathbf{i}} + \hat{\mathbf{j}} - 4\hat{\mathbf{k}})$$

or

$$\mathbf{r} = (1 + 3t + 4u)\hat{\mathbf{i}} + (1 - 4t + u)\hat{\mathbf{j}} + (2 - 3t - 4u)\hat{\mathbf{k}}$$

(ii) If $\mathbf{r} = \mathbf{d}$, then we must have

$$1 + 3t + 4u = 2 \qquad (1)$$

$$1 - 4t + u = 6 \qquad (2)$$

$$2 - 3t - 4u = \alpha \qquad (3)$$

Solving equations 1 and 2 gives

$$t = -1 \text{ and } u = 1.$$

Then Equ. 3 gives

$$\alpha = 2 + 3 - 4 = 1.$$

**Exercise 4c**

1. The points A and B have position vectors $\mathbf{a} = 2\hat{\imath} - \hat{\jmath} + 3\hat{\mathbf{k}}$ and $\mathbf{b} = \hat{\imath} + \hat{\jmath} - \hat{\mathbf{k}}$, in the usual notation.
   (i) Find, in vector form, the equation of the line $\overleftrightarrow{AB}$.
   (ii) Find the values of $\alpha$ and $\beta$ if the point C with position vector where $\mathbf{c} = 3\hat{\imath} + \alpha\hat{\jmath} + \beta\hat{\mathbf{k}}$ lies on the line $\overleftrightarrow{AB}$.
2. The points A, B and C have position vectors $\mathbf{a} = 2\hat{\imath} - \hat{\jmath} + 3\hat{\mathbf{k}}$, $\mathbf{b} = \hat{\imath} + \hat{\jmath} - \hat{\mathbf{k}}$ and $\mathbf{c} = 3\hat{\imath} + 3\hat{\jmath} - 2\hat{\mathbf{k}}$, in the usual notation.
   (i) Find, in vector form, the equation of the plane ABC.
   (ii) Does the point D with position vector $\mathbf{d} = 4\hat{\imath} + 13\hat{\jmath} + \alpha\hat{\mathbf{k}}$ line in the plane: (a) when $\alpha = 16$; (b) when $\alpha = -16$?
3. Show that the points A, B, C and D, with position vectors $\mathbf{a} = 2\hat{\imath} - \hat{\jmath} + 2\hat{\mathbf{k}}$, $\mathbf{b} = \hat{\imath} - \hat{\jmath}$, $\mathbf{c} = \hat{\imath} + \hat{\jmath} + 3\hat{\mathbf{k}}$ and $\mathbf{d} = \frac{1}{2}\hat{\imath} + \frac{1}{2}\hat{\mathbf{k}}$ are coplanar.
4. A, B, C and D have position vectors $\mathbf{a} = 2\mathbf{u} + 3\mathbf{v} + \mathbf{w}$, $\mathbf{b} = 3\mathbf{u} - \mathbf{v} + 2\mathbf{w}$, $\mathbf{c} = \mathbf{u} - 2\mathbf{v} + 3\mathbf{w}$ and $\mathbf{d} = 3\mathbf{u} - 8\mathbf{v} + 4\frac{1}{3}\mathbf{w}$ referred to the basis $\{\mathbf{u}, \mathbf{v}, \mathbf{w}\}$. Find the position vector $\mathbf{e}$ of the point of intersection of the lines AB and CD.
5. If O and $P_0$ are fixed points, describe the set of points $\{P: \mathbf{OP} = \mathbf{OP}_0 + \alpha\mathbf{d}\}$ where $\mathbf{d}$ is a given vector and $\alpha$ takes all real values. What is the significance of each of the cases $\alpha < 0$, $\alpha = 0$, $\alpha > 0$? (AEB)

## 4.9 Miscellaneous Exercises 4

1. The points A and B have position vectors **a** and **b** respectively referred to some origin O.
   (i) If C divides AB in the ratio 3:5, give **c** in terms of **a** and **b**.
   (ii) If $2\mathbf{a} + 3\mathbf{b} + \alpha\mathbf{c} = \mathbf{0}$, and C is on the line AB, find $\alpha$ and give the ratio in which C divides AB.
   (iii) If A divides BC in the ratio $-2:7$, give **c** in terms of **a** and **b**.
2. ABCD is a quadrilateral, and E is the mid-point of AB. DEBC is a parallelogram. Find the position vector of the point F of intersection of AC and DE, giving your answer in terms of the position vectors **a** and **c** of A and C.
3. In the triangle OAB, M is the mid-point of AB; C is a point on OM such that $OC = \frac{1}{2}CM$ and X is a point on OB such that $OX = 2XB$. The line XC is produced to meet OA at Y. Find OY/YA and XC/CY. (MME)
4. O is the origin and A and B are points whose position vectors are **a** and **b** respectively. Illustrate clearly, on a diagram, the points C, D and E such that

$$\mathbf{OC} = \mathbf{a} + \mathbf{b} \quad \mathbf{OD} = \tfrac{1}{2}\mathbf{a} + \mathbf{b} \quad \mathbf{OE} = \tfrac{1}{3}\mathbf{b}.$$

Given that F is the mid-point of OD, find the vectors **EC** and **EF** in terms of **a** and **b**. Hence show that E, F and C line on a straight line. (C)

5. In Fig. 4.12, X is the mid-point of AB and Y is the mid-point of OX. Given

that $\overrightarrow{OA}$ and $\overrightarrow{OB}$ represent the vectors **a** and **b** respectively, show that $\overrightarrow{OX}$ represents the vector $\frac{1}{2}(\mathbf{a} + \mathbf{b})$ and write down the vector $\overrightarrow{OY}$.

P is the point on OB such that $OP = \frac{3}{4}OB$. The line PQ is parallel to AO and $PQ = \frac{3}{4}AO$. Find, in terms of **a** and **b**, the vectors $\overrightarrow{OP}$ and $\overrightarrow{OQ}$.

Show that OYBQ is a parallelogram. (C)

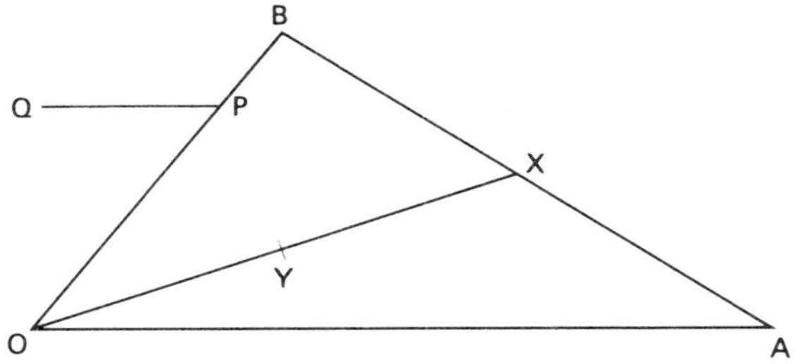


**Fig. 4.12.** Question 5.

6. O, A, B and C are points such that $\overrightarrow{OA} = \mathbf{a}$, $\overrightarrow{OB} = \mathbf{b}$, $\overrightarrow{OC} = k\mathbf{a} + l\mathbf{b}$, where $k$ and $l$ are numbers. Express $\overrightarrow{AB}$, $\overrightarrow{AC}$ and $\overrightarrow{BC}$ in terms of $k$, $l$, **a** and **b**, and show that if $k + l = 1$, then AB, AC and BC are in the same direction. State the conclusion that follows from this, concerning the points A, B and C, and express the ratio AC:CB in terms of $k$ and $l$.

X and Y are points such that $\overrightarrow{OX} = \frac{2}{3}\mathbf{a}$ and $\overrightarrow{OY} = 2\mathbf{b}$. Express $\overrightarrow{XY}$ in terms of **a** and **b**, and hence show that the point Z, given by $\overrightarrow{OZ} = \overrightarrow{OX} + \frac{1}{4}\overrightarrow{XY}$, is the mid-point of AB. (L)

7. In the triangle OAB, L is the mid-point of OA, and M is a point on OB such that $OM/MB = 2$. P is the mid-point of LM, and the line AP is produced to meet OB at Q.

Given that $\overrightarrow{OA} = \mathbf{a}$ and $\overrightarrow{OB} = \mathbf{b}$, find, in terms of **a** and **b**: (i) $\overrightarrow{OP}$, (ii) $\overrightarrow{AP}$. If $\overrightarrow{AQ} = h\,\overrightarrow{AP}$ and $\overrightarrow{OQ} = k\,\overrightarrow{OB}$, find $h$, $k$, AP/PQ and OQ/QB. (MME)

8. The position vectors of points A, B, C relative to a fixed origin O are **a**, **b**, **c** respectively. If D is the mid-point of AB, and if E is the point which divides CB internally in the ratio 1:2, write down the position vectors of D and E in terms of **a**, **b**, **c**.

Show that the mid-point F of CD is on AE and find the ratio AF:FE. (JMB)

9. Three non-coplanar vectors **a**, **b**, **c** are given in three-dimensional space, and a fourth vector **d** is expressed in terms of them in the form

$$\mathbf{d} = \alpha\mathbf{a} + \beta\mathbf{b} + \gamma\mathbf{c}.$$

Two lines are drawn: one is parallel to **b** and through the point with position vector **a**; the other is parallel to **d** and through the point with position vector **c**. Prove that these two lines meet: (i) if, (ii) only if $\alpha + \gamma = 0$.

A parallelepiped has three adjacent edges OA, OB, OC, and P, A′, B′, C′ are the vertices opposite to O, A, B, C respectively. Prove by a purely geometrical argument that a line through C (other than CA′) meets AC′: (i) if, and (ii) only if it also meets A′C′.

Establish the equivalence of these two results. (MEI)

# 5
# Coordinate Systems

## 5.1 Polar coordinates

We have already met plane polar coordinates in earlier chapters, but we will here summarize the properties that we need.

Any point P in a plane may be described by means of *polar coordinates* $(r, \theta)$ as follows: select in the plane an arbitrary, fixed origin O and an arbitrary fixed unit position vector $\mathbf{\hat{a}}$. Then $r$ is the length of $\overrightarrow{OP}$, and is necessarily positive; and $\theta$ is the angle between $\mathbf{\hat{a}}$ and the position vector $\overrightarrow{OP}$, measured anticlockwise from $\mathbf{\hat{a}}$. $\theta$ is not unique, as will be seen below.

The fixed direction and sense determined by $\mathbf{\hat{a}}$ is called the *initial line* (see Fig. 5.1). Thus the point A in Fig. 5.2 has polar coordinates (1, O), B has polar coordinates $(2, 45°)$ or $(2, \frac{1}{4}\pi$ rad), and C has polar coordinates $(1{\cdot}5, -\frac{1}{2}\pi$ rad). We see from this diagram that the point C may equally well be described as $(1{\cdot}5, 3\pi/2)$ or as $(1{\cdot}5, -5\pi/2)$, or more generally, as $(1{\cdot}5, (2n - \frac{1}{2})\pi)$ for any integer value of $n$.

Some definitions of polar coordinates admit the possibility of $r$ being negative, in which case the point A in Fig. 5.2 could be described as $(-1, \pi)$. The point D has coordinates $(1, \pi)$ and determines the positive sense for $r$ in the direction specified by $\theta = \pi$.

We now observe that the equation $\theta = \alpha$, where $\alpha$ is a constant, describes a half-line. Fig. 5.3 shows the half-lines $\theta = \pi/6$, $\theta = \pi/3$ and $\theta = 4\pi/3$, for example. If we allow negative values of $r$, then the equation $\theta = \pi/3$ is the equation of the whole line $\overleftrightarrow{AB}$ in the diagram. The context should make it clear whether such an equation describes all the line, or half of it.

Thus any straight line through the origin has an equation of the form $\theta$ = constant.

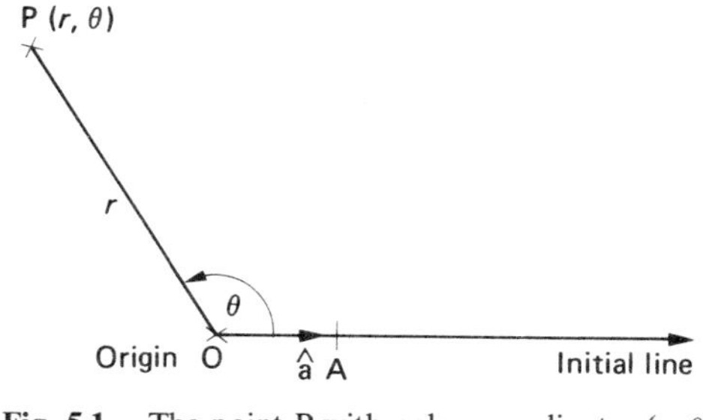


**Fig. 5.1.** The point P with polar coordinates $(r, \theta)$.

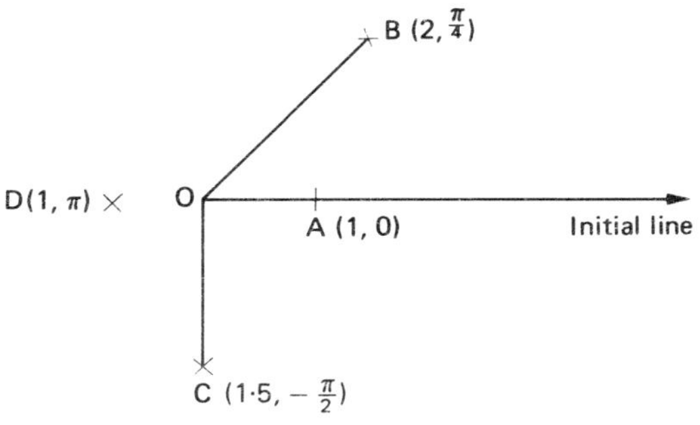


**Fig. 5.2.** Some points and their polar coordinates.

In general, the equation of a straight line has the form $r\cos(\theta - \alpha) = p$, where $p$ and $\alpha$ are constants.

The line $r\cos(\theta - \alpha) = p$ passes through the point $(p, \alpha)$, and is such that the perpendicular from O to the line has length $p$ and makes an angle $\alpha$ with the initial line. (See Exercise 5*a*, question 4, for an indication of the proof of this result.)

It is also worth noting that the equations $r$ = constant all represent circles, centred on the origin, with that constant as radius. Also, a circle *through* the origin with centre $(a, 0)$ has equation $r = 2a\cos\theta$, where $a$ is the radius. In general, *any* circle has an equation of the form

$$r^2 + c^2 - 2rc\cos(\theta - \alpha) = A^2$$

where $A$, $c$ and $\alpha$ are constants. This circle has centre $(c, \alpha)$ and radius $A$. (See Exercise 5*a*, question 5, for an indication of the proof of this result.)

We will be dealing with polar equations of conics in a later chapter. For the polar

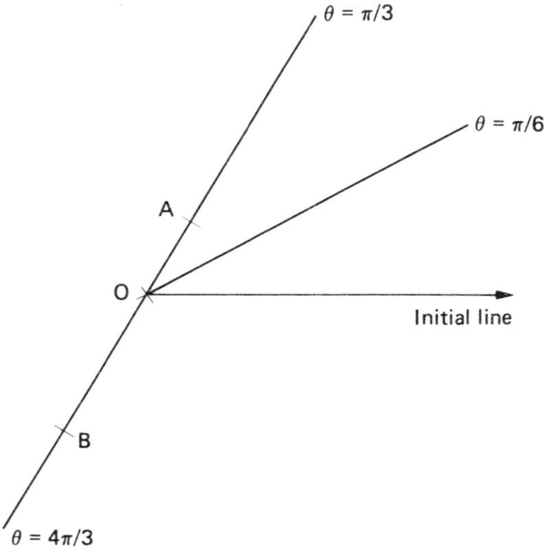


**Fig. 5.3.** Some half-lines and their polar equations.

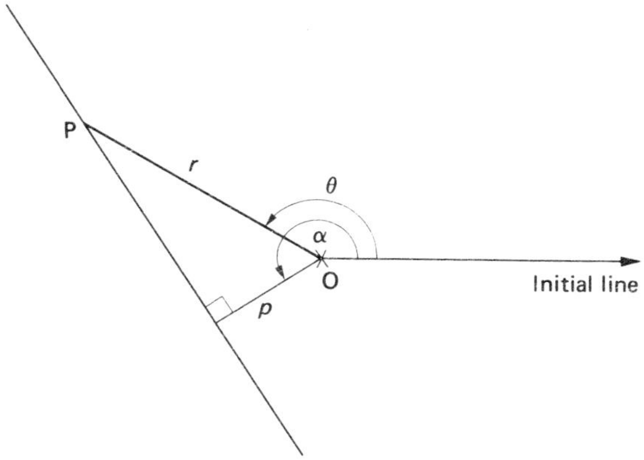


Fig. 5.4. The straight line $r\cos(\theta - \alpha) = p$.

equations of other curves, and their sketches, the reader is referred to more specialized texts.

**Worked Example 5.1**

The point A has polar coordinates $(4, \frac{1}{2}\pi)$, and B has polar coordinates $(3, \pi)$.
(i) Find the equation of the straight line AB.
(ii) Find the equation of the circle, centre A and radius 4.

*Solution*

We refer to Fig. 5.5.

(i) Suppose OC is the perpendicular from O onto $\overleftrightarrow{AB}$, and suppose $A\hat{O}C = \beta$. The $O\hat{B}A = \beta$, and we see that $\tan\beta = \frac{4}{3}$. Thus $\beta = \arctan(\frac{4}{3})$. Also, the length of OC is $3\sin\beta = 3 \times \frac{4}{5}$ since AB = 5. Hence the line $\overleftrightarrow{AB}$ has equation

$$r\cos(\theta - \beta - \tfrac{1}{2}\pi) = 12/5,$$

using the equation given on page 82.

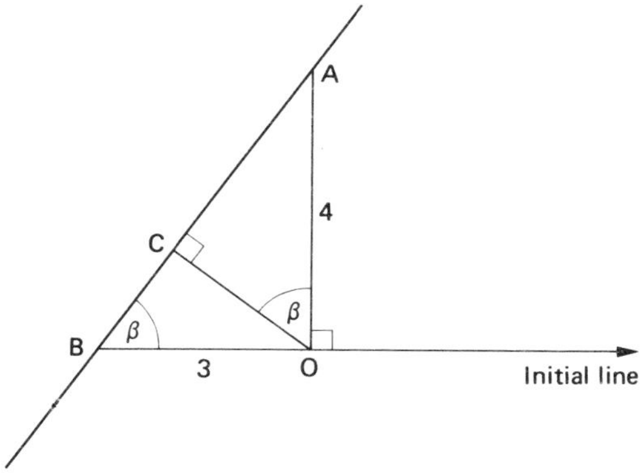


Fig. 5.5. Worked example 5.1.

(ii) The circle has centre $(4, \frac{1}{2}\pi)$ and radius 4. Therefore we may use the equation from page 82 to give the equation of the circle as

$$r^2 + 4^2 - 2 \times r \times 4 \times \cos(\theta - \tfrac{1}{2}\pi) = 4^2.$$

Therefore

$$r^2 - 8r\cos(\theta - \tfrac{1}{2}\pi) = 0$$

and so

$$r^2 - 8r\sin\theta = 0$$

is the required equation.

**Worked Example 5.2**

Find the coordinates of the points where the straight line with equation $r\cos(\theta - \frac{1}{4}\pi) = 4$ meets each of the following:

(i) the straight line with equation $r\cos\theta = 4$;
(ii) the straight line with equation $\theta = \frac{1}{2}\pi$;
(iii) the circle with equation $r = 5$.

*Solution*

(i) we refer to Fig. 5.6. The two straight lines meet at the point C. OA and OB are the perpendiculars from O onto the lines, and are both of length 4. Suppose $A\hat{O}C = \alpha$. Then

$$r\cos\alpha = 4 = r\cos(\alpha - \tfrac{1}{4}\pi)$$

Therefore $\cos\alpha = \cos(\alpha - \frac{1}{4}\pi)$, and so $\alpha = \pi/8$. Hence $OC = 4 \times \sec(\pi/8) = 4{\cdot}3296 \approx 4{\cdot}33$. Hence the lines meet at C $(4{\cdot}33, \pi/8)$.

(ii) The line $\theta = \frac{1}{2}\pi$ meets the line $r\cos(\theta - \frac{1}{4}\pi) = 4$, where $r\cos(\frac{1}{2}\pi - \frac{1}{4}\pi) = 4$.

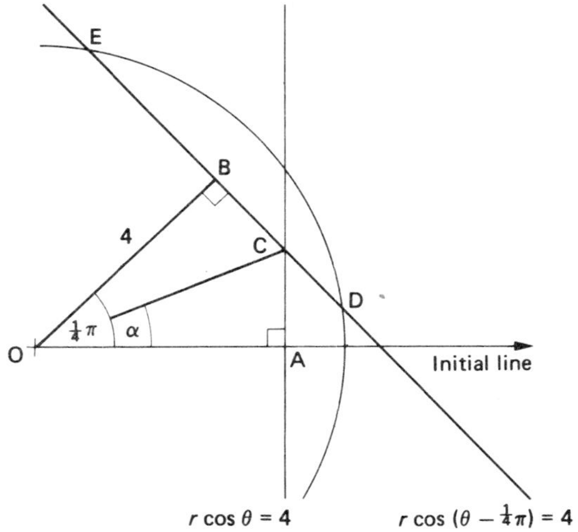


**Fig. 5.6.** Worked example 5.2.

Therefore $r \times \frac{1}{2}\sqrt{2} = 4$, and hence $r = 4\sqrt{2}$. Hence the two straight lines meet at $(4\sqrt{2}, \frac{1}{2}\pi)$.

(iii) The line meets the circle $r = 5$ at points D and E, where $5\cos(\theta - \frac{1}{4}\pi) = 4$. Therefore

$$\cos(\theta - 45°) = 0{\cdot}8 = \cos(36{\cdot}9°)$$

Therefore

$$\theta - 45° = 36{\cdot}9° \quad \text{or} \quad \theta - 45° = -36{\cdot}9°$$

Therefore

$$\theta = 81{\cdot}9° \quad \text{or} \quad \theta = 8{\cdot}1°$$

Hence the straight line meets the circle at D(5, 8·1°) and E(5, 81·9°).

## 5.2 Radial and transverse unit vectors

Now consider any point P in the plane, and suppose that P has polar coordinates $(r, \theta)$. Then P may be described in vector form by $\overrightarrow{OP} = r\hat{\mathbf{r}}$, where $\hat{\mathbf{r}}$ is a unit position vector in the direction and sense $\overrightarrow{OP}$. The restriction on sense is unnecessary if $r$ is allowed to be negative. Clearly, $\hat{\mathbf{r}}$ is not a fixed unit vector, as it depends on the (variable) polar angle $\theta$ of the point P. It will be called the *radial unit vector*. There is a vector $\hat{\boldsymbol{\theta}}$ at right angles to $\hat{\mathbf{r}}$, and 90° anticlockwise from it. This vector is called the *transverse unit vector*. The vector $\hat{\boldsymbol{\theta}}$ makes an angle $\theta + \frac{1}{2}\pi$ with the initial line.

**Worked Example 5.3**

P is the point with polar coordinates $(2, \frac{1}{4}\pi)$, and radial and transverse unit vectors $\hat{\mathbf{r}}$ and $\hat{\boldsymbol{\theta}}$ as above. Find the polar coordinates of the points with the following vectors:
(i) $\hat{\mathbf{r}}$ (ii) $\hat{\boldsymbol{\theta}}$ (ii) $\hat{\mathbf{r}} + \hat{\boldsymbol{\theta}}$ (iv) $3\hat{\mathbf{r}} - 4\hat{\boldsymbol{\theta}}$

*Solution*

We refer to Fig. 5.8.

(i) From the diagram, the point A has position vector $\hat{\mathbf{r}}$ and polar coordinates $(1, \frac{1}{4}\pi)$.

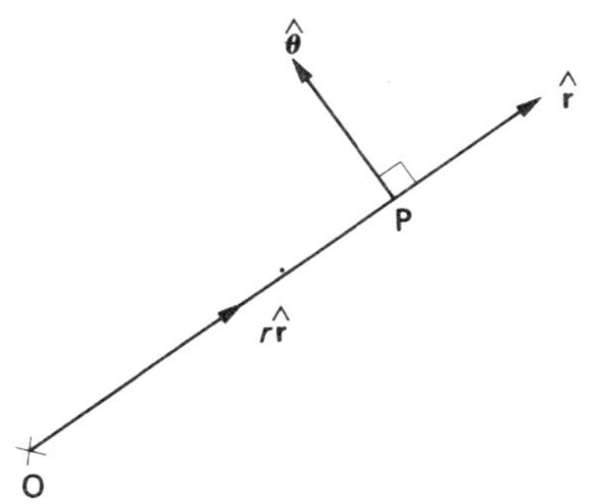


**Fig. 5.7.** The radial and transverse unit vectors $\hat{\mathbf{r}}$ and $\hat{\theta}$

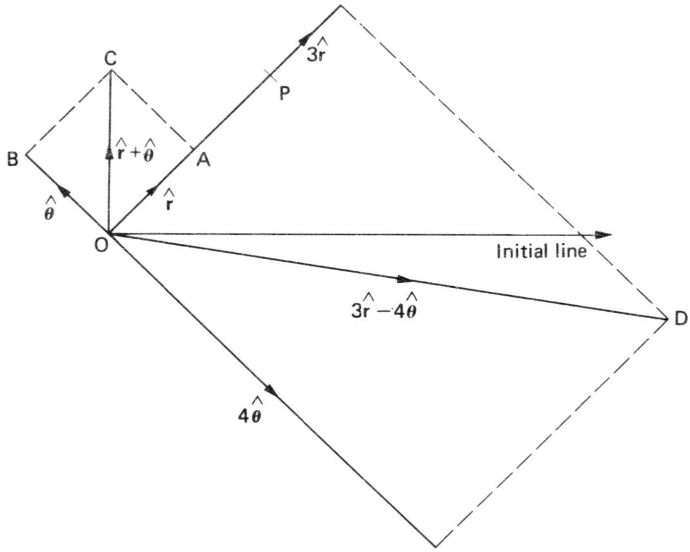


**Fig. 5.8.** Worked example 5.3.

(ii) Hence the point B with position vector $\hat{\boldsymbol{\theta}}$ has polar coordinates $(1, \frac{3}{4}\pi)$.
(iii) The point C with position vector $\hat{\mathbf{r}} + \hat{\boldsymbol{\theta}}$ has polar coordinates $(\sqrt{2}, \frac{1}{2}\pi)$, since OACB is a square of side 1.
(iv) The point D has position vector $3\hat{\mathbf{r}} - 4\hat{\boldsymbol{\theta}}$. By Pythagoras' theorem, the length of OD is 5. Also, $\tan(\mathrm{A\hat{O}D}) = 4/3$, and so $\mathrm{A\hat{O}D} = 53{\cdot}1°$. Hence D has polar coordinates $(5, -8{\cdot}1°)$.

## Exercise 5*a*

1. Sketch on the same diagram the half-lines given by equations (i) and (ii) and the circles given by equations (iii) and (iv).
(i) $\theta = 0$ (ii) $\theta = \pi/3$
(iii) $r = 2$ (iv) $r = 4\cos\theta$

2. A has polar coordinates (4, 90°). Sketch the circle on OA as diameter, and find its polar equation. Find also the equations of the circles: (i) with centre O, passing through A; (ii) with centre A, passing through O.
3. A and B are the points with polar coordinates (3, 30°) and (3, 90°) respectively. Find the equation of the circle on AB as diameter, stating clearly the coordinates of the centre of the circle, and its radius.
4. A is a point on the initial line. B has polar coordinates $(p, \alpha)$, where $\alpha$ is an acute angle, and where $\mathrm{O\hat{B}A}$ is a right angle. C is the point $(r, \theta)$ on the line AB, where $\theta$ is an acute angle greater than $\alpha$. Draw a clearly labelled diagram to display this information, and hence show that the equation of the straight line ABC is $r\cos(\theta - \alpha) = p$. Note that this establishes the general form of the equation of the straight line for the particular configuration drawn here; it is left to the reader to extend his argument to establish the result for other configurations.

5. The origin O lies outside the circle with centre C and radius A. The initial line cuts the circle in the points R and S. Suppose C has polar coordinates $(c, \alpha)$, where $\pi/2 > \alpha > 0$, and suppose that P is a point on the circle with polar coordinates $(r, \theta)$, with $\theta > \alpha$. Prove that $r^2 + c^2 - 2rc\cos(\theta - \alpha) = A^2$.

Note that this establishes the general form of the equation of the circle with centre C and radius A, again for a particular configuration. Again, it is left to the reader to extend his argument to establish the result for other configurations.

6. Find, in their simplest forms, the equations of the straight lines joining the following pairs of points:

(i) A $(4, 0)$ and B $(4, \pi)$;
(ii) A $(4, 0)$ and C $(4, \pi/3)$;
(iii) B $(4, 0)$ and C $(4, \pi/3)$.

7. Find the coordinates of the points where the straight line with equation $r\cos(\theta - \frac{1}{2}\pi) = 2$ meets each of the following:

(i) the straight line with equation $r + 2\sec\theta = 0$;
(ii) the straight line with equation $\theta = \pi/6$;
(iii) the circle with equation $r = 3$.

8. P is the point with polar coordinates $(3, \pi/3)$, and radial and transverse unit vectors $\hat{\mathbf{r}}$ and $\hat{\boldsymbol{\theta}}$, as in the text. Find the polar coordinates of the points with the following position vectors: (i) $\hat{\mathbf{r}}$, (ii) $\hat{\boldsymbol{\theta}}$, (iii) $\hat{\mathbf{r}} + \hat{\boldsymbol{\theta}}$, (iv) $2\hat{\mathbf{r}} - 2\hat{\boldsymbol{\theta}}$, (v) $2\hat{\boldsymbol{\theta}} - 2\hat{\mathbf{r}}$, (v) $2\hat{\mathbf{r}} + 5\hat{\boldsymbol{\theta}}$.

## 5.3 Plane Cartesian coordinates

We have already assumed that the reader is familiar with the idea of plane Cartesian coordinates $(x, y)$—we will now re-define them in a way that uses vectors. Select an origin O, and two perpendicular unit vectors $\hat{\mathbf{i}}$ and $\hat{\mathbf{j}}$, with $\hat{\mathbf{j}}$ 90° anticlockwise from $\hat{\mathbf{i}}$. Use these to define axes O$x$ and O$y$ respectively. Then any point P whose position vector $\mathbf{p}$ may be written as $\mathbf{p} = x\hat{\mathbf{i}} + y\hat{\mathbf{j}}$ is said to have rectangular Cartesian coordinates $(x, y)$. Suppose also that P has polar coordinates $(r, \theta)$. Then we see that $(x, y)$ and $(r, \theta)$ are connected by the relations $x = r\cos\theta$ and

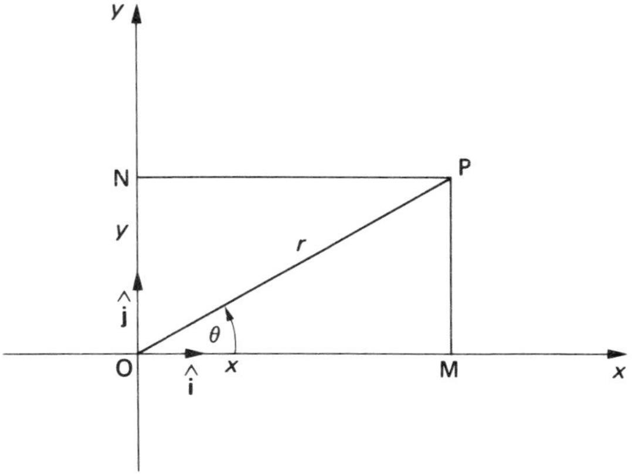


**Fig. 5.9.** The point P with polar coordinates $(r, \theta)$ and Cartesian coordinates $(x, y)$.

$y = r\sin\theta$, for all angles $\theta$, not just for acute angles, as might be suggested by the diagram.

Thus the position vector **p** of P may be written as

$$\mathbf{p} = x\hat{\mathbf{i}} + y\hat{\mathbf{j}} = (r\cos\theta)\hat{\mathbf{i}} + (r\sin\theta)\hat{\mathbf{j}}$$

and in turn corresponds to the column vector

$$\begin{pmatrix} x \\ y \end{pmatrix} = \begin{pmatrix} r\cos\theta \\ r\sin\theta \end{pmatrix}$$

The angles between **p** and the axes will be seen to be important later, especially in the three-dimensional extension. They are called the *direction angles* of **p**, and are $\theta$ and $90° - \theta$ respectively. We will also be interested in the cosines of these angles, namely $\cos\theta$ and $\cos(90° - \theta) = \sin\theta$, and these are called the *direction cosines* of the vector **p**. Direction angles and direction cosines are similarly defined to determine the direction of *any* line, not necessarily through the origin. Either direction angles or direction cosines may be used to specify the direction of any line relative to Cartesian axes.

Another very useful, connected, idea is that of *direction ratios*. Suppose the direction cosines of a line are $a$ and $b$. Then the pair of numbers $\lambda a$ and $\lambda b$ is a possible pair of direction ratios for the line. They correspond to our intuitive notion of being able to describe the direction of a straight line by a statement like 'two along and three up'—the 2 and the 3 would be suitable direction ratios.

**Worked Example 5.4**

The points P and Q have Cartesian coordinates (3, 4) and (2, 5) respectively, and column vectors

$$\mathbf{p} = \begin{pmatrix} 3 \\ 4 \end{pmatrix} \text{ and } \quad \mathbf{q} = \begin{pmatrix} 2 \\ 5 \end{pmatrix}$$

(i) Find the direction cosines of the line PQ.

(ii) Find the Cartesian and polar coordinates of the point with column vector $\mathbf{p} + \mathbf{q}$.

(iii) Find the length of the position vector corresponding to the column vector $2\mathbf{p} - \mathbf{q}$.

*Solution*

(i) The bound vector **PQ** is equivalent to

$$\mathbf{q} - \mathbf{p} = \begin{pmatrix} -1 \\ -1 \end{pmatrix}$$

and so the angle between the $x$-axis and $\overrightarrow{PQ}$ is 135°; and the angle between $\overrightarrow{PQ}$ and the $y$-axis is 45°. Hence the direction cosines of PQ are $\cos 135°$ and $\cos 45°$, i.e. $-\frac{1}{2}\sqrt{2}$ and $\frac{1}{2}\sqrt{2}$.

Alternatively, we could say that the angle between $\overrightarrow{QP}$ and the $x$-axis is 45°, so that the direction cosines of PQ are $\cos 45°$ and $\cos 135°$, i.e. $\frac{1}{2}\sqrt{2}$ and $-\frac{1}{2}\sqrt{2}$.

Hence the direction cosines of a line PQ are not unique—there is one set if we consider the line as $\overrightarrow{PQ}$, and another set if we consider it as $\overrightarrow{QP}$. Either set of direction cosines is sufficient to specify the direction of $\overrightarrow{PQ}$; the two different sets correspond to opposite senses. The direction of the line could also be specified

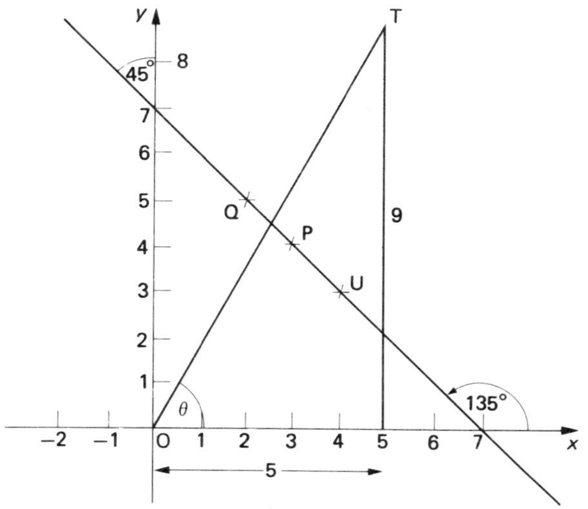


**Fig. 5.10.** Worked example 5.4.

by direction ratios $-1$ and 1, for example; or by 1 and $-1$, or by 2 and $-2$, etc.

(ii) $\mathbf{p} + \mathbf{q} = \begin{pmatrix} 3 + 2 \\ 4 + 5 \end{pmatrix} = \begin{pmatrix} 5 \\ 9 \end{pmatrix} = \mathbf{t}$

corresponding to the point T, say. Hence T has Cartesian coordinates (5, 9). By Pythagoras' theorem, $OT^2 = 5^2 + 9^2 = 106$ and so $OT = 10{\cdot}3$ (3S). Also $\tan\theta = 9/5 = 1{\cdot}8$ and so $\theta = 60{\cdot}9°$. Hence T has polar coordinates $(10{\cdot}3, 60{\cdot}9°)$.

(iii) $2\mathbf{p} - \mathbf{q} = \begin{pmatrix} 6 - 2 \\ 8 - 5 \end{pmatrix} = \begin{pmatrix} 4 \\ 3 \end{pmatrix} = \mathbf{u}$

corresponding to point U, say. By Pythagoras' theorem, OU = 5, and so the length of the position vector corresponding to $2\mathbf{p} - \mathbf{q}$ is 5.

## 5.4 Three-dimensional Cartesian coordinates

In three dimensions, we now take three unit vectors: $\hat{\mathbf{i}}$ and $\hat{\mathbf{j}}$ as before, and $\hat{\mathbf{k}}$ perpendicular to both so that $\hat{\mathbf{i}}, \hat{\mathbf{j}}, \hat{\mathbf{k}}$ satisfies the right-hand screw rule. This means that a screwdriver turning through a right angle from $\hat{\mathbf{i}}$ to $\hat{\mathbf{j}}$, and perpendicular to both, would drive a screw in the direction and sense of $\hat{\mathbf{k}}$. $\hat{\mathbf{i}}$, $\hat{\mathbf{j}}$ and $\hat{\mathbf{k}}$ determine the three axes O$x$, O$y$ and O$z$ respectively, which may be remembered as east, north, and upwards. Then any point P whose position vector $\mathbf{p}$ may be written as $\mathbf{p} = x\hat{\mathbf{i}} + y\hat{\mathbf{j}} + z\hat{\mathbf{k}}$ is said to have rectangular Cartesian coordinates $(x, y, z)$. Suppose the length of OP is $r$, and that the position vector $\overrightarrow{OP}$ makes an angle $\theta_1$ with O$x$. Then we see that $x = r\cos\theta_1$. Similarly, $y = r\cos\theta_2$ and $z = r\cos\theta_3$, where $\theta_2$ and $\theta_3$ are the angles between $\overrightarrow{OP}$ and O$y$ and O$z$, respectively. These three angles, $\theta_1$, $\theta_2$ and $\theta_3$, are the *direction angles* of the line OP, and their cosines are the *direction cosines* of the line. As in the two-dimensional case, either direction angles or direction cosines may be used to specify the direction of a straight line. The direction angles and direction cosines of *any* line PQ are defined to be the direction

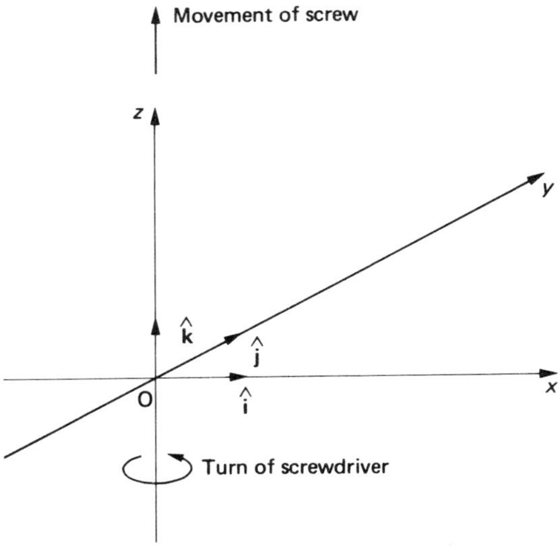


**Fig. 5.11.** Three-dimensional Cartesian axes.

angles and direction cosines of *either* the position vector **a** which is equivalent to $\overrightarrow{PQ}$, *or* the position vector **b** which is equivalent to $\overrightarrow{QP}$. In other words, we consider a line parallel to PQ, but through the origin.

Often, we use *direction ratios* to specify the direction. A set of direction ratios consists of scalar multiples of the direction cosines; e.g. $\{5\cos\theta_1, 5\cos\theta_2, 5\cos\theta_3\}$ is just one possible set of direction ratios. Although we have used set notation the *order* of the elements is, of course, not arbitrary.

We saw above that $x = r\cos\theta_1$, $y = r\cos\theta_2$ and $z = r\cos\theta_3$. Hence the position vector **r** of P may be written as

$$\mathbf{r} = (r\cos\theta_1)\hat{\mathbf{i}} + (r\cos\theta_2)\hat{\mathbf{j}} + (r\cos\theta_3)\hat{\mathbf{k}}$$

Hence

$$\frac{1}{r}\mathbf{r} = \cos\theta_1\hat{\mathbf{i}} + \cos\theta_2\hat{\mathbf{j}} + \cos\theta_3\hat{\mathbf{k}}$$

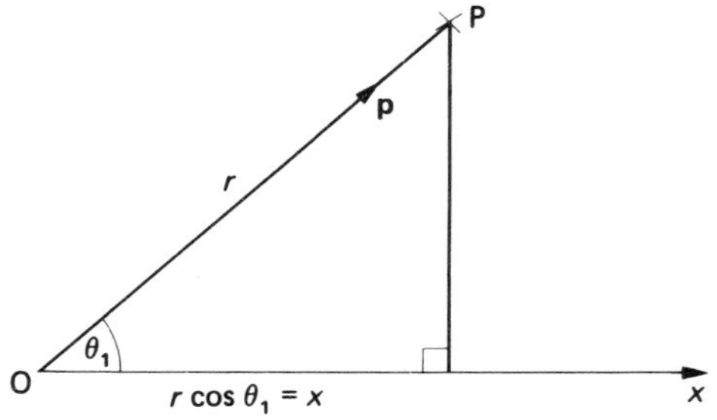


**Fig. 5.12.** The position vector $\overrightarrow{OP}$ and the $x$-axis.

In other words, the vector $\mathbf{r}/r$ has components which are the direction cosines of $\mathbf{r}$. The direction cosines therefore specify a unit vector in the direction and sense of $\mathbf{r}$, and this specification is unique. This uniqueness is justifiable by a consideration of linear independence (see Chapter 2). Similarly, a set of direction ratios will be the components of some vector in the direction of $\mathbf{r}$, but not necessarily in the same sense.

The length of the unit vector $\mathbf{r}/r$ is also given by $(\cos\theta_1)^2 + (\cos\theta_2)^2 + (\cos\theta_3)^2$, and so

$$(\cos\theta_1)^2 + (\cos\theta_2)^2 + (\cos\theta_3)^2 = 1$$

The position vector $\mathbf{p} = x\hat{\mathbf{i}} + y\hat{\mathbf{j}} + z\hat{\mathbf{k}}$ corresponds directly to the column vector

$$\begin{pmatrix} x \\ y \\ z \end{pmatrix}$$

and we will say that the point P has column vector

$$\mathbf{p} = \begin{pmatrix} x \\ y \\ z \end{pmatrix}$$

Suppose that

$$\mathbf{p}(u) = x(u)\hat{\mathbf{i}} + y(u)\hat{\mathbf{j}} + z(u)\hat{\mathbf{k}}$$

Then we know that

$$\mathbf{p}'(u) = x'(u)\hat{\mathbf{i}} + y'(u)\hat{\mathbf{j}} + z'(u)\hat{\mathbf{k}}$$

Therefore the derivative $\mathbf{p}'(u)$ of

$$\mathbf{p}(u) = \begin{pmatrix} x(u) \\ y(u) \\ z(u) \end{pmatrix} \quad \text{is} \quad \mathbf{p}'(u) = \begin{pmatrix} x'(u) \\ y'(u) \\ z'(u) \end{pmatrix}.$$

**Worked Example 5.5**

P has Cartesian coordinates (2, −1, −2), and Q has Cartesian coordinates (3, 1, −2).

(i) Find the length of OP, and hence find the direction cosines of $\overrightarrow{OP}$.
(ii) Find direction ratios for $\overrightarrow{PQ}$.

*Solution*

(i) The length of OP is $\sqrt{2^2 + (-1)^2 + 2^2} = 3$. Hence the direction cosines of $\overrightarrow{OP}$ are $\frac{2}{3}$, $-\frac{1}{3}$ and $-\frac{2}{3}$. Note that the direction cosines of $\overrightarrow{PO}$ are $-\frac{2}{3}$, $\frac{1}{3}$ and $\frac{2}{3}$.

(ii) $\overrightarrow{PQ}$ has column vector

$$\begin{pmatrix} 3 \\ 1 \\ -2 \end{pmatrix} - \begin{pmatrix} 2 \\ -1 \\ -2 \end{pmatrix} = \begin{pmatrix} 1 \\ 2 \\ 0 \end{pmatrix}$$

Hence {1, 2, 0} is a possible set of direction ratios for $\overrightarrow{PQ}$; as are {−1, −2, 0}, {2, 4, 0}, {7·3, 14·6, 0}, to name just three more possibilities.

**Worked Example 5.6**

The bound vector **PQ** has direction ratios {2, −1, 2} and length 6. The point P has Cartesian coordinates (3, −1, −2).

(i) Find the direction cosines of **PQ**;
(ii) find the coordinates of Q;
(iii) find the angle between **q** and O$x$.

*Solution*

(i) The column vector

$$\begin{pmatrix} 2 \\ -1 \\ 2 \end{pmatrix}$$

has magnitude $\sqrt{2^2 + (-1)^2 + 2^2} = 3$, and is therefore the column vector for $\frac{1}{2}$**PQ**. Therefore the direction cosines of $\frac{1}{2}$**PQ** (and so also of **PQ**) are $\frac{2}{3}, -\frac{1}{3}, \frac{2}{3}$.

(ii) The column vector for **PQ** = **q** − **p** is

$$6\begin{pmatrix} 2/3 \\ -1/3 \\ 2/3 \end{pmatrix} = \begin{pmatrix} 4 \\ -2 \\ 4 \end{pmatrix}$$

Therefore

$$\mathbf{q} = \begin{pmatrix} 3 \\ -1 \\ -2 \end{pmatrix} + \begin{pmatrix} 4 \\ -2 \\ 4 \end{pmatrix} = \begin{pmatrix} 7 \\ -3 \\ 2 \end{pmatrix}$$

and Q has coordinates (7, −3, 2).

(iii) $|\mathbf{q}| = \sqrt{7^2 + (-3)^2 + 2^2} = \sqrt{62}$. Hence $\cos\theta_1 = 7/\sqrt{62}$, where $\theta_1$ is the angle between **q** and O$x$. Hence $\theta_1 \approx 27{\cdot}2°$.

**Exercise 5*b***

1. Find the polar coordinates of the points with the following Cartesian coordinates: (a) (3, 4); (b) (−5, 12); (c) (−8, −15); (d) (9, −40). Give the angle both in degrees and in radians.

2. Find the Cartesian coordinates of the points with the following polar coordinates, where the angles are given in degrees: (a) (2, 30); (b) (4, 135); (c) (3, 240); (d) (4, 300).

3. Find the Cartesian coordinates of the points with the following polar coordinates, where the angles are given in radians: (a) $(2{\cdot}3, \frac{1}{4}\pi)$; (b) $(2{\cdot}2, \pi)$; (c) $(4{\cdot}1, 6\pi/5)$; (d) $(3{\cdot}2, 7\pi/4)$.

4. Find the direction cosines of the lines joining the following pairs of points: (a) (−2, −3) and (3, 1); (b) (−3, −2) and (−1, 2); (c) the origin and (0, 4); (d) (−1, 3) and (−3, −2).

5. The points A and B have Cartesian coordinates (3, −2) and (−1, −1) respectively, and column vectors **a** and **b**.

(i) Find the direction cosines of the bound vector **BA**.
(ii) Find the Cartesian coordinates of the point with column vector **a** + 2**b**.
(iii) Find the polar coordinates of the point with column vector 2**a** − 3**b**.

6. Find the direction cosines of the lines joining the following pairs of points: (a) (2, 1, 2) and (2, −1, −2); (b) (2, −3, −2) and (0, 1, 3); (c) (−1, −3, 2) and (4, 4, 2); (d) (2, −3, 5) and (3, −2, 3).

7. A has Cartesian coordinates (3, −2, 2) and B has Cartesian coordinates (−1, −1, −1).

(i) Find the direction ratios and direction cosines for **AB**.

(ii) Find direction ratios and direction cosines for **OA** and **OB**.

8. The bound vector **PQ** has direction ratios −1, −2, 2 and length 4. The point P has Cartesian coordinates (−1, −1, 2).

(i) Find the direction cosines of **PQ**.

(ii) Find the coordinates of Q.

(iii) Find the angle between **q** and O$x$.

## 5.5 Cylindrical polar coordinates

In this and the next section, we will define two more common three-dimensional coordinate systems which the reader may meet at a later stage. We will relate them to the Cartesian coordinates already defined, but will not dwell on them unduly.

Firstly, we will define *cylindrical polar coordinates*. Suppose that the point P has Cartesian coordinates $(x, y, z)$, and that Q is the point in the $xy$-plane with Cartesian coordinates $(x, y, 0)$. Suppose that Q has polar coordinates $(r, \theta)$ referred to the same origin O, and the axis O$x$ as initial line. Then P has cylindrical polar coordinates $(r, \theta, z)$.

We thus see that the Cartesian coordinates $(x, y, z)$ and the cylindrical polar coordinates $(r, \theta, z)$ of P are connected by the equations $r\cos\theta = x$, $r\sin\theta = y$, $z = z$.

It is worth noting at this stage the following facts, which the reader is left to investigate further for himself:

(1) The set of points P such that $r$ has some constant value $a$ is a cylindrical shell shell of radius $a$, and with the $z$-axis as the axis of the cylinder.

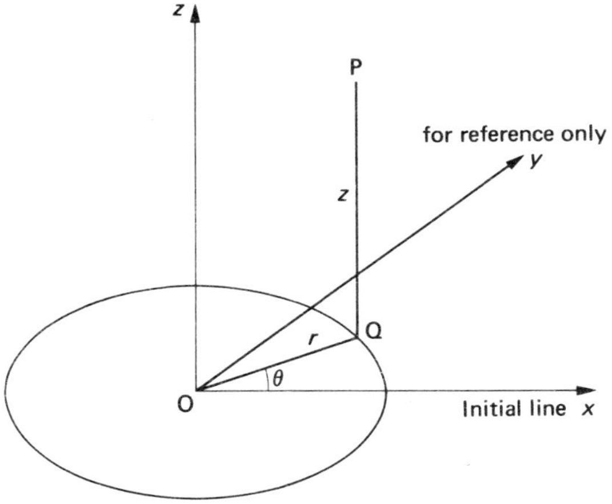


**Fig. 5.13.** The point P with cylindrical polar coordinates $(r, \theta, z)$.

(2) The set of points P such that $\theta$ has some fixed value $\alpha$ is a half-plane through the origin and containing the $z$-axis.
(3) The set of points P such that $z$ has some fixed value $c$ is a plane parallel to the plane containing the axes of $x$ and $y$.

## 5.6 Spherical polar coordinates

The other system of coordinates is that of *spherical polar coordinates*. Suppose, again, that P and Q are the points with Cartesian coordinates $(x, y, z)$ and $(x, y, 0)$ respectively. Then we define the spherical polar coordinates $(r, \theta, \phi)$ of P by:

$$r = |\overrightarrow{OP}|,$$
$$\theta = \text{the angle between } \overrightarrow{OP} \text{ and } Oz,$$

and

$$\phi = \text{the angle between } \overrightarrow{Ox} \text{ and } \overrightarrow{OQ} \text{ as shown in Fig. 5.14.}$$

We thus see that the Cartesian coordinates $(x, y, z)$ and the spherical polar coordinates $(r, \theta, \phi)$ of P are connected by the equations $x = r\sin\theta\cos\phi$, $y = r\sin\theta\sin\phi$ and $z = r\cos\theta$.

It is worth noting at this stage the following facts, which the reader is left to investigate further for himself:
(1) The set of points P such that $r$ has some constant value $a$ is a spherical shell, centre the origin and radius $a$.
(2) The set of points P such that $\theta$ has some constant value $\alpha$ is a conical shell of vertical angle $2\alpha$ and having $0z$ as its axis.
(3) The set of points P such that $\phi$ has some constant value $\beta$ is a half-plane containing the origin and the $z$-axis.

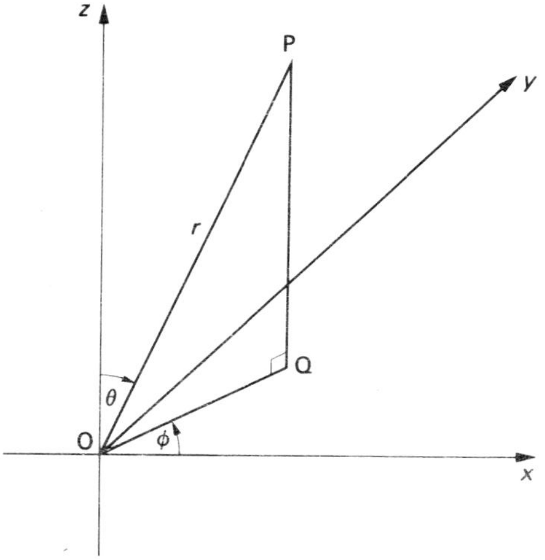


**Fig. 5.14.** The point P with spherical polar coordinates $(r, \theta, \phi)$.

## 5.7 Miscellaneous Exercises 5

1. Sketch on the same diagram the straight lines and circles given by the following polar equations:
(a) $r = 2$; (b) $\theta = 2$ rad, (c) $r = 2\cos\theta$, (d) $r\cos(\theta - 210°) = 2$.

2. A has polar coordinates $(3, 3\pi/2)$. Sketch the circle on OA as diameter, and find its polar equation. Find also the equations of the circles:
(a) with centre O, passing through A;
(b) with centre A, passing through O.

3. Find the polar equation of the circle, centre $(2, \pi/6)$ and radius 4. Find the equation of the tangent to this circle at the point $(6, \pi/6)$.

4. Find, in their simplest forms, the equations of the straight lines joining the following pairs of points:
(a) A$(3, 0)$ and B$(5, \pi)$;
(b) A$(3, 0)$ and C$(4, \frac{1}{2}\pi)$;
(c) B$(5, \pi)$ and C$(4, \frac{1}{2}\pi)$.

5. P is the point with polar coordinates $(4, 4\pi/3)$, and radial and transverse unit vectors $\hat{\mathbf{r}}$ and $\hat{\boldsymbol{\theta}}$, defined in the usual way. Find the polar coordinates of the points with the following position vectors:
(i) $\hat{\mathbf{r}}$, (ii) $\hat{\boldsymbol{\theta}}$, (iii) $-\hat{\mathbf{r}} + \hat{\boldsymbol{\theta}}$, (iv) $2\hat{\mathbf{r}} - 3\hat{\boldsymbol{\theta}}$.

6. Find the polar coordinates of the points with the following Cartesian coordinates: (a) $(2, -3)$; (b) $(9, 3)$; (c) $(-7, -8)$; (d) $(-4, -3)$. Give the angle both in degrees and in radians.

7. Find the Cartesian coordinates of the points with the following polar coordinates, where the angles are given in radians: (a) $(3{\cdot}7, 9\pi/8)$, (b) $(4{\cdot}3, 4{\cdot}3)$, (c) $(5{\cdot}5, 7\pi/3)$, (d) $(6, 6)$.

8. The points F and G have Cartesian coordinates $(4, 4)$ and $(-3, 5)$ respectively, and column vectors $\mathbf{f}$ and $\mathbf{g}$.
(i) Find the direction cosines of the bound vector **FG**.
(ii) Find the Cartesian coordinates of the point with column vector $2\mathbf{f} - 3\mathbf{g}$.
(iii) Find the polar coordinates of the point with column vector $3\mathbf{f} + 4\mathbf{g}$.

9. K has Cartesian coordinates $(2, -4, 1)$ and L has Cartesian coordinates $(-1, 2, 3)$.
(i) Find direction ratios and direction cosines for **KL**.
(ii) Find the angle between **KL** and O$x$.

10. The bound vector **MN** has direction ratios $-1, -1, 3$ and length 5. The point M has coordinates $(5, 3, -6)$.
(i) Find the coordinates of N.
(ii) Find the angle between **ON** and O$z$.

11. Find the cylindrical polar coordinates and the spherical polar coordinates of the points with the following Cartesian coordinates, giving the angles in degrees: (a) $(2, 2, 1)$, (b) $(1, -3, 2)$, (c) $(4, 5, -2)$, (d) $(-2, -2, 4)$.

12. (a) The point A has cylindrical polar coordinates $(3, 60°, 5)$. Find its Cartesian coordinates and its spherical polar coordinates. (b) The point B has spherical polar coordinates $(3, 60°, 120°)$. Find its Cartesian coordinates and its cylindrical polar coordinates.

13. In three-dimensional Euclidean space with Cartesian coordinates $(x, y, z)$, points A and B are given by $(2, 1, 1)$ and $(1, -4, 2)$. Prove that the sphere with AB as diameter passes through the origin. (SMP)

# 6
# Relative Velocity

## 6.1 Linear motion

Suppose you are travelling in a car, on a motorway, at 60 km $h^{-1}$. If another car overtakes you, you may well estimate his velocity as follows:

'I am travelling at 60 km $h^{-1}$; he is doing about 30 km $h^{-1}$ more then I am; therefore he is travelling at about 90 km $h^{-1}$''. The important figure here is the 30: this is called the velocity of the other car *relative to* your car; the velocity at which you observe the other car to be gaining on you. The velocity of the second car relative to your car is about 30 km $h^{-1}$.

Now consider the driver of the other car. He might argue:

'I am travelling at 90 km $h^{-1}$; he is doing about 30 km $h^{-1}$ less than I am; therefore he is travelling at about 60 km $h^{-1}$''. Again, the 30 is the important figure. Your velocity relative to the second car is $-30$ km $h^{-1}$; if the other driver could see nothing else, he might think you were reversing towards him at 30 km $h^{-1}$.

Thus your velocity relative to him is $-30$ km $h^{-1}$, whilst his velocity relative to you is $+30$ km $h^{-1}$. The two are necessarily equal and opposite.

Relative to a lorry travelling in the slow lane at 40 km $h^{-1}$, the velocities of the two cars are 20 km $h^{-1}$ and 50 km $h^{-1}$. Relative to a man repairing a puncture on the hard shoulder, the velocities of the two cars are 60 km $h^{-1}$ and 90 km $h^{-1}$—the actual velocities. It will often be convenient to imagine actual velocities as relative to some object which is fixed on the ground.

Remember, then, that the value given to the velocity of a car depends on who is observing the car, and their relative motion.

Now let us try to formalise what we have just done. Suppose the velocity of the first car may be represented by the vector $60\hat{\mathbf{v}}$, where $\hat{\mathbf{v}}$ is a unit vector determining the direction and sense of that car's motion. Then the velocity of the second car is represented by $90\hat{\mathbf{v}}$ The velocity of the second car relative to the first is given by $90\hat{\mathbf{v}} - 60\hat{\mathbf{v}} = 30\hat{\mathbf{v}}$—which we described earlier as $+30$ km $h^{-1}$. Similarly, the velocity of the first car relative to the second is given by

$$60\hat{\mathbf{v}} - 90\hat{\mathbf{v}} = -30\hat{\mathbf{v}} = \text{velocity of first car} - \text{velocity of second car}$$

The *relative speed* in each case is 30 km $h^{-1}$, the magnitude of each relative velocity.

**Worked example 6.1**

If the lengths of both the cars in the above explanation are 5 m, for how long will the two cars overlap?

*Solution*

The nose of the faster car has to travel two car lengths (10 m) at the relative speed of 30 km h$^{-1}$ in order to complete the overtaking. Thus

$$\text{time taken} = \frac{\text{distance travelled}}{\text{relative speed}}$$

$$= \frac{10 \text{ m}}{30 \text{ km h}^{-1}}$$

$$= 1{\cdot}2 \text{ s}$$

**Worked example 6.2**

(a) A fast train, moving at 150 km h$^{-1}$, is travelling towards a slow train, moving at 65 km h$^{-1}$, on a straight, level track. Find the velocity of each relative to the other. If the fast train is 225 m long, and the slow train is 150 m long, for how long will the two trains overlap?

(b) The fast train later overtakes another slow train, also 150 m long and moving at 65 km h$^{-1}$ along a parallel track. How long does the overtaking take?

*Solution*

(a) Suppose the velocity of the fast train is represented by $150\hat{\mathbf{v}}$, where $\hat{\mathbf{v}}$ is a unit vector in the direction and sense of the fast train's motion. Then the velocity of the slow train is represented by $-65\hat{\mathbf{v}}$. Therefore the velocity of the fast train relative to the slow train is given by

$$\text{velocity of fast train} - \text{velocity of slow train} = 150\hat{\mathbf{v}} - (-65\hat{\mathbf{v}}) = 215\hat{\mathbf{v}}$$

This is the velocity at which a passenger in the slow train imagines the fast train to be travelling past him. The same relative velocity would also occur if the slow train was not moving and the fast train was actually travelling at 215 km h$^{-1}$; or if both trains were travelling at $107\frac{1}{2}$ km h$^{-1}$; etc.

The velocity of the slow train relative to the fast train is $(-65\hat{\mathbf{v}}) - 150\hat{\mathbf{v}} = -215\hat{\mathbf{v}}$– equal in magnitude, but opposite in sense. The time of overlap is given by

$$\frac{225 \text{ m} + 150 \text{ m}}{215 \text{ km h}^{-1}} = \frac{270}{43} \text{ s} \approx 6{\cdot}28 \text{ s}$$

(b) The velocity of the fast train relative to the second slow train is $(150\hat{\mathbf{v}}) - (65\hat{\mathbf{v}}) = 85\hat{\mathbf{v}}$. The time of overtaking is given by

$$\frac{225 \text{ m} + 150 \text{ m}}{85 \text{ km h}^{-1}} = \frac{270}{17} \text{ s} \approx 15{\cdot}9 \text{ s}$$

**Exercise 6*a***

1. A car of length 5 m and speed 100 km h$^{-1}$ overtakes another car of length 4·5 m and speed 85 km h$^{-1}$. How long does the manœuvre take?

2. A car of length 5 m and speed 100 km h$^{-1}$ takes 1·2 s to overtake a lorry travelling at 50 km h$^{-1}$. How long is the lorry?

3. One boy cycles twice as fast as another boy walks, and both are travelling on the same straight road. If the velocity of the cyclist relative to the walker is $v$, find the possible values of the cyclist's speed, in terms of $v$.

4. An express train moves with speed $u$, and a goods train with speed $v$ along straight parallel tracks. Both trains are 250 m long. If they are travelling towards each other, they take 8 seconds to pass; if they are travelling in the same sense, they take 16 seconds to pass. Find $u$ and $v$.

5. Three particles A, B and C travel in a straight line with velocities $a\hat{\mathbf{v}}$, $b\hat{\mathbf{v}}$ and $c\hat{\mathbf{v}}$ respectively, where $\hat{\mathbf{v}}$ is a fixed unit vector. Find the velocity of A relative to B, and the velocity of C relative to B. Find the connection between $a$, $b$ and $c$ if

velocity of A relative to B − velocity of C relative to A

= 2 × (velocity of C relative to B).

6. Two particles A and B have velocities $t\hat{\mathbf{v}}$ and $t^2\hat{\mathbf{v}}$ respectively, where $\hat{\mathbf{v}}$ is a fixed unit vector, and $t$ represents time. Find when they are stationary relative to each other.

## 6.2 Relative velocity law

Consider two toy boats, a red one and a blue one, sailing on a lake in different directions, watched by their owner on the bank. Their velocities may be described in different ways as follows:

*the red one*

in absolute terms, travelling due north at some speed; (1)
by the owner, travelling towards me at some speed; (2)
by the blue one, always on my port side and getting nearer. (3)

*the blue one*

in absolute terms, on a bearing of 330° at some speed; (4)
by the owner, travelling towards a point on my left at some speed; (5)
by the red one, always on my starboard side and getting nearer. (6)

Immediately, we observe that, since the owner is stationary, he will observe the actual velocities of the boats, and so the pairs (1) and (2), and (4) and (5), are identical. This is borne out by Fig. 6.1.

The velocities described by (3) and (6) are called the velocities of the boats relative to one another. If R stands for the red boat, and B for the blue boat, then

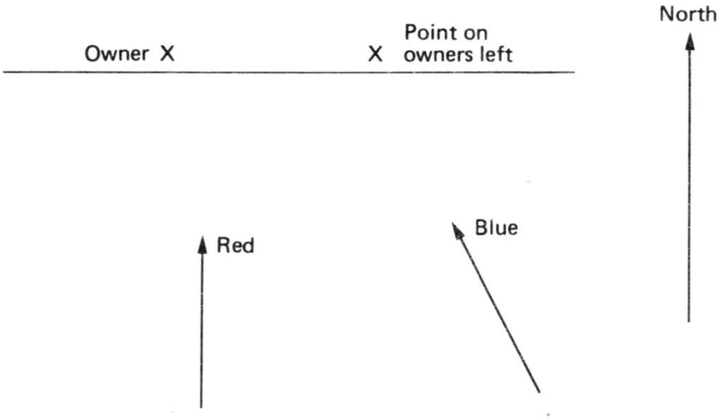


**Fig. 6.1.** Two toy boats on a lake.

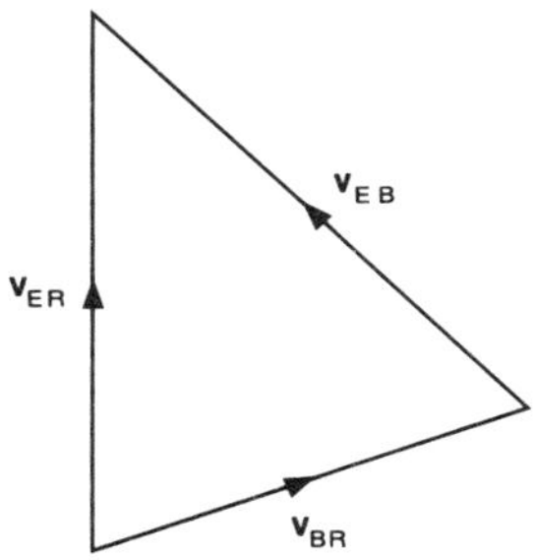


**Fig. 6.2.** The relative velocity law, $\mathbf{v}_{EB} + \mathbf{v}_{BR} = \mathbf{v}_{ER}$.

*the velocity of R relative to B* is the velocity of R as observed by B, and we will write it as $\mathbf{v}_{BR}$. Similarly, the velocity of B relative to R is denoted by $\mathbf{v}_{RB}$. For convenience, the actual velocities of B and R may be regarded as velocities relative to the earth—which is really what they are—and denoted by $\mathbf{v}_{EB}$ and $\mathbf{v}_{ER}$ respectively.

Now, we may imagine the velocity of R relative to the earth as comprising two components: the velocity of R relative to B, and the velocity of B relative to the earth. This gives us the *relative velocity law*:

$$\mathbf{v}_{EB} + \mathbf{v}_{BR} = \mathbf{v}_{ER} \tag{7}$$

Notice that the repeated suffix B on the left-hand side is the one that does not appear on the right-hand side.

Alternatively, the position of R relative to B may be written as $\mathbf{BR} = \mathbf{r} - \mathbf{b}$, where $\mathbf{b}$ and $\mathbf{r}$ are the position vectors of B and R respectively relative to some origin O. Then

$$\frac{d}{dt}(\mathbf{BR}) = \mathbf{v}_{BR} = \dot{\mathbf{r}} - \dot{\mathbf{b}} = \mathbf{v}_{ER} - \mathbf{v}_{EB}$$

and we have proved the relative velocity law (7) by another method.

Furthermore, we have $\mathbf{BR} = -\mathbf{RB}$. Hence, differentiating with respect to $t$ gives $\mathbf{v}_{BR} = -\mathbf{v}_{RB}$. Therefore, the relative velocities $\mathbf{v}_{BR}$ and $\mathbf{v}_{RB}$ are equal in magnitude and direction but opposite in sense.

A possible application of the relative velocity law (7) will be shown in the worked examples that follow.

This law may be generalized to consideration of the relative motion of any three bodies A, B, and C. The law then becomes

$$\mathbf{v}_{AB} + \mathbf{v}_{BC} = \mathbf{v}_{AC} \tag{8}$$

since $\mathbf{AB} + \mathbf{BC} = \mathbf{AC}$.

## 6.3 Worked examples

### Worked example 6.3

On a lake, a yellow boat is travelling at 5 m s$^{-1}$ due west, and a green boat is travelling at 4 m s$^{-1}$ towards the north-east. Find the velocity of the green boat relative to the yellow one.

*Solution*

From above, we have that $\mathbf{v}_{EY} + \mathbf{v}_{YG} = \mathbf{v}_{EG}$, or

$$\mathbf{v}_{YG} = \mathbf{v}_{EG} - \mathbf{v}_{EY} = \text{velocity of green boat} - \text{velocity of yellow boat}$$

as in the linear case. These vectors, and their magnitudes are shown in Fig. 6.3, where the required relative velocity has magnitude $v$, and is towards $\beta$ degrees north of east. By the cosine rule;

$$\begin{aligned} v^2 &= 4^2 + 5^2 - 2 \times 4 \times 5 \times \cos 135° \\ &= 16 + 25 + 40 \times \cos 45° \\ &= 69{\cdot}284 \end{aligned}$$

Therefore

$$v = 8{\cdot}324 \text{ m s}^{-1} \approx 8{\cdot}32 \text{ m s}^{-1}$$

By the sine rule,

$$\sin \beta = \frac{4 \times \sin 135°}{8{\cdot}324} = \sin 19{\cdot}8°$$

Therefore

$$\beta = 19{\cdot}8°$$

Thus the velocity of the green boat relative to the yellow one is $8{\cdot}32 \text{ m s}^{-1}$ on a bearing of $070{\cdot}2°$.

**Worked example 6.4**

A rectangular skating rink is 40 m long and 20 m wide. Skater A starts at the mid-point of a short side and skates at $4 \text{ m s}^{-1}$ parallel to the long sides. Skater B starts at the mid-point of the long side on A's left, and skates towards the *opposite* corner on *his* left at $4 \text{ m s}^{-1}$. Find the velocity of B relative to A, and the shortest distance between them.

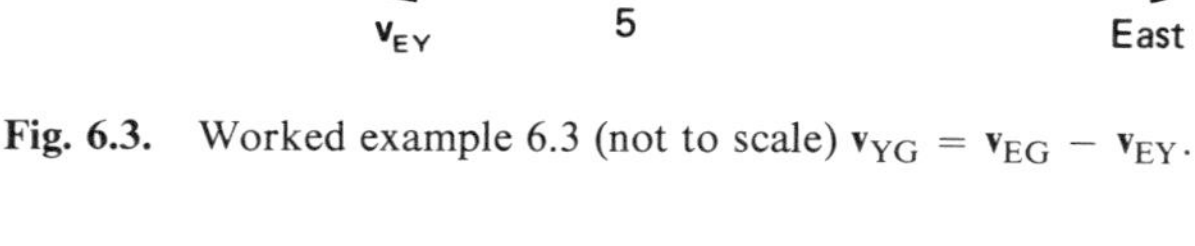

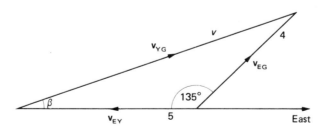

**Fig. 6.3.** Worked example 6.3 (not to scale) $\mathbf{v}_{YG} = \mathbf{v}_{EG} - \mathbf{v}_{EY}$.

*Solution*

Suppose the starting positions of A and B are $A_0$ and $B_0$ respectively, as shown in Fig. 6.4. The velocity of B relative to A is given by $\mathbf{v}_{AB} = \mathbf{v}_B - \mathbf{v}_A$, where $\mathbf{v}_A$ is the velocity of A, and $\mathbf{v}_B$ is the velocity of B. These velocities are shown in Fig. 6.5, where the dotted line is parallel to the short sides of the rink.

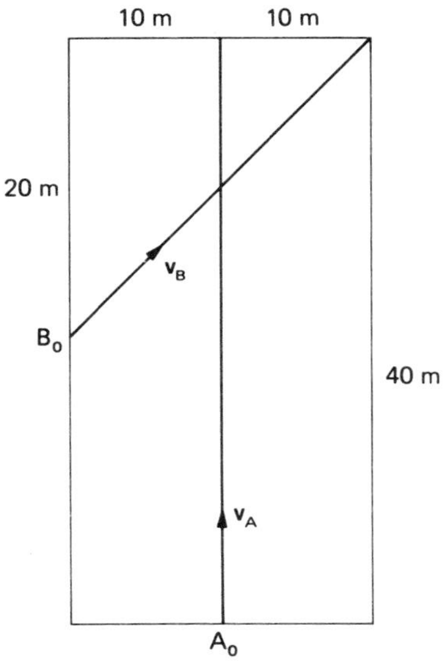


**Fig. 6.4.** Worked example 6.4.

The triangle shown is isosceles. Therefore $45 + \theta = \frac{1}{2}(180 - 45) = 67\frac{1}{2}$, and so $\theta = 22\frac{1}{2}°$. Also, if $v$ is the speed of B relative to A,

$$v^2 = 4^2 + 4^2 - 2 \times 4 \times 4 \times \cos 45° = 32(1 - \cos 45°) = 16(2 - \sqrt{2})$$

Therefore

$$v = \sqrt{16(2 - \sqrt{2})} \text{ m s}^{-1} \approx 3{\cdot}06 \text{ m s}^{-1}$$

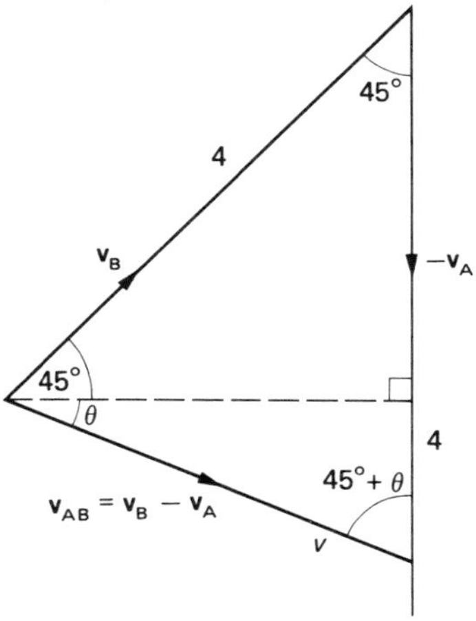


**Fig. 6.5.** Finding the relative velocity $\mathbf{v}_{AB}$.

Therefore the velocity of B relative to A is $3{\cdot}06\ \text{m s}^{-1}$, making an angle $22\frac{1}{2}°$ with the short sides of the rink, measured clockwise. This is shown again on Fig. 6.6, where the sides of the rink are also shown. We may now imagine A to be stationary at $A_0$, while B is moving with velocity $\mathbf{v}_{AB}$. Therefore the shortest distance between A and B is the distance $A_0B_1$ where $A_0B_1$ is perpendicular to $\mathbf{v}_{AB}$.

From Fig. 6.6,

$$SR = 20 \tan 22\tfrac{1}{2}°$$

thus

$$RQ = 20(1 - \tan 22\tfrac{1}{2}°)$$

and so

$$\begin{aligned} CA_0 &= \tfrac{1}{2}(B_0P + RQ) \\ &= \tfrac{1}{2} \times 20 \times (2 - \tan 22\tfrac{1}{2}°) \\ &= 10(2 - \tan 22\tfrac{1}{2}°) \end{aligned}$$

therefore

$$\begin{aligned} A_0B_1 &= CA_0 \cos 22\tfrac{1}{2}° \\ &= 10(2 - \tan 22\tfrac{1}{2}°) \cos 22\tfrac{1}{2}° \end{aligned}$$

But $\tan 22\frac{1}{2}° = \sqrt{2} - 1$ and $\cos 22\frac{1}{2}° = 1/\sqrt{4 - 2\sqrt{2}}$. Therefore

$$A_0B_1 = \frac{10(3 - \sqrt{2})}{\sqrt{4 - 2\sqrt{2}}} \approx 14{\cdot}6\ \text{m}$$

Alternatively, this could have been solved by scale drawing; particularly the last part, where the calculations are not particularly easy.

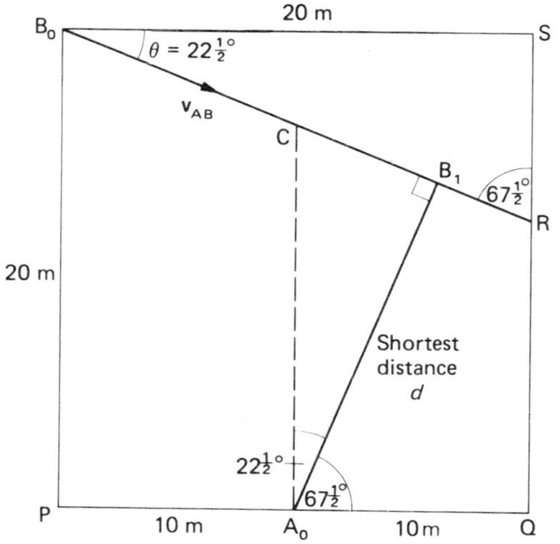


**Fig. 6.6.** Finding the shortest distance $d = A_0B_1$.

**Worked example 6.5**

At time $t = 0$ s, particles A and B have position vectors $\mathbf{a} = 2\hat{\mathbf{i}} - 3\hat{\mathbf{j}} + \hat{\mathbf{k}}$ and $\mathbf{b} = \hat{\mathbf{i}} + \hat{\mathbf{j}} + 2\hat{\mathbf{k}}$ respectively. They move with velocity vectors $\mathbf{v}_A = \hat{\mathbf{i}} + \frac{1}{4}\hat{\mathbf{j}} - \frac{1}{2}\hat{\mathbf{k}}$ and $\mathbf{v}_B = 1\frac{1}{4}\hat{\mathbf{i}} - \frac{3}{4}\hat{\mathbf{j}} - \frac{3}{4}\hat{\mathbf{k}}$ respectively. Show that they collide, and find their common position when they do so. The velocity of a third particle C relative to A is in the direction of $\hat{\mathbf{i}} + \hat{\mathbf{j}} - \hat{\mathbf{k}}$, and the velocity of C relative to B is in the direction of $2\hat{\mathbf{i}} - 2\hat{\mathbf{k}}$. Find the velocity of C.

*Solution*

The velocity of B relative to A is $\mathbf{v}_{AB} = \mathbf{v}_B - \mathbf{v}_A = \frac{1}{4}\hat{\mathbf{i}} - \hat{\mathbf{j}} - \frac{1}{4}\hat{\mathbf{k}}$. The position of B relative to A at time $t$ is given by

$$\begin{aligned}\mathbf{AB}(t) &= \mathbf{AB}(0) + \mathbf{v}_{AB}t \\ &= (\hat{\mathbf{i}} + \hat{\mathbf{j}} + 2\hat{\mathbf{k}}) - (2\hat{\mathbf{i}} - 3\hat{\mathbf{j}} + \hat{\mathbf{k}}) + t(\tfrac{1}{4}\hat{\mathbf{i}} - \hat{\mathbf{j}} - \tfrac{1}{4}\hat{\mathbf{k}}) \\ &= -\hat{\mathbf{i}} + 4\hat{\mathbf{j}} + \hat{\mathbf{k}} + t(\tfrac{1}{4}\hat{\mathbf{i}} - \hat{\mathbf{j}} - \tfrac{1}{4}\hat{\mathbf{k}})\end{aligned}$$

The particles will be at the same location if $\mathbf{AB} = \mathbf{0}$. In this example, we see that $\mathbf{AB} = \mathbf{0}$ for $t = 4$ s. Hence the particles collide after 4 seconds, at which time

$$\begin{aligned}\mathbf{a} = \mathbf{b} &= (2\hat{\mathbf{i}} - 3\hat{\mathbf{j}} + \hat{\mathbf{k}}) + 4(\hat{\mathbf{i}} + \tfrac{1}{4}\hat{\mathbf{j}} - \tfrac{1}{2}\hat{\mathbf{k}}) \\ &= 6\hat{\mathbf{i}} - 2\hat{\mathbf{j}} - \hat{\mathbf{k}}\end{aligned}$$

For the third particle C, we have

$$\mathbf{v}_{AC} = \alpha(\hat{\mathbf{i}} + \hat{\mathbf{j}} - \hat{\mathbf{k}}) = \mathbf{v}_C - (\hat{\mathbf{i}} + \tfrac{1}{4}\hat{\mathbf{j}} - \tfrac{1}{2}\hat{\mathbf{k}})$$

and

$$\mathbf{v}_{BC} = \beta(2\hat{\mathbf{i}} - 2\hat{\mathbf{k}}) = \mathbf{v}_C - (1\tfrac{1}{4}\hat{\mathbf{i}} - \tfrac{3}{4}\hat{\mathbf{j}} - \tfrac{3}{4}\hat{\mathbf{k}})$$

where $\alpha$ and $\beta$ are constants. Therefore

$$\begin{aligned}\mathbf{v}_C &= (1 + \alpha)\hat{\mathbf{i}} + (\tfrac{1}{4} + \alpha)\hat{\mathbf{j}} + (-\tfrac{1}{2} - \alpha)\hat{\mathbf{k}} \\ &= (1\tfrac{1}{4} + 2\beta)\hat{\mathbf{i}} - \tfrac{3}{4}\hat{\mathbf{j}} + (-\tfrac{3}{4} - 2\beta)\hat{\mathbf{k}}\end{aligned}$$

Therefore

$$1 + \alpha = 1\tfrac{1}{4} + 2\beta$$
$$\tfrac{1}{4} + \alpha = -\tfrac{3}{4}$$

and so

$$\alpha = -1 \quad \text{and} \quad \beta = -5/8$$

from which it is seen that $-\frac{1}{2} - \alpha = -\frac{3}{4} - 2\beta$ is consistent. Therefore the velocity of C is $\mathbf{v}_C = -\frac{3}{4}\hat{\mathbf{j}} + \frac{1}{2}\hat{\mathbf{k}}$.

**Exercise 6*b***

1. One ship steams at 15 km h$^{-1}$ on a bearing of 045°; and another at 10 km h$^{-1}$ on a bearing of 200°. Find the velocity of each relative to the other.
2. A road and a railway are perpendicular, and meet at a level crossing. A car travelling at a steady speed of 60 km h$^{-1}$ passes the level crossing 3 s before a train travelling at a steady speed of 100 km h$^{-1}$. Find the velocity of the car relative to the

train. Find also when they are closest to each other, and how far apart they are at that time.

3. Explain why vertically falling rain makes lines on the window of a moving train which are not vertical. In a train travelling at 60 km $h^{-1}$, a man notices that the lines of the rain are at 80° to the vertical when the rain is falling vertically. Find the speed of the rain.

4. A man travelling northwards at 10 km $h^{-1}$ observes the wind to be coming from the south-west. If he increases his speed to 15 km $h^{-1}$, the wind now appears to come from the west. Find the actual velocity of the wind.

5. At time $t = 0$ s, particles A and B have position vectors $\mathbf{a} = 3\hat{\imath} + \hat{\jmath} - \hat{k}$ and $\mathbf{b} = 2\hat{\imath}$, respectively. They move with velocity vectors $\mathbf{v}_A = 2\hat{\imath} - \hat{\jmath} + \hat{k}$ and $\mathbf{v}_B = 5\hat{\imath} + \alpha\hat{\jmath} + \beta\hat{k}$. Find the values of $\alpha$ and $\beta$ if it is known that the particles collide, and find their common position when they do so.

6. Particles A and B start simultaneously from points which have position vectors $-11\mathbf{i} + 17\mathbf{j} - 14\mathbf{k}$ and $-9\mathbf{i} + 9\mathbf{j} - 32\mathbf{k}$ respectively. The velocities of A and B are constant and represented by $6\mathbf{i} - 7\mathbf{j} + 8\mathbf{k}$ and $5\mathbf{i} - 3\mathbf{j} + 17\mathbf{k}$ respectively. Show that A and B will collide.

A third particle C moves so that its velocity relative to A is parallel to the vector $2\mathbf{i} + 3\mathbf{j} + 4\mathbf{k}$ and its velocity relative to B is parallel to the vector $\mathbf{i} + 2\mathbf{j} + 3\mathbf{k}$. Find the velocity and initial position of C if all three particles collide simultaneously.(L)

7. Two boats A and B have velocity vectors $\mathbf{u}$ and $\mathbf{v}$ respectively. Show, with the aid of a sketch, how to find the velocity of A relative to B.

The boats A and B are racing when there is a wind of 10 knots blowing from due north. A is sailing at 6 knots on a bearing of 045°. Find the direction of the wind relative to A. (Give bearings correct to the nearest degree.)

At the same time B is sailing at 6 knots on a bearing of 315°. Find the direction of the wind relative to B and the velocity of A relative to B.

The boat A then rounds a buoy and sails on a bearing of 225°. If its new speed relative to B is 10 knots, find its actual speed. (MEI)

## 6.4 Miscellaneous exercises 6

1. A car of length 5 m has speed 110 km $h^{-1}$, and is travelling on a bearing of 030°.
   (a) Find its velocity relative to another car, also of length 5 m, which is travelling on the same bearing with a speed of 85 km $h^{-1}$. If the first car overtakes the second car, find the time taken for the overtaking.
   (b) Find the velocity of the second car relative to a train travelling on a bearing of 060° at 145 km $h^{-1}$.

2. Particles A and B start simultaneously from points with position vectors $-4\hat{\imath} + 7\hat{\jmath} + 11\hat{k}$ and $5\hat{\imath} - 6\hat{\jmath} - 3\hat{k}$ respectively. The velocities of A and B are constant and represented by the vectors $6\hat{\imath} + (5/3)\hat{\jmath} + (7/3)\hat{k}$ and $3\hat{\imath} + 6\hat{\jmath} + 7\hat{k}$ respectively. Show that the particles collide, and find the position vector of the point where they collide.

After the collision, A continues with the same velocity, but B's velocity changes to that represented by $6\hat{\imath} - 3\hat{\jmath}$. Find the velocity of B relative to A, and the distance between the particles 6 seconds after the collision.

3. A man walking along a horizontal road at 1·5 m $s^{-1}$ is facing the rain, which appears to him to be falling uniformly with a speed of 4 m $s^{-1}$ in the direction which

makes an angle of 60° with the horizontal. Find, by calculation or by drawing, the actual speed of the rain and the angle which its actual direction makes with the horizontal.

Find also the speed which the rain would appear to the man to have and the angle which its direction would appear to make with the horizontal if the man turned round and walked at $1 \cdot 5$ m s$^{-1}$ in the direction opposite to that in which he was previously walking. (L)

4. (i) With O as origin, P is the point (1, 2), Q is the point (2, −1) and R is the point (3, −2). If $2\overrightarrow{PQ} + 3\overrightarrow{QR} = 5\overrightarrow{OS}$, find the coordinates of S.

(ii) A train is travelling due north at 25 m s$^{-1}$ and a car, visible from the train, is travelling in a north-easterly direction at 20 m s$^{-1}$. Find, graphically or by calculation, the magnitude and direction of the car's velocity as it appears to a person sitting in the train. (L)

5. A ship X, at a point O, is moving due east at 10 km h$^{-1}$. At the same moment another ship Y, at a point 8 km due north of O, is moving due south at 16 km h$^{-1}$. Find, by drawing, the distance between the ships in kilometres, when they are nearest together. (C)

6. Relative to a ship which is travelling due north at a speed of 10 knots, the velocity of a speedboat is in the direction N 45° E. Relative to a second ship which is travelling due south at a speed of 10 knots, the velocity of the speedboat is in the direction N 30° E. Prove that the speedboat is travelling in the direction N $\theta$° E where $\tan\theta = \sqrt{3} - 1$, and find its speed. (L)

7. A man bicycling at a constant speed $u$ finds that when his velocity is $u\mathbf{j}$ the velocity of the wind appears to be $\frac{1}{2}v_1(\mathbf{i} - \sqrt{3}\mathbf{j})$, where $\mathbf{i}$ and $\mathbf{j}$ are unit vectors in the east and north directions respectively; but when his velocity is $\frac{1}{2}u(-\sqrt{3}\mathbf{i} + \mathbf{j})$ the velocity of the wind appears to be $v_2\mathbf{i}$. Prove that the true velocity of the wind is $\frac{1}{6}\sqrt{3}u(\mathbf{i} + \sqrt{3}\mathbf{j})$, and find $v_1$ and $v_2$ in terms of $u$. (L)

8. Two particles A and B are moving with constant velocity vectors $\mathbf{v}_1 = 5\mathbf{i} + 3\mathbf{j} - \mathbf{k}$ and $\mathbf{v}_2 = 3\mathbf{i} + 4\mathbf{j} - 3\mathbf{k}$ respectively. Find the velocity vector of A relative to B. At time $t = 0$ the particle A is at the point whose position vector is $-4\mathbf{i} + 7\mathbf{j} - 6\mathbf{k}$. If A collides with B when $t = 5$, find the position vector of B at $t = 0$.

The velocity of A relative to a third moving particle C is in the direction of the vector $2\mathbf{i} + \mathbf{j} - 2\mathbf{k}$ and the velocity of B relative to C is in the direction of the vector $2\mathbf{i} + 3\mathbf{j} - 6\mathbf{k}$. Find the magnitude and direction of the velocity of C. (L)

9. A smugglers' boat with a maximum speed of 12 knots is at a position A. Information is received that a patrol boat, 20 nautical miles due south of A, is travelling at a constant 30 knots due north. In what direction should the smugglers' boat steer to keep as far as possible out of the way of the patrol boat?

What is then the least distance apart of the two boats in the subsequent motion?

On another occasion a similar problem arises with the same boats, but this time the patrol boat is observed to be 20 nautical miles 30° west of south from A. Find the corresponding direction and least distance apart. (MEI)

10. Rain is falling vertically, hitting the front windscreen of a car at right angles. The car is travelling at 10 m s$^{-1}$ and the windscreen is inclined at 30° to the horizontal; what is the velocity of the raindrops? Assume the windscreen is plane.

Rain with the same vertical velocity component falls on the same windscreen which is at rest, on a day when a steady wind is blowing into the screen, and hits the screen at an angle of 30° to the normal. Find the velocity of the wind.

Find also the direction of the rain relative to the car when the car is travelling:

(i) at 10 m $s^{-1}$ against the wind;

(ii) at 10 m $s^{-1}$ at right angles to the wind. (MEI)

11. At a given instant, a ship P travelling due E at a speed of 30 km $h^{-1}$ is 7 km due north of a second ship Q which is travelling N $\theta°$ W at a speed of 14 km $h^{-1}$, where $\tan\theta = \frac{3}{4}$. Show that the speed of Q relative to P is 40 km $h^{-1}$ and find the direction of the relative velocity.

The ships continue to move with uniform velocities. Find correct to three significant figures:

(i) the distance between the ships when they are nearest together;

(ii) the time taken, in minutes, to attain this shortest distance.

If initially, the course of Q had been altered to bring the ships as close as possible, the speed of Q and the speed and course of P being unchanged, find the direction of this new course. (JMB)

12. The position vectors of the vertices A and B of a triangle ABC are $\mathbf{i} - 2\mathbf{j}$ and $5\mathbf{i}$ respectively. A particle starts to move from A to B with constant speed $\sqrt{5}$ units and a second particle starts simultaneously starts to move from B to C with constant velocity vector $\mathbf{i} - \mathbf{j}$. Find the velocity vector of the second particle relative to the first and the shortest distance between the particles in the subsequent motion.

A third particle is moving along AC. Relative to the first particle, it is moving in the direction $5\mathbf{i} - 2\mathbf{j}$ and relative to the second particle it is moving in the direction $\mathbf{i}$. Find the velocity vector of the third particle and the position vector of the point C. (AEB)

# 7
# Forces (i)

## Introduction

In Chapter 1, we assumed that the reader had some qualitative idea about the concept of *force*. We used this idea to show that forces on a body could be represented by localized line vectors (§1.14), and used an experimental example to show how this could lead us to a suitable definition of addition of localized line vectors to be analogous to the combination of forces on a body.

We will now define *force* to be the physical quantity which changes the momentum of a particle according to the law

$$\mathbf{F} = \frac{\mathrm{d}}{\mathrm{d}t}(m\mathbf{v}) \quad \text{(Newton's second law)}$$

where $m\mathbf{v}$ is the momentum of the body in kg m s$^{-1}$, and $\mathbf{F}$ is the force in newton (N), or kg m s$^{-2}$.

With this definition, we see that force is a vector quantity, which is in accord with our intuitive observations that forces have magnitude, direction and sense and may be combined using the triangle law of addition.

In this chapter, we shall look at useful ways of representing forces to lead to efficient solutions of problems; qualitative details will follow in Chapter 8.

## 7.1 Representation of forces by directed line segments

For our purposes, we may always represent a force by a directed line segment, in component form as the sum of two or more forces, or in coordinate form as a column vector, whichever is the most convenient. For the present we shall concentrate on its representation by a directed line segment, where the length of the directed line segment represents the magnitude of the force.

Whether we should represent a force by a free vector, a position vector, a localized line vector or a bound vector will depend on the situation. Naturally, we shall use free vectors or position vectors wherever possible, as these are the most easily handled.

Fig. 7.1 shows two forces, represented by $\mathbf{F}_1$ and $\mathbf{F}_2$ applied respectively to: (i) a particle P; and (ii) a solid block.

In case (i), all the forces applied to the *particle* may be regarded as *position vectors*, since they must all act through the point P.

In case (ii), we expect different results with $\mathbf{F}_1$ applied in the two locations shown.

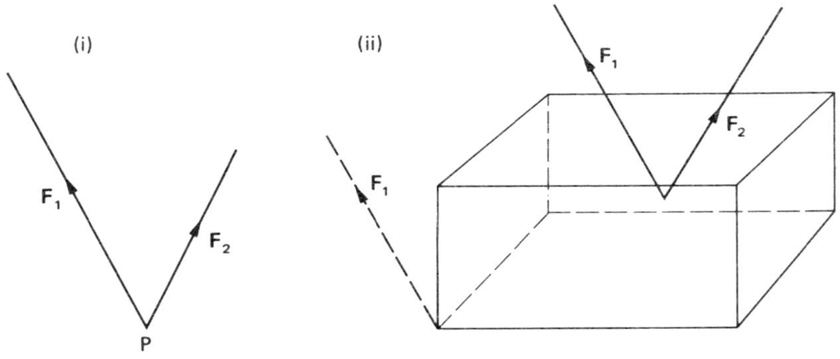


**Fig. 7.1.** Two forces acting on: (i) a particle; (ii) a solid block.

Assuming that the block is a *rigid body* (i.e. its shape is not changed by the forces), *localized line vectors* are required to represent the forces.

## 7.2 Forces on a particle

Consider the effect of several forces acting on a particle. We define the *resultant* of a set of forces to be the vector sum of the forces.
Fig. 7.2 shows the resultant of the forces $\mathbf{F}_1$ and $\mathbf{F}_2$ acting on the particle P in Fig. 7.1. We often mark the resultant with a double arrow to distinguish it from its components.

**Worked Example 7.1**

Forces of 3N and 5N act on a particle, making an angle of 60° with each other. Find the magnitude and direction of their resultant.

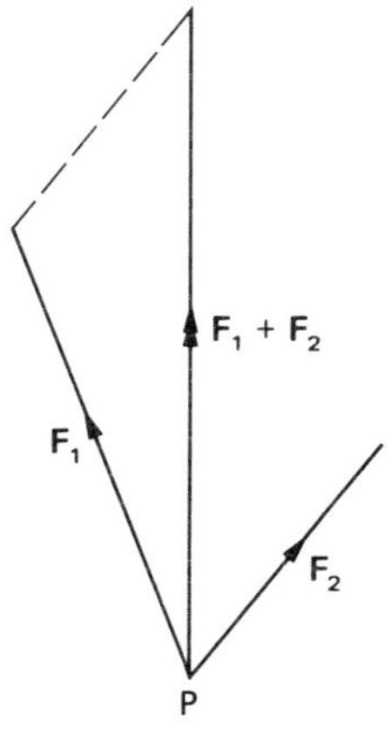


**Fig. 7.2.** The resultant of two forces.

*Solution*

For the solution, we draw a combined diagram, showing both the forces and their magnitudes (Fig. 7.3). Let the resultant have magnitude $F$, and make an ange $\theta$ with the 5N force. Using the cosine rule,

$$\begin{aligned} F^2 &= 3^2 + 5^2 - 2 \times 3 \times 5 \times \cos 120^\circ \\ &= 9 + 25 + 15 \\ &= 49 \end{aligned}$$

therefore

$$F = 7\text{N}$$

Using the sine rule,

$$\frac{\sin \theta}{3} = \frac{\sin 120^\circ}{7}$$

and so

$$\theta = 21{\cdot}8^\circ$$

Therefore the resultant is 7N, making an angle of 21·8° with the larger component.

The effect of applying forces $\mathbf{F}_1$, $\mathbf{F}_2$, $\mathbf{F}_3$, $\mathbf{F}_4$ of constant magnitude and direction to a particle P may well be to move the particle. This seems to be at variance with the representation of the forces by position vectors, which are defined relative to some *fixed* origin O, and not relative to a *moving* origin P.

Fig. 7.4 shows the forces acting on P in the two different positions $P_1$ and $P_2$. This diagram is a convenient way of representing two pieces of information: (a) the forces involved; and (b) the displacement of P. When we combine forces, on a particle, their positions in space are irrelevant; we only need to know that they act through a point. The force diagram needed for this is shown in Fig. 7.5. The resultant is applied to P, wherever P may be.

We may add the forces as position vectors as shown in Fig. 7.6; the order in which we treat them does not matter since vector addition is both commutative

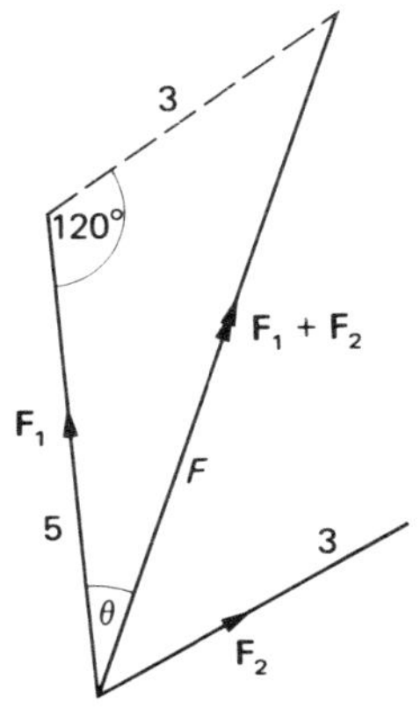


**Fig. 7.3.** Worked example 7.1.

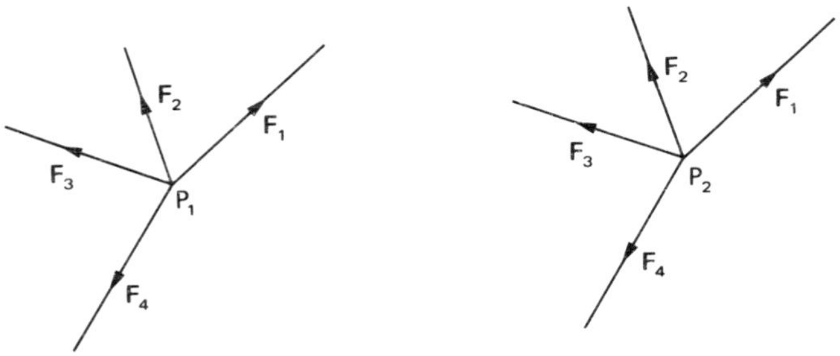


**Fig. 7.4.** Four forces on a particle at two different locations.

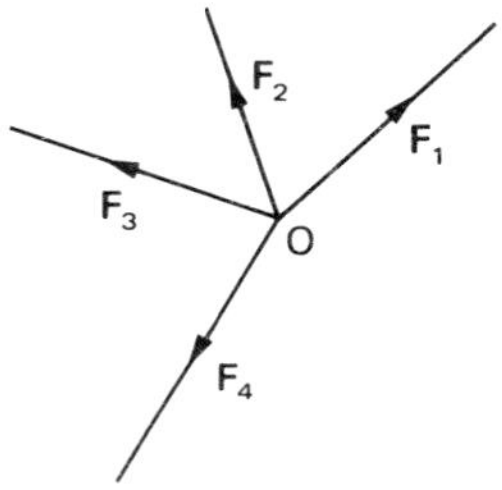


**Fig. 7.5.** Position vectors representing four forces on a particle.

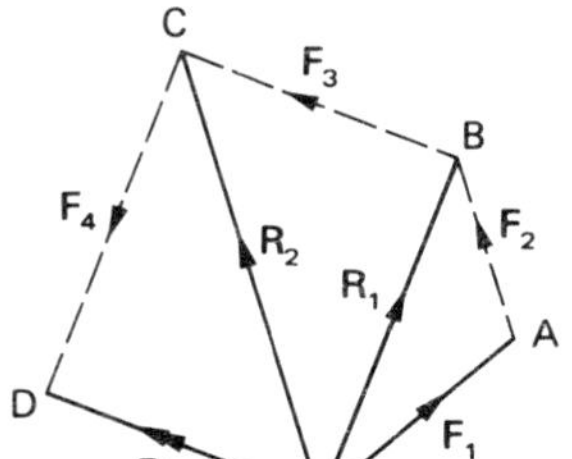


**Fig. 7.6.** A force polygon.

and associative. $\mathbf{R}_1 = \mathbf{F}_1 + \mathbf{F}_2$ is the resultant of $\mathbf{F}_1$ and $\mathbf{F}_2$; $\mathbf{R}_2 = \mathbf{R}_1 + \mathbf{F}_3$; and $\mathbf{R} = \mathbf{R}_2 + \mathbf{F}_4 = \mathbf{F}_1 + \mathbf{F}_2 + \mathbf{F}_3 + \mathbf{F}_4$ is the resultant of the four forces. The diagram is arranged so that the arrows on the components follow each other, so that the resultant is the join of the tail of the first component vector to the head of the last. The polygon PABCD is called a *force polygon*.

**Exercise 7*a***

1. Find the resultant of the forces shown in the diagram:

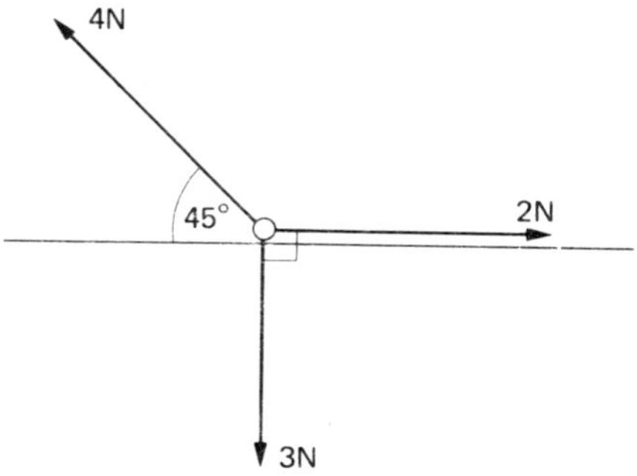


2. Find the resultant of the forces shown in the diagram:

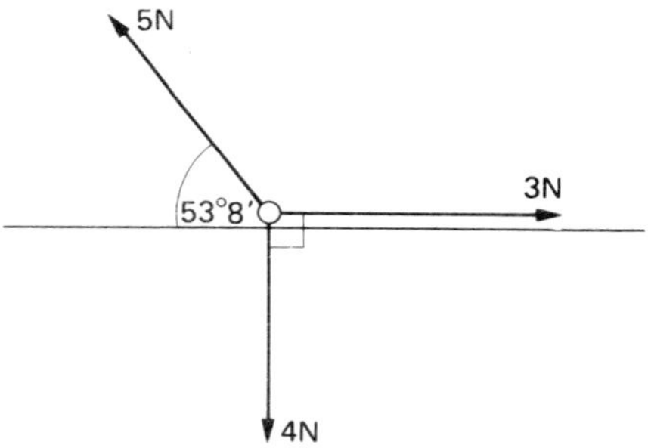


3. The forces acting on a particle may be represented by the following column vectors:

$$\begin{pmatrix}2\\1\\3\end{pmatrix}\text{N}, \begin{pmatrix}3\\2\\1\end{pmatrix}\text{N}, \begin{pmatrix}-4\\1\\-2\end{pmatrix}\text{N}.$$

Find their resultant as a column vector and give its magnitude and direction cosines.

4. The forces acting on a particle may be represented by the column vectors:

$$\begin{pmatrix}-1\\0\\2\end{pmatrix}\text{N}, \begin{pmatrix}2\\1\\-1\end{pmatrix}\text{N}, \begin{pmatrix}-1\\-1\\-1\end{pmatrix}\text{N}.$$

Find their resultant. What can you deduce?

5. Forces of 4 N and 5 N acting at 60° to each other are applied to a particle. By drawing a force triangle find a third force which will make the resultant of the three forces zero.

6. Four men, Alan, Brian, Clive and Desmond, pull with forces of equal magnitude on four ropes attached to a barrel. The ropes of men with adjacent initial letters are inclined at 72° to each other, and no two men pull in the same direction. Draw a force polygon. Can you draw any conclusions?

## 7.3 Equilibrium

A particle is in *equilibrium* if it is acted upon by a number of forces with zero resultant. If the forces are $\mathbf{F}_1$, $\mathbf{F}_2$, ..., $\mathbf{F}_n$, then we have $\mathbf{F}_1 + \mathbf{F}_2 + \cdots + \mathbf{F}_n = \mathbf{0}$ as the condition for the particle to be in equilibrium. Fig. 7.7 shows the force polygons for two particles in equilibrium. The force polygons are closed figures, with no side corresponding to a resultant. Notice that the arrows are in the same cyclic directions.

Problems involving equilibrium will be dealt with in qualitative detail in Chaper 8. For the present the concept is all we require, and we may re-state it as follows, using Newton's second law. If a particle of constant mass is moving with constant velocity, then it has constant linear momentum, i.e. the rate of change of its momentum is zero. Thus, by Newton's law, the resultant force acting on it is zero—in other words, the forces acting on it are in equilibrium.

If two forces are in equilibrium, they will have the same magnitude and direction, but opposite sense. If three forces are in equilibrium, then a necessary (but not sufficient) condition is that they are coplanar. This is so since they must be capable of being represented by the sides of a triangle, as in Fig. 7.7(a). We may use this latter fact to demonstrate that certain forces *cannot* be in equilibrium. For, suppose a particle is placed at the origin of three-dimensional Cartesian coordinates, and acted upon by three non-zero forces in the directions of the axes. Then the particle cannot be in equilibrium. Notice that we do not need to know the magnitudes of the forces; only that they are all non-zero.

## 7.4 Components of forces

We know that if two vectors expressed in component form are equal, then the corresponding components are also equal, i.e. if

$$\mathbf{r} = r_1\hat{\mathbf{i}} + r_2\hat{\mathbf{j}} + r_3\hat{\mathbf{k}} \quad \text{and} \quad \mathbf{s} = s_1\hat{\mathbf{i}} + s_2\hat{\mathbf{j}} + s_3\hat{\mathbf{k}}$$

then $\mathbf{r} = \mathbf{s} \iff r_i = s_i$ for $i = 1, 2, 3$. This result has wide applications in force problems, where the constraints of the system naturally lead us to choose particular directions for our unit vectors.

Suppose a particle has the form of a bead sliding along a rigid wire, as in Fig. 7.8. Suppose it is acted upon by force $\mathbf{F}_1$ of magnitude 4 N, acting at 30° to the wire, and $\mathbf{F}_2$ of magnitude 2 N perpendicular to the wire. Since the bead is constrained to

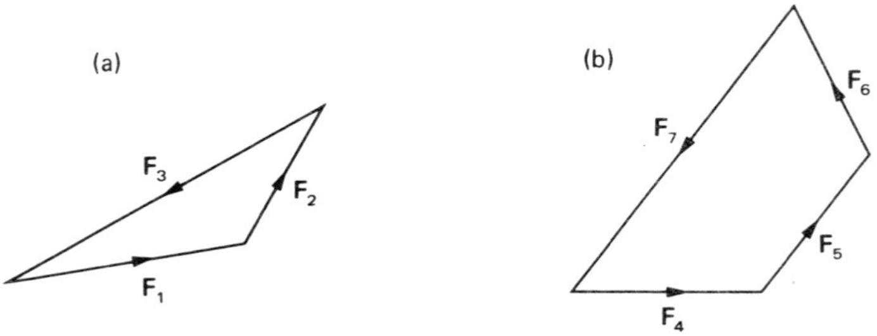


**Fig. 7.7.** The force polygons for two particles in equilibrium. (a) $\mathbf{F}_1 + \mathbf{F}_2 + \mathbf{F}_3 = 0$; (b) $\mathbf{F}_4 + \mathbf{F}_5 + \mathbf{F}_6 + \mathbf{F}_7 = 0$.

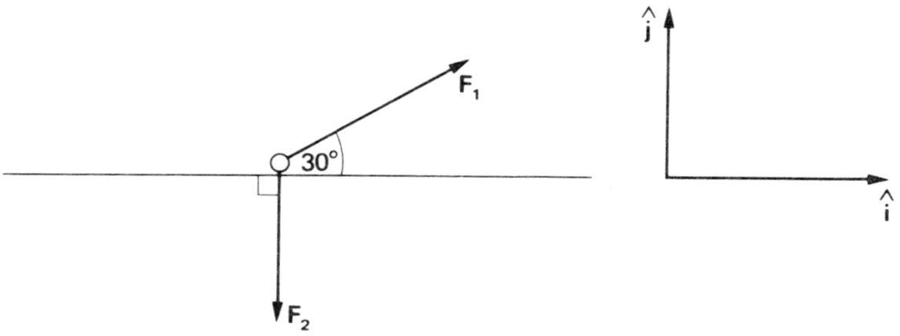


**Fig. 7.8.** A bead on a wire.

move in the line of the wire, it is convenient to choose directions for our unit vectors so that one of them is along the wire. Let $\hat{\mathbf{i}}$ and $\hat{\mathbf{j}}$ be unit forces of 1 N acting respectively along the wire and perpendicular to the wire, as shown in Fig. 7.8. Then we may write

$$\mathbf{F}_1 = (4\cos 30°\,\hat{\mathbf{i}} + 4\sin 30°\,\hat{\mathbf{j}})\text{ N and }\mathbf{F}_2 = -2\hat{\mathbf{j}}\text{ N}$$

That is

$$\mathbf{F}_1 = (2\sqrt{3}\hat{\mathbf{i}} + 2\hat{\mathbf{j}})\text{ N and }\mathbf{F}_2 = -2\hat{\mathbf{j}}\text{ N.}$$

Now $\mathbf{F}_1 + \mathbf{F}_2 = 2\sqrt{3}\hat{\mathbf{i}}$ N, which demonstrates immediately that the resultant force on the bead acts along the wire.

We could, alternatively, express this example in column-vector notation, where the column vector

$$\begin{pmatrix} x \\ y \end{pmatrix} \text{ represents } x\hat{\mathbf{i}} + y\hat{\mathbf{j}}.$$

Then $\mathbf{F}_1 = \begin{pmatrix} 2\sqrt{3} \\ 2 \end{pmatrix}$ N and $\mathbf{F}_2 = \begin{pmatrix} 0 \\ -2 \end{pmatrix}$ N

We have assumed a result which is fundamental to our later quantitative study of forces. We have resolved a force into components in order to make our solution of the problem easier.

In general, suppose that we are given a force **F**, and have already chosen component directions $\hat{\mathbf{i}}$ and $\hat{\mathbf{j}}$. Then we may write $\mathbf{F} = F_1\hat{\mathbf{i}} + F_2\hat{\mathbf{j}}$, where $F_1 = F\cos\alpha$ and $F_2 = F\cos(90° - \alpha) = F\sin\alpha$, $\alpha$ and $90° - \alpha$ being the direction angles of **F**. The two force diagrams shown in Fig. 7.9 are then equivalent; (a) shows the given

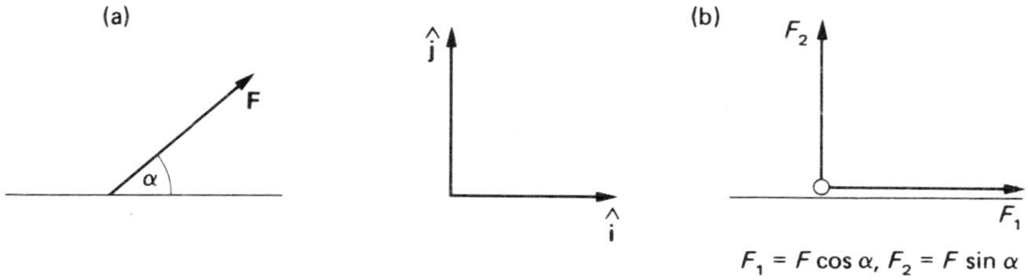


**Fig. 7.9.** Two equivalent force diagrams.

force **F**; and (b) shows its components and is often easier to use. We have, on these diagrams, used a convention which we will adopt, namely that on force diagrams we may choose to write the magnitudes of the forces against the arrows, rather than the representative vectors.

## 7.5 Forces on particles

We have so far only considered properties of forces, rather than the forces themselves. We now look for 'natural' forces which may act on a particle. First, we state Newton's third law:

Each force has an equal and opposite reaction

This is in accord with our experience. If you try to push a car, say, then you transmit an equal and opposite force through your feet to the ground. As we know, the nature of the surface may be such that we cannot exert a large force without sliding (for instance, when pushing on ice). The force which attempts to prevent two surfaces sliding is called *friction*. Occasionally, there may be forces other than friction attempting to prevent motion, or opposing an attempt to move an object. Such forces are called *resistances*, and we often use the expression *the resistance* to mean the resultant of all resistance forces, including friction.

Consider a particle of mass $m$ at rest on a horizontal plane, as in Fig. 7.10(a). Since its momentum is constant, there can be no resultant force acting. But, can we deduce that there is *no* force acting? We know that we cannot since the particle has weight. The *weight* of a particle is the force acting on it due to the attraction of the earth, and may be regarded as acting vertically downwards. A quantitative treatment will be given in Chapter 8. We will represent the weight by **W**. This cannot be the only force acting, or the particle would be falling. The equal and

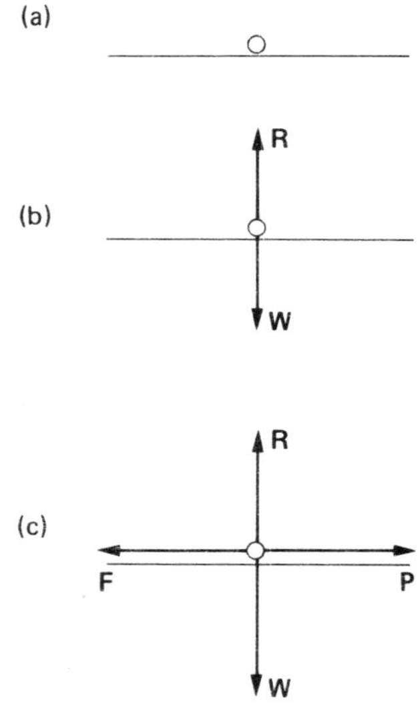


**Fig. 7.10.**

opposite force acting in this case is the *normal reaction* of the plane. We will represent this as **R**, as in Fig. 7.10(b). We know that $\mathbf{W} + \mathbf{R} = \mathbf{0}$ if the particle is at rest.

Suppose another force **P** is applied to the particle, parallel to the plane. Will the particle move? This depends on the nature of the surface, and on the frictional force created.

We have said that *friction* is the force which opposes the sliding of two surfaces. It has the following properties:

(1) It depends on the nature of the surfaces. (Rubber against rubber would give a different effect to rubber against ice.)
(2) It is independent of the area of contact.
(3) It opposes the direction of the applied force and is equal in magnitude to it, subject to:
(4) It has a maximum value (called *limiting friction*) which is in magnitude proportional to the normal reaction. If **F** is the limiting friction and **R** the normal reaction, then $F \propto R$, or $F = \mu R$, where $\mu$ is the *coefficient of friction*, and depends on the surfaces in contact. So, in general, $F \leqq \mu R$.

Hence, in the above example of a particle, the force **P** will be opposed by a frictional force **F**, as in Fig. 7.10(c), and $\mathbf{F} + \mathbf{P} = \mathbf{0}$ since the particle is in equilibrium.

If $P$ is increased, then $F$ will increase with it up to the value $\mu R$. If $P > \mu R$, then there will be a resultant force $P - \mu R$ parallel to the plane and the particle will slide on the plane. In practice, sliding friction is slightly less than limiting friction—this means that, if $P = \mu R$ and the particle is pushed gently it will actually accelerate, rather than not. In our model, we assume that sliding friction is equal to limiting friction, as the error consequent to this assumption is small.

We conventionally describe a surface as *smooth* if it will offer no frictional force at all, and *rough* otherwise. A smooth surface is obviously an idealized situation.

## 7.6 Forces on bodies

We may extend the ideas of the previous section to forces on bodies. The *weight* of a body acts vertically downwards through a point G, called its *centre of gravity*. We shall see later how to locate this point and how it is related to the *centre of mass*. For the present we shall regard these two points as coincident.

We shall use the result that, for a symmetric, homogeneous, body, the centre of mass is centrally located—for example, the centre of a sphere or of a disc, the middle of a rod, the centroid of a triangle, etc. Note that the point G need not be a physical property of the body.

A body resting on level ground will experience a normal reaction. Any surface is capable of providing a reaction normal to the surface and limited only by its physical nature. Such normal reactions are present in most practical problems. For example, consider a wheel standing at rest on the ground. The normal reaction is a force equal and opposite to the weight. If the wheel is loaded, then the normal reaction will increase correspondingly until a point is reached where the ground cannot support the stress. Further loading will cause the wheel to sink as the additional weight cannot be opposed and there is now a resultant force downwards.

Suppose a body is being pulled on a smooth, horizontal plane by means of a string. Clearly a force is being transmitted by the string. This force is called *tension*.

Usually, we consider the string to have zero or negligible mass, and call it a *light string*. Often we say that a string is *inelastic*, meaning that it will not stretch when a force is applied to it. A string can only transmit a force when it is taut, and then only along its line.

In Fig. 7.11, A is a particle connected to the body B by a light, inextensible string. If a force $P$ is applied to A, horizontally and away from B, then the forces acting on the body and the particle will be as in the diagram; namely the weight $W$ of the body, the normal reaction $R$ of the ground, the tensions $T_1$ and $T_2$ in the string, and the applied force $P$. Since the applied force is being transmitted by the string, $T_1 = T_2$; we have inserted the subscripts for clarity, and they would not normally be shown.

We may sometimes use a rod or strut which is capable of transmitting a force under *thrust* or *compression*, as in Fig. 7.12, which shows the forces acting if the string in Fig. 7.11 is replaced by a rigid rod and the force $P$ is reversed in sense. Note the equal and opposite thrusts in the rod. A rigid rod or strut may also transmit forces perpendicular to its line.

Sometimes, we have to deal with *elastic* strings or springs. In this case an experimental law, *Hooke's law* applies (see Chapter 8). At present it is sufficient to note that such a string will stretch in proportion to the resultant force applied.

If we have two struts, they may be freely joined by a *smooth hinge*. In such a hinge, there will be *no* resistance to turning (such as might be caused by rust), but there will be a normal reaction in some direction. This may be shown as a single force or as two components. It is usual to use rectangular component directions, either horizontal and vertical, or with one direction parallel to one of the struts. These three possibilities are shown in Fig. 7.13.

Suppose a light, inextensible string passes round a *smooth peg*, which may be assumed to have negligible size. Then the tension in the string has the same magnitude on either side of the peg, and there will be a normal reaction of the peg on the string bisecting the angle between the portions of the string. Fig. 7.14(a) shows the forces, and Fig. 7.14(b) shows the force polygon, which demonstrates the assertion of equal angles since it is an isosceles triangle.

Strings may also pass round *smooth pullies*, and again the tension in the string will have equal magnitude on either side of a pulley.

Fig. 7.15 shows a pulley, with equal masses suspended on either side at A and B. The four tensions marked are all equal. $R$ is the reaction of the pulley support, $w$ is the weight of the pulley, and $W$ the weight of each mass.

A *lamina* is any planar body, i.e. lies wholly in a plane. Laminas have a number of simple properties and we use them as a model for bodies of negligible thickness or bodies of uniform cross section where the situation concerns only a plane

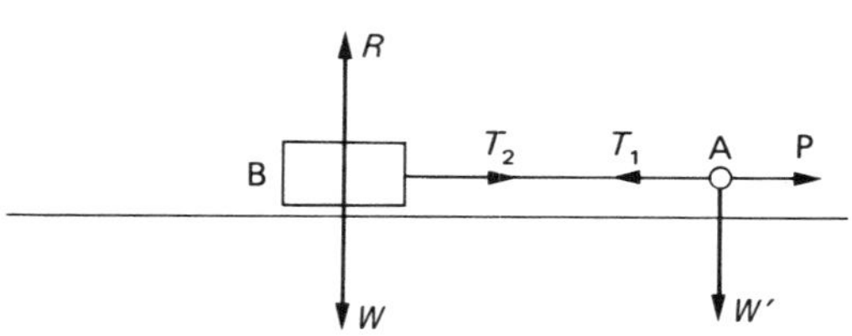


**Fig. 7.11.**

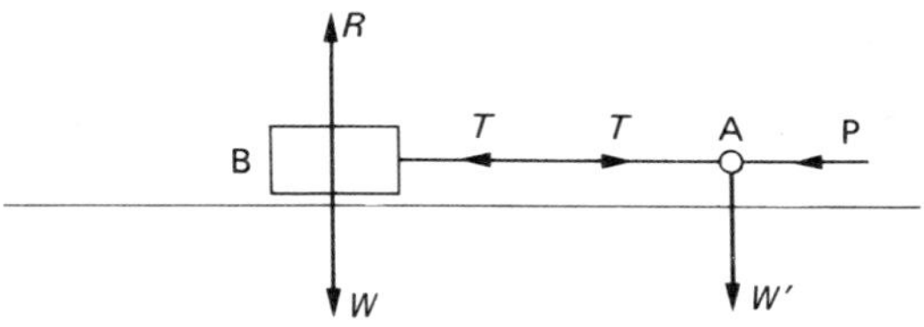


Fig. 7.12.

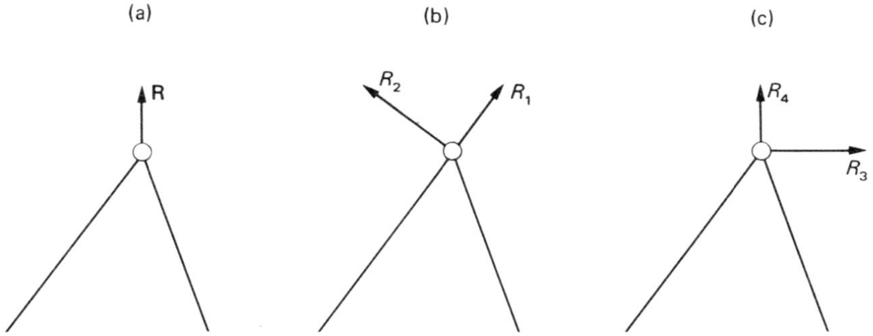


Fig. 7.13. Three equivalent force diagrams.

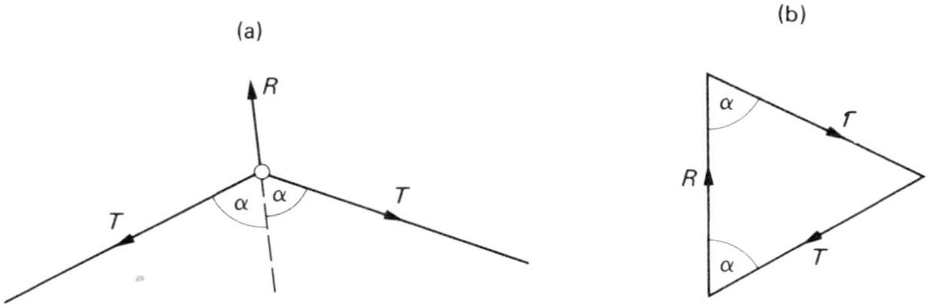


Fig. 7.14.

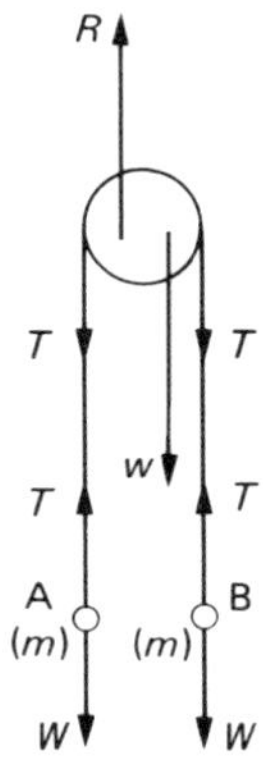


Fig. 7.15.

parallel to that of the uniform cross section. For example, a piece of card may be assumed to be a lamina.

## 7.7 Worked examples

It is not always necessary to show *all* of the forces which may be put in a diagram. We may show the normal reaction of the ground on a body, but may not need to show the normal reaction of the body on the ground. If we are considering a system as a whole, we may not need to put in equal and opposite tensions or compressions in, say, every constituent strut in a framework.

In particular we may consider separately component parts of a system as long as we show clearly *all* the forces acting on each of those parts. As an example, Fig. 7.16(a) shows separately the body and the particle from Fig. 7.11, and the forces acting on each, while Fig. 7.16(b) shows the forces acting on the system as a whole, with the equal and opposite tensions omitted.

### Worked Example 7.2

Show the forces acting on a uniform thin rod resting on a rough horizontal surface and leaning against a smooth vertical surface, tied by a string at its centre. The string is half the length of the rod and is tied to a point on the line of intersection of the surfaces. Indicate the nature of the forces.

*Solution*

The solution is contained in Fig. 7.17, where $W$ is the weight of the rod, $T$ is the tension in the string, $R$ and $S$ are normal reactions, and $F$ is frictional. The equal and opposite tension $T$ in the string is not shown, as it is not a force on the rod. Nor do we show the equal and opposite thrusts (or tensions) in this or any rod.

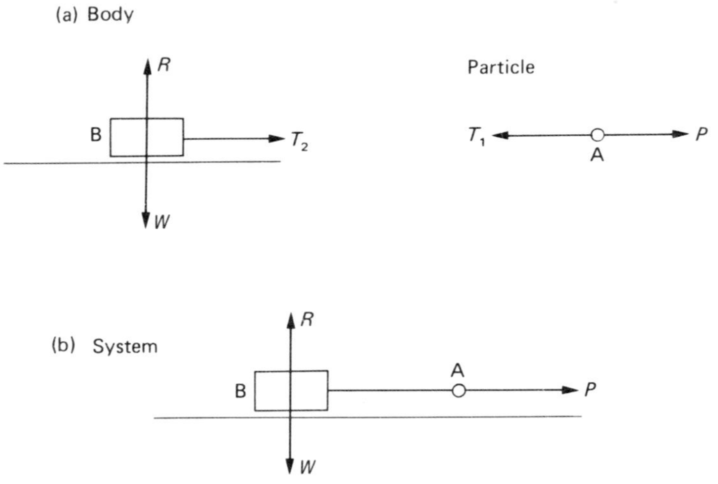


**Fig. 7.16.**

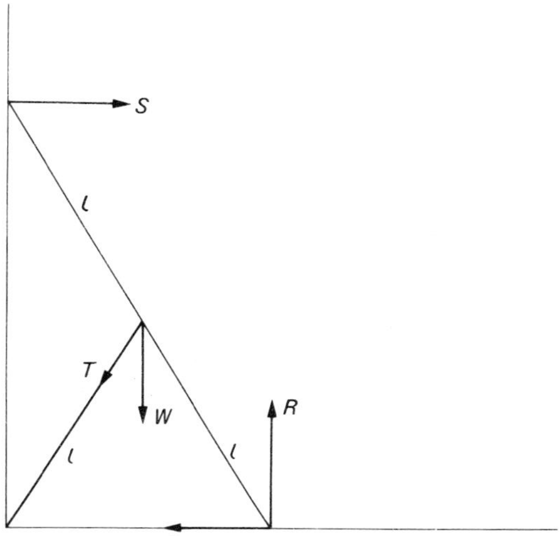


**Fig. 7.17.** The solution to worked example 7.2.

### Worked Example 7.3

A pulley of weight $W$ is suspended by a light inextensible string from a ceiling. A further light inextensible string hangs over the pulley with masses of weight $w_1$ and $w_2$ attached to its ends. Show all the forces acting on the pulley, string and particles.

*Solution*

The solution is Fig. 7.18, which is self-explanatory.

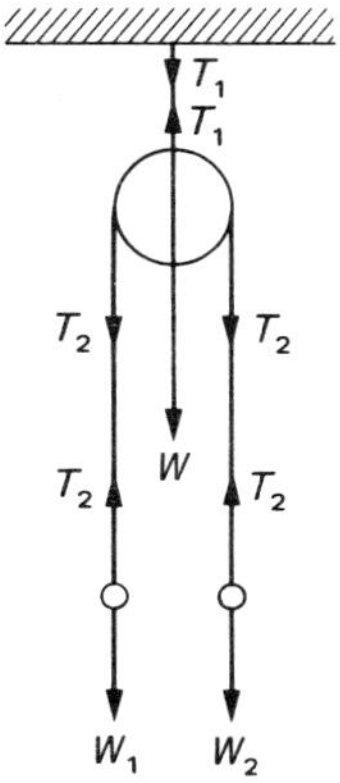


**Fig. 7.18.** The solution to worked example 7.3.

**Worked Example 7.4**

Show the forces acting on a step ladder held together by a light inextensible string, with a smooth hinge at the top, and standing on a smooth horizontal surface.

*Solution*

The solution is Fig. 7.19. If the ladder is uniform and symmetrical, then $R = S$, $W_1 = W_2$ and $\mathbf{Q} = \mathbf{0}$.

**Exercise 7*b***

For each question, draw a diagram to show the forces acting.

1. A particle hanging by a thread from the ceiling. Also name the forces.

2. A particle of mass $m$ rests on a rough plane inclined at an angle $\alpha$ to the horizontal.

3. To the particle in question 3 a force **P** is applied horizontally in the plane of the line of greatest slope of the plane so that the particle is just about to slip *up* the plane.

4. A uniform ladder rests against a vertical wall and a horizontal floor.
(a) both surfaces are smooth;
(b) the floor is rough and the wall smooth;
(c) both surfaces are rough.
Comment.

5. A man pulls a sledge on horizontal ground by means of a rope inclined at 30° to the horizontal. The tension in the rope is 80 N and the ground offers a resistance of 32 N to the sledge. A second identical sledge is now fixed to the first by means of a horizontal rope.

6. Two particles of masses $m$ and $m'$ are attached to each other by a string which passes over a smooth pulley, the axle of which is supported from the ground by a rigid vertical rod.

7. A lamina is in the form of a regular pentagon ABCDE of side $a$. It rests horizontally on wooden legs, each of length $a$ and inclined at 75° to the horizontal. The tops of the legs are positioned at the centroids of the triangles ABC, ADC and AEC.

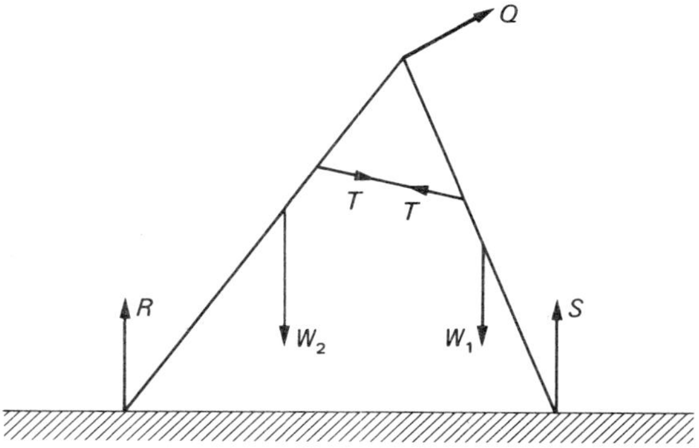


**Fig. 7.19.** The solution to worked example 7.4.

# 8
# Forces (ii)

## 8.1 Newton's second law

We have already said that Newton's second law states that a force acting on a particle causes a change of momentum proportional to the magnitude of the force and in the direction of the force. If **F** is the force, then we may write

$$\mathbf{F} \propto \frac{\mathrm{d}}{\mathrm{d}t}(m\mathbf{v}) \quad \text{or} \quad \mathbf{F} = k\frac{\mathrm{d}}{\mathrm{d}t}(m\mathbf{v})$$

where $k$ is a constant.

The SI system of units defines the unit of force to be *1 newton* (1 N) in such a way that $k = 1$ when the mass $m$ is in kg, and the velocity $\mathbf{v}$ in m s$^{-1}$. Then we may state *Newton's second law* as

$$\mathbf{F} = \frac{\mathrm{d}}{\mathrm{d}t}(m\mathbf{v}) \qquad \text{(A)}$$

or

$$\mathbf{F} = m\frac{\mathrm{d}\mathbf{v}}{\mathrm{d}t} = m\mathbf{a} \text{ if } m \text{ is constant} \qquad \text{(B)}$$

Thus 1 N is the force required to give a constant mass of 1 kg an acceleration of magnitude 1 m s$^{-2}$. Both forms (A) and (B) of Newton's second law are very important.

Now suppose the force **F** is represented by the column vector

$$\mathbf{F} = \begin{pmatrix} F_1 \\ F_2 \\ F_3 \end{pmatrix}$$

and the velocity **v** by the column vector

$$\mathbf{v} = \begin{pmatrix} v_1 \\ v_2 \\ v_3 \end{pmatrix}.$$

Then, from (A),

$$\begin{pmatrix} F_1 \\ F_2 \\ F_3 \end{pmatrix} = \frac{\mathrm{d}}{\mathrm{d}t}\begin{pmatrix} mv_1 \\ mv_2 \\ mv_3 \end{pmatrix} = \begin{pmatrix} \frac{\mathrm{d}}{\mathrm{d}t}(mv_1) \\ \frac{\mathrm{d}}{\mathrm{d}t}(mv_2) \\ \frac{\mathrm{d}}{\mathrm{d}t}(mv_3) \end{pmatrix}$$

That is,

$$F_i = \frac{\mathrm{d}}{\mathrm{d}t}(mv_i) \quad \text{for } i = 1, 2, 3$$

Thus Newton's second law may be applied in each component direction separately; and thus in *any* direction since the component directions were chosen arbitrarily.

**Worked Example 8.1**

A particle moves so that its displacement $\mathbf{x}$ at time $t$ is

$$\mathbf{x} = \begin{pmatrix} 3t^2 \\ 2t - 3 \\ 1 - t^3 \end{pmatrix}$$

Find the force on the particle if:
(a) its mass is 3 kg;
(b) its mass at time $t$ is $(3 - \beta t)$, where $\beta$ is a positive constant;
In (b), find also the force at the instant when the mass becomes zero.

*Solution*

For all the parts,

$$\mathbf{x} = \begin{pmatrix} 3t^2 \\ 2t - 3 \\ 1 - t^3 \end{pmatrix}$$

and so

$$\mathbf{v} = \begin{pmatrix} 6t \\ 2 \\ -3t^2 \end{pmatrix}$$

(a) Since the mass is constant,

$$\mathbf{F} = 3\mathbf{a} = 3\frac{\mathrm{d}\mathbf{v}}{\mathrm{d}t} = \begin{pmatrix} 18 \\ 0 \\ -18t \end{pmatrix}$$

(b)

$$\mathbf{F} = \frac{\mathrm{d}}{\mathrm{d}t}(m\mathbf{v}) = \frac{\mathrm{d}}{\mathrm{d}t}\begin{pmatrix} 6t(3 - \beta t) \\ 2(3 - \beta t) \\ -3t^2(3 - \beta t) \end{pmatrix} = \frac{\mathrm{d}}{\mathrm{d}t}\begin{pmatrix} 18t - 6\beta t^2 \\ 6 - 2\beta t \\ -9t^2 + 3\beta t^3 \end{pmatrix}$$

therefore

$$\mathbf{F} = \begin{pmatrix} 18 - 12\beta t \\ -2\beta \\ -18t + 9\beta t^2 \end{pmatrix}$$

(c) $m = 0$ for $t = 3/\beta$, in which case

$$\mathbf{F} = \begin{pmatrix} -18 \\ -2\beta \\ 27/\beta \end{pmatrix}$$

## 8.2 Weight

Weight is the force acting on a body due to the gravitational attraction of the earth. The precise nature of this force is not properly known, but its effects have been extensively studied.

*Newton's law of gravitation* states that between any two particles of masses $m_1$ and $m_2$, distance $d$ apart, there is a gravitational attraction of magnitude $F$ towards each other, where

$$F \propto \frac{m_1 m_2}{d^2} \text{ or } F = \frac{G m_1 m_2}{d^2}$$

This constant of proportionality $G$ is the *universal gravitational constant* and has the value of $6{\cdot}67 \times 10^{-11}\ \text{m}^3\ \text{kg}^{-1}\ \text{s}^{-2}$. These results are an example of an inverse square law of attraction. They may be extended to cover systems of particles which form bodies, but this is outside the scope of our present study.

We may quote the following result: the gravitational attraction between a solid sphere of homogeneous material, and mass $M$, and a particle of mass $m$ outside the sphere is the same as that between the particle, and a particle of mass $M$ at the centre of the sphere.

In our model, the earth is just such a sphere. Thus the gravitational attraction of the earth on a particle P of mass $m$ at a distance $d(\geq R)$ from the centre of the earth is $GMm/d^2$, where $M$ is the mass of the earth and $R$ its radius. It is this force that we call the *weight* of the particle. We may write the weight as $m\mathbf{g}$, where $g = |\mathbf{g}| = GM/d^2$, and the unit vector $\hat{\mathbf{g}}$ in the direction and sense of $\mathbf{g}$ is directed towards the centre of the earth (see Fig. 8.1).

For many systems that we consider, the radial distances involved are small in comparison with $d$, and we may regard $d$ as a constant with value $R$. Thus

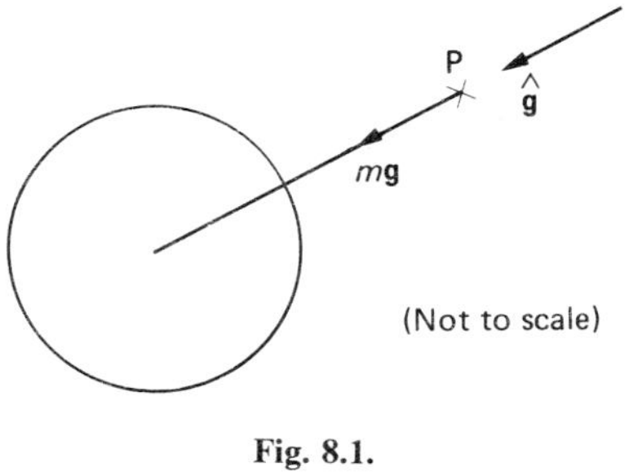


Fig. 8.1.

$GM/d^2 \approx GM/R^2$ is approximately constant. Hence **g** and $g$ may be regarded as constants. Under these assumptions, $g$ has the value $9{\cdot}80665$ m s$^{-2}$, which is usually approximated to $9{\cdot}81$ m s$^{-2}$. Hence the acceleration with which any particle (or body) will fall freely under gravity may be taken as **g**. Thus, applying Newton's second law, we see that the weight of a mass of 1 kg is approximately $9{\cdot}81$ N; or, more generally, a mass $m$ has weight $m\mathbf{g}$.

For any two points near one another, the vectors towards the centre of the earth may be regarded as parallel, and both 'vertically downwards'—locally, we use a plane as our model of the earth's surface. Also, the attraction $Gmm'/d^2$ between two nearby masses is so small that it may be neglected in comparison with their weights—so long as neither of the masses approaches the mass of the earth, which is unlikely.

As a summary of the results about gravity and weight, we have:

(1) the attraction between two bodies in a problem is neglected, unless one of the bodies is the earth or similarly massive;

(2) the acceleration of any body falling freely under gravity is taken as constant and independent of the mass, provided that the body is above the earth and the distance fallen is small compared with the radius of the earth;

(3) two bodies near one another have weights which act in parallel directions.

(4) since the earth is not a perfect sphere made of homogeneous material, then there are local, small variations in the value of $g$, and in the direction of **g**. We neglect these at the present.

## 8.3 The constant acceleration formulae

We now establish some oft-quoted and useful formulae which apply to a particle moving under a constant acceleration **a**. In particular, they will apply in the case $\mathbf{a} = \mathbf{g}$.

We know from Chapter 3 that

$$\mathbf{v}(t) - \mathbf{v}(0) = \int_0^t \mathbf{a}(t)\mathrm{d}t \tag{1}$$

and

$$\mathbf{x}(t) - \mathbf{x}(0) = \int_0^t \mathbf{v}(t)\mathrm{d}t \tag{2}$$

in the usual notation, as used in that chapter.

For these formulae, we suppose that the particle is moving through the origin with velocity **u** at the start of time, i.e. $\mathbf{x}(0) = \mathbf{0}$ and $\mathbf{v}(0) = \mathbf{u}$. Also, **a** is constant. Therefore from Equ. 1

$$\mathbf{v} - \mathbf{u} = \mathbf{a}\int_0^t \mathrm{d}t = \mathbf{a}\left[t\right]_0^t = t\mathbf{a}$$

Thus

$$\mathbf{v} = \mathbf{u} + \mathbf{a}t \tag{I}$$

Hence from Equ. 2

$$\mathbf{x} - \mathbf{0} = \int_0^t (\mathbf{u} + \mathbf{a}t)\mathrm{d}t = \left[\mathbf{u}t + \tfrac{1}{2}t^2\mathbf{a}\right]_0^t$$

and thus

$$\mathbf{x} = \mathbf{u}t + \tfrac{1}{2}\mathbf{a}t^2 \qquad \text{(II)}$$

Using Equations I and II we have

$$\mathbf{a} = \frac{\mathbf{v} - \mathbf{u}}{t} = \frac{\mathbf{x} - \mathbf{u}t}{\tfrac{1}{2}t^2}$$

thus

$$t\mathbf{v} - t\mathbf{u} = 2\mathbf{x} - 2t\mathbf{u}$$

and

$$\mathbf{x} = \tfrac{1}{2}(\mathbf{u} + \mathbf{v})t \qquad \text{(III)}$$

A further formula presents more difficulty without a knowledge of scalar products, and will not be proved until Chapter 14. It is

$$v^2 = u^2 + 2ax\cos\theta \qquad \text{(IV)}$$

where $\theta$ is the angle between **a** and **x**. This, unlike Equations I to III, is a scalar equation rather than a vector equation.

Usually, we will be applying these formulae to particles moving in a straight line. In that case, the vectors may be replaced by their magnitudes and $\cos\theta = \cos 0 = 1$. Then the formulae become:

$$v = u + at \qquad \text{(I)}$$

$$x = ut + \tfrac{1}{2}at^2 \qquad \text{(II)}$$

$$x = \tfrac{1}{2}(u + v)t \qquad \text{(III)}$$

$$v^2 = u^2 + 2ax \qquad \text{(IV)}$$

Equ. IV may be proved in this case by eliminating $t$ from Equations I and III. We give some examples of the use of Equ. IV; the others, particularly Equations I and II were amply demonstrated in Chapter 3.

**Worked Example 8.2**

(a) If a stone is dropped, then it is subjected to an acceleration $g$ in a vertical line; $u = 0$ m s$^{-2}$. Therefore $v^2 = 2gh$ gives the velocity after dropping through a height $h$, from Equ. IV above.

(b) If a stone is thrown upwards from ground level with speed $u$, $v^2 = u^2 - 2gh$. The stone reaches the top of its flight when $v = 0$, i.e. when $h = u^2/2g$.

**Worked Example 8.3**

(a) A particle accelerates from rest to 12 m s$^{-1}$ in travelling 5 m. Find its acceleration.

(b) A particle starts with a speed of 3 m s$^{-1}$ and accelerates at 7 m s$^{-2}$. Find its speed after it have travelled 6 m.

*Solution*

(a) By Equ. IV,

$$12^2 = 0^2 + 2 \times a \times 5 \quad \Rightarrow \quad a = 144/10 = 14{\cdot}4 \text{ m s}^{-2}$$

(b) By Equ. IV,

$$v^2 = 3^2 + 2 \times 7 \times 6 = 9 + 84 = 93$$

and so

$$v \approx 9{\cdot}64 \text{ m s}^{-1}$$

## 8.4 Applications of Newton's second law

We are now in a position to discuss the motion of particles subjected to a system of forces. Then following points should be clearly borne in mind:

(a) always draw a clear diagram showing all the forces acting on the system, subject to

(b) do not confuse your diagram by showing the reactions to forces on parts of the system which are not being considered;

(c) if the particle is essentially one-dimensional, use only components in that named direction.

**Worked Example 8.4**

A constant force of 8 N is applied to a mass of 2 kg for 3 s. How far does it move in that time if it was initially stationary?

*Solution*

Using Newtons' second law, $F = ma$, we have $8 = 2a$ and so $a = 4 \text{ m s}^{-2}$ in the direction of the force. By the constant acceleration formula of Equ. II, $x = \frac{1}{2} \times 4 \times 3^2 = 18$ m.

**Worked Example 8.5**

(a) A sledge of mass 45 kg is towed over rough horizontal ground by a rope inclined at 60° to the horizontal. If the ground offers a constant resistance to sliding of 20 N, and the tension in the rope is 50 N, find the acceleration of the sledge.

(b) A second identical sledge is now attached to the first by means of a horizontal rope. Find the angle $\alpha$ which the rope attached to the first sledge must make with the horizontal if both sledges just move when a force of the same magnitude is applied. What is the tension in the connecting rope?

(c) Find the common acceleration of the sledges, and the tension in the connecting rope, if the rope to the first sledge is now inclined at an angle of arccos $(0{\cdot}9)$ to the horizontal, the tension in it remaining the same.

*Solution*

(a) Fig. 8.2 shows all the forces, and the acceleration. We have only given values to the relevant forces, which are those having components parallel to the plane. We apply Newton's second law parallel to the plane, that is in the $\hat{\mathbf{i}}$ direction. Then

$$50 \cos 60° - 20 = 45 \times a \quad \text{since the mass is constant;}$$

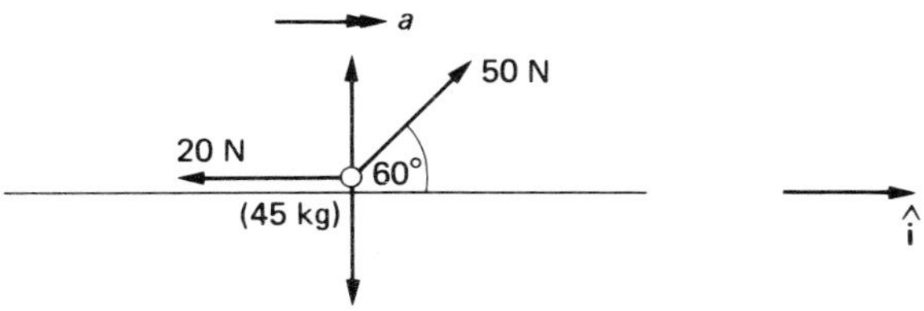


Fig. 8.2.

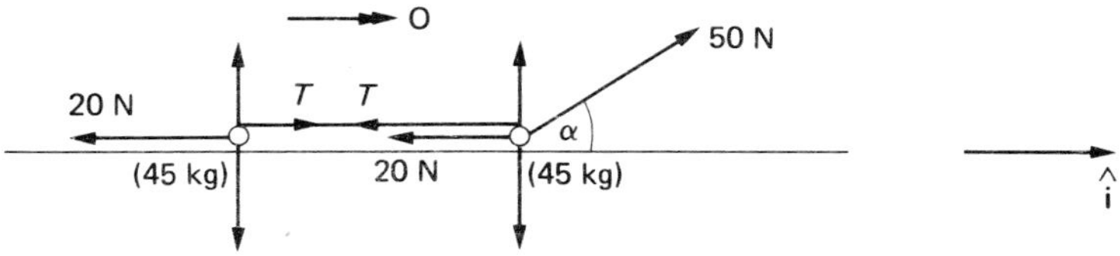


Fig. 8.3.

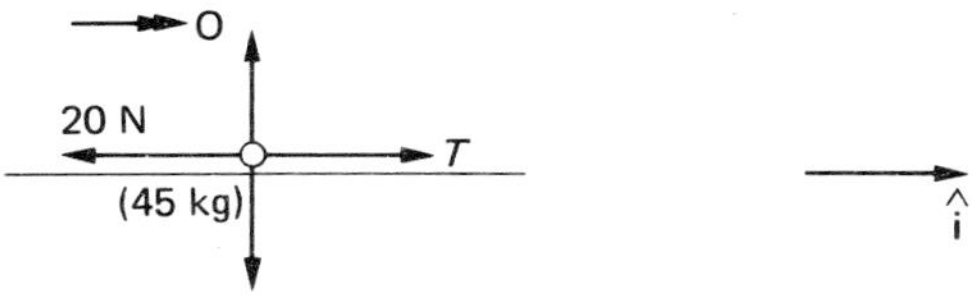


Fig. 8.4.

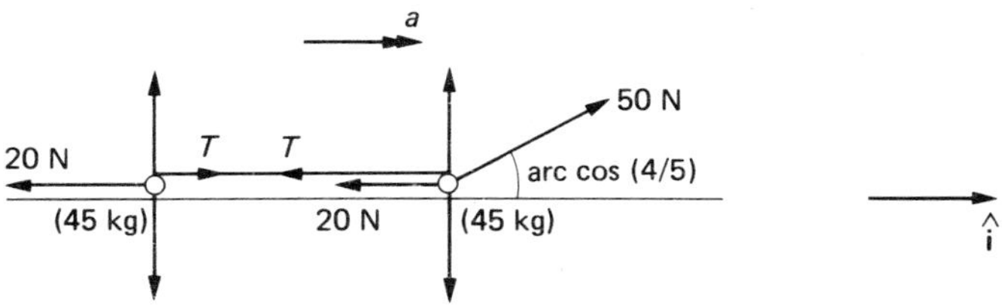


Fig. 8.5.

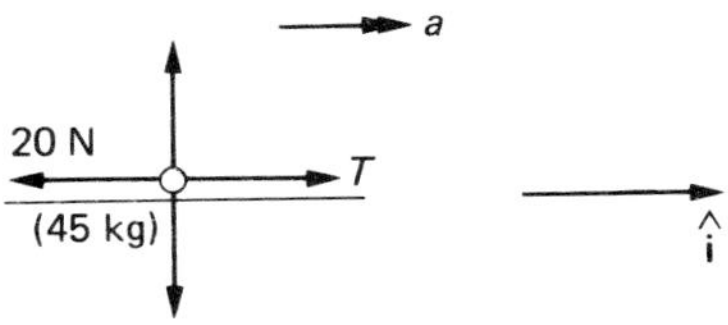


Fig. 8.6.

and so

$$a = \frac{50 \times \frac{1}{2} - 20}{45} = \frac{1}{9}\text{ m s}^{-2}$$

(b) Fig. 8.3 shows the forces acting on the two sledges considered as a single unit, and Fig. 8.4 shows the forces on the second sledge alone. Apply Newton's second law in the $\hat{\imath}$ direction to the whole system:

$$50 \cos \alpha - 20 - 20 = (45 + 45) \times 0$$

thus

$$\cos \alpha = 40/50 \text{ and so } \alpha = \arccos(4/5)$$

Apply Newton's second law in the $\hat{\imath}$ direction to the second sledge:

$$T - 20 = 45 \times 0, \text{ and so } T = 20 \text{ N}.$$

(c) Figs. 8.5 and 8.6 show, respectively, the whole system and the second sledge. Apply Newton's second law in the $\hat{\imath}$ direction to the whole system:

$$50 \times 0{\cdot}9 - 20 - 20 = 90a$$

thus

$$a = \frac{45 - 40}{90} = \frac{1}{18}\text{ m s}^{-2}$$

Apply Newton's second law in the $\hat{\imath}$ direction to the second sledge:

$$T - 20 = 45 \times \frac{1}{18} \text{ and so } T = 20 + 2{\cdot}5 = 22{\cdot}5 \text{ N}$$

**Worked Example 8.6**

A light inextensible smooth string hangs over a smooth pulley, and has masses $m$ and $m'$ attached to its ends. If the system is released from rest, find the acceleration of the masses and the tension in the string.

*Solution*

Let us assume that $m' > m$. (If $m' = m$, the system remains in equilibrium.) Then, if the mass $m$ has an acceleration $a\hat{\jmath}$ (i.e. upwards), the mass $m'$ will have an acceleration $-a\hat{\jmath}$ (i.e. downwards), as shown in Fig. 8.7. Apply Newton's second law in the $\hat{\jmath}$ direction:

to the mass $m$: $T - Mg = ma$

to the mass $m'$: $T - m'g = m'(-a)$.

Subtract these equations:

$$(m' - m)g = (m + m')a$$

thus

$$a = \frac{(m' - m)g}{m' + m}$$

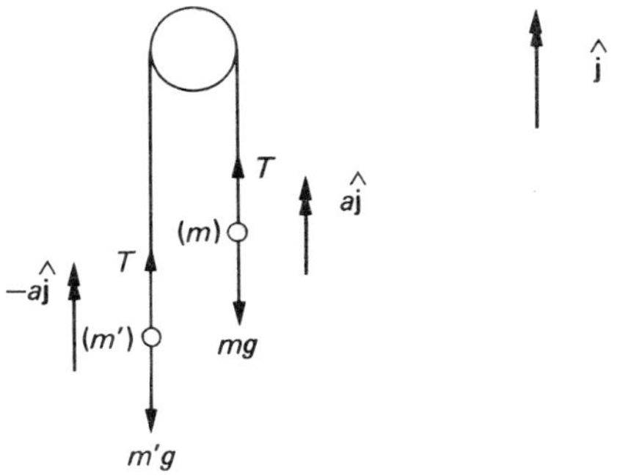


Fig. 8.7.

Therefore

$$T = mg + ma = mg\left(1 + \frac{m' - m}{m' + m}\right) = \frac{2mm'g}{m + m'}$$

**Worked Example 8.7**

A sledge of mass 12 kg is released from rest on a slope inclined at 30° to the horizontal. The coefficient of friction between the sledge and the slope is 0·1. Find: (a) the acceleration of the sledge; (b) the speed of the sledge after it has travelled 10 m; and (c) the distance travelled by the sledge in reaching a speed of 25 m s$^{-1}$.

*Solution*

For a moving body, the frictional force is given by $F = \mu R$, where $R$ is the normal reaction and $\mu$ the coefficient of friction. In Fig. 8.8, we show the weight in two components, and mark the friction as $0{\cdot}1R$.

Apply Newton's second law:

perpendicular to the plane: $R = 12g \cos 30° = 6g\sqrt{3}$

parallel to the plane: $12g \sin 30° - 0{\cdot}1 \times 6g\sqrt{3} = 12a$

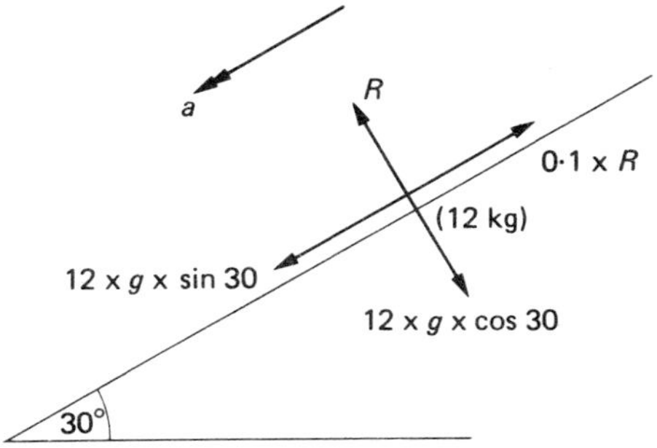


Fig. 8.8.

Therefore

$$a = g \times \tfrac{1}{2} - g \times \sqrt{3}/20 = 0{\cdot}4134 \times 9{\cdot}81 = 4{\cdot}056\ \text{m s}^{-2} \approx 4{\cdot}06\ \text{m s}^{-2}$$

Now $v^2 = u^2 + 2gx$ and $u = 0$. Therefore $v^2 = 2ax$.
For (b), $x = 10$ m, thus $v^2 = 2 \times 4{\cdot}056 \times 10$, and so $v = 9{\cdot}006\ \text{m s}^{-1} \approx 9{\cdot}01\ \text{m s}^{-1}$.
For (c), $v = 25\ \text{m s}^{-1}$, thus $625 = 2 \times 4{\cdot}056 \times x$, and so $x = 77{\cdot}04$ m $\approx 77{\cdot}0$ m.

**Exercise 8*a***

1. Find in magnitude and direction the acceleration of an object of mass 3 kg acted upon by forces $2\mathbf{i} + 3\mathbf{j}$ N and $3\mathbf{i} - 4\mathbf{j}$ N.

2. A railway truck begins to run down an incline with an initial velocity of 1 m s$^{-1}$. After travelling for 100 m its velocity is 3 m s$^{-1}$. Calculate the acceleration of the truck. If the mass of the truck is 10 tonne and the frictional resistance is 4500 N, calculate the angle of the incline.

3. A locomotive pulls a load of 200 tonne (engine *plus* carriages) on the level against a resistance of 70 N t$^{-1}$. Find the acceleration when the maximum tractive force of 64 000 N is used. If steam is shut off when the train is going down an incline of angle $\beta = \arcsin(1/400)$, calculate the resulting retardation (i.e. negative acceleration), assuming that the resistance is the same as in the preceding case.

4. A body accelerates uniformly from rest to 15 m s$^{-1}$. Find the force acting if the mass of the body is 6 kg, in the cases when the body reaches its greatest speed over (a) 12 s, (b) 12 m.

5. A force of 6 N accelerates a body from rest to 25 m s$^{-1}$. The mass of the body is 4 kg. Find the acceleration, the distance travelled, and the time taken.

6. A body of mass 8 kg is dropped vertically through a liquid which offers a resistance of 2 N kg$^{-1}$. The body nevertheless manages to acquire a speed of 12 m s$^{-1}$. Find the time taken to do so, and the distance travelled in this time.

7. A train of mass $M$ is moving with zero acceleration against a resistance equal in magnitude to $k$ times its weight. Find its acceleration if it maintains the same tractive force, and slips a coach of mass $m$.

8. Find the acceleration of a particle of mass $m$ if it slides down a slope of angle $\alpha$, along a line making an angle $\beta$ with the line of greatest slope.

9. A balloon and its ballast has mass $M$, of which $m$ is the mass of the ballast. They fall with acceleration $a$, and when their combined velocity is $v$, the ballast is discarded. If the balloon comes to rest in a distance $x$, prove that $(M - m)v^2 = 2(mg - Ma)x$.

10. Masses of 2 kg and 5 kg are suspended over a smooth pulley by means of a light inextensible string. The system is released from rest. Find the acceleration of the masses, the tension in the string, and the time taken for one of the masses to move 1 m.

11. A mass of 4 kg lies 3 m from the edge of a smooth horizontal rectangular table, and is attached to a light inextensible string, which passes over a small pulley at the edge of the table to a mass of 1 kg which hangs freely. The system is released from rest. How long does it take for the 4 kg mass to reach the edge of the table?

12. An engine applies a net tractive force of 5000 N to three identical coaches, each of mass 10 tonne. The resistance to motion of each coach is 500 N and the mass of the whole train is 75 tonne. Find the acceleration of the train and the tension in each coupling.

13. Assume: (a) the earth is a sphere of radius 6371 km (this is the mean radius of the earth); (b) the acceleration due to gravity everywhere on the surface has the value of 9·807 m $s^{-2}$, which is the approximation to 4S of the standard value $g_n = 9{\cdot}80665\ \mathrm{m\,s^{-2}}$; (c) $G = 6{\cdot}67 \times 10^{-11}\ \mathrm{m^3\,kg^{-1}\,s^{-2}}$.

Find:

(i) the weight of a 1 kg mass on the surface of the earth;
(ii) the mass of the earth;
(iii) gravity at 5 km above the surface, and the percentage error in using $g_n$ instead;
(iv) the angle between the gravity vectors for particles 1000 km apart on the surface of the earth. Find the magnitude of the mean of these two vectors, and the percentage error in using $g_n$ in its stead.

14. A particle slides down a plane of angle $\alpha$ with constant velocity. Find its acceleration if the slope is increased to $2\alpha$.

## 8.5 Hooke's law

All materials stretch when under tension, and it is an experimental fact that many do so according to *Hooke's law*. This states that the tension in the material is proportional to the *extension*, which is defined as the magnitude of the displacement caused by the tension. Elastic strings and springs may be regarded as obeying this law at all times. In reality, *all* materials stretch to a certain extent, and obey Hooke's law for tensions not in excess of a certain value. When the tension reaches that value, the material reaches its *elastic limit*, and for greater tensions may deform or even break. Certain coil springs may also obey this law in compression.

Suppose a force **T** is applied along a string of *natural* (that is, unstretched) *length a*; that the string is fixed at one end, and obeys Hooke's law. Suppose the force **T** causes an extension **x** (see Fig. 8.9). Then the tension in the string is $-\mathbf{T}$, with magnitude $T = |\mathbf{T}|$. Hooke's law states that

$$T \propto x \quad \text{or} \quad T = kx$$

where the constant of proportionality $k$ is called the *stiffness* of the string, and has units N $m^{-1}$ since $T$ is in newton and $x$ in metre. Numerically, $k$ gives the magnitude of the tension required to produce unit extension. Hooke's law may also be written as $T = \lambda x/a$, where $a$ is the natural length of the string and $\lambda$ is the *modulus of elasticity*. $\lambda$ is in newton and is the actual force required to produce unit extension. $\lambda$ is the same for all strings or springs of the same material, while $k$ depends on the length of any given string or spring. In future, for our purposes, all elastic strings and springs will be considered to obey Hooke's law (HL).

**Worked Example 8.8**

An elastic string has stiffness 0·4 N $m^{-1}$ and is subject to a tension of 5 N. Find the extension.

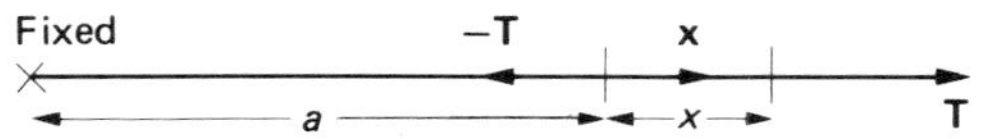


**Fig. 8.9.**

*Solution*

By HL, the extension $x$ is given by $5 = 0{\cdot}4x$, and so $x = 12{\cdot}5$ m.

**Worked Example 8.9**

A light elastic spring of natural length $a$ and stiffness $k$ is suspended from a fixed point and hangs vertically with a particle of mass $m$ attached to the lower end.

(a) If the system is allowed to hang in equilibrium, the spring is extended by a length $b$. Find $b$.

(b) If the particle is now pulled down a further small distance and released, investigate the motion of the system.

*Solution*

(a) We refer to Fig. 8.10. Using HL, $T = kb$. Applying Newton's second law in the $\hat{\mathbf{j}}$ direction: $mg - T = 0$, and so $T = mg$. Therefore $mg = kb$ and hence $b = mg/k$.

(b) We refer to Fig. 8.11. Suppose the extension at time $t$ is described by $x(t)\hat{\mathbf{j}} = x\hat{\mathbf{j}}$, that is, the particle is below the equilibrium position for $x$ positive, and above for $x$ negative. Then the acceleration of the particle is $\ddot{x}\hat{\mathbf{j}}$. Using HL, $T = k(b + x)$.

Applying Newton's second law in the $\hat{\mathbf{j}}$ direction: $mg - T = m\ddot{x}$. Therefore

$$mg - k\left(\frac{mg}{k} + x\right) = m\ddot{x}$$

thus $\quad mg - mg - kx = m\ddot{x}$

and so $$m\ddot{x} = -kx \tag{1}$$

This is the equation of motion of the particle.

We note that Equ. 1 is a second-order differential equation with general solution $x = A \sin t\sqrt{(k/m)} + B \cos t\sqrt{(k/m)}$, where $A$ and $B$ are constants which depend on physical conditions. The particle oscillates in *simple harmonic motion.* It returns to its starting position (or to any position on its path) at regular time intervals $2\pi\sqrt{(m/k)}$. This time is called the *period* of the oscillation.

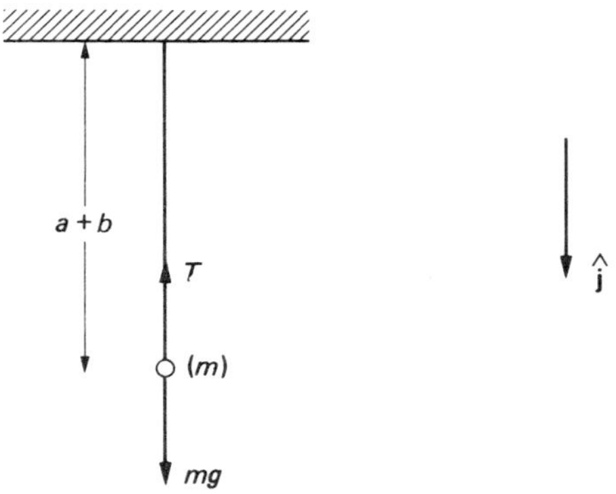


**Fig. 8.10.**

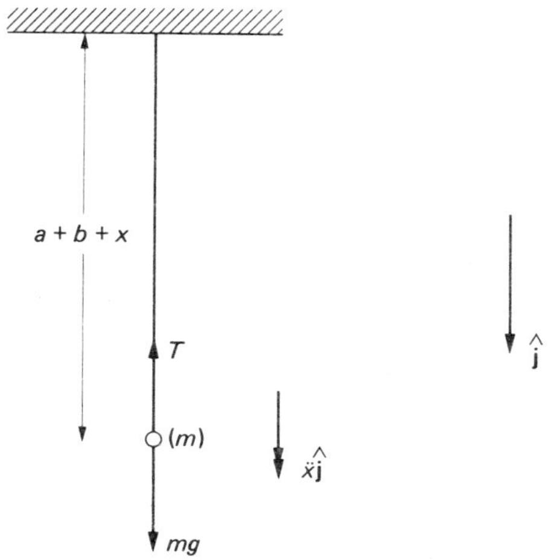


**Fig. 8.11.**

**Worked Example 8.10**

Suppose $n$ identical light elastic strings, each of natural length $a$ and stiffness $k$, are joined together to form a single elastic string, of natural length $na$. Find its stiffness $k'$.

*Solution*

If a tension $T$ is applied to the long string, there will be a tension $T$ in each short string. The total extension will be $nT/k$, by HL. If we consider the long string, then the tension in this string is also $T$, and $T = k'\,nT/k$, by HL, since its extension is $nT/k$. Therefore $k'n/k = 1$, and so $k' = k/n$—emphasizing that $k$ depends on the length of the string. Note, however, that, for each short string, $\lambda = ka$; and, for the long string, $\lambda = k'(na) = (k/n)na = ka$. The values are the same since $\lambda$ depends only on the material.

**Exercise 8*b***

1. Find the extension in a spring of natural length 0·5 m and stiffness 2·5 N m$^{-1}$ when subject to a tension of 4 N. What is the tension in the spring when it is stretched to twice its natural length?

2. A particle of mass 3 kg is a long way from the edge of a smooth horizontal table, and is attached to an elastic string which is fixed to the table, and to a light inelastic string which passes over a smooth pulley at the edge of the table. A mass of 4 kg hangs from the end of this string. The two strings lie in the same vertical plane, and initially the 4 kg mass is held so that both strings are taut but the elastic one is unstretched. The system is now released from rest. Find the acceleration of the 4 kg mass when it has fallen 1 m, given that if it is lowered gently through 8 m from the initial position, the system reaches equilibrium. (Leave your answer as a multiple of $g$.)

3. Two springs each of natural length 0·5 m and negligible mass are joined to a particle of mass 2 kg resting on a smooth horizontal table, and stretched between two fixed points A and B 1·5 m apart. If the spring attached to A has stiffness 2 N m$^{-1}$, and the other has stiffness 3 N m$^{-1}$, find the equilibrium position of the particle. Describe the motion if the particle is displaced a small distance from this equilibrium position.

4. Two identical strings of natural length 0·5 m and stiffness 2·5 N m$^{-1}$ are attached at one end to points on the ceiling 0·5 m apart. The other ends are joined to a heavy particle which is allowed to hang in equilibrium. Find the weight of the particle if it causes each string to stretch to twice its natural length.

## 8.6 Accelerations in systems

We have already worked problems involving single pulleys. We shall now consider systems involving several pulleys. With these it is important to keep the following points in mind:

(1) the magnitude of the tension in a string is constant for the whole of the string;
(2) Newton's second law may be applied separately to parts of a system;
(3) Newton's second law should be used to relate the net force acting on a particle and its resulting acceleration relative to a fixed point in space, and *not* to relate relative forces and relative accelerations.

**Worked Example 8.11**

Two equal pulleys have fixed axles in the same horizontal plane. A light inextensible string passes over the pulleys and under a third, movable, pulley of mass $M$ which hangs between them. To the ends of the string are attached particles of masses $m$ and $2m$. The parts of the string supporting the middle pulley hang vertically. Discuss the motion of the system when released from rest.

*Solution*

We refer to Fig. 8.12. Suppose that the tension in the string is $T$ and that the particles $m$, $2m$ and the pulley have respective accelerations $a_1\hat{\mathbf{j}}$, $a_2\hat{\mathbf{j}}$ and $a_3\hat{\mathbf{j}}$, where $\hat{\mathbf{j}}$ is chosen vertically upwards, and clearly $a_1$, $a_2$ and $a_3$ cannot all be positive.
Apply Newton's second law in the $\hat{\mathbf{j}}$ direction:

to the mass $m$: $\quad T - mg = ma_1 \qquad (1)$

to the mass $2m$: $\quad T - 2mg = 2ma_3 \qquad (2)$

to the pulley: $\quad 2T - Mg = Ma_2 \qquad (3)$

Now the accelerations of the particles and the pulley are related. For, suppose that their respective displacements in time $t$ are $x_1\hat{\mathbf{j}}$ for Q, $x_2\hat{\mathbf{j}}$ for P and $x_3\hat{\mathbf{j}}$ for R. Then $x_1\hat{\mathbf{j}} + x_3\hat{\mathbf{j}} = -2x_2\hat{\mathbf{j}}$ in order that the string remains taut along its length. If we differentiate this twice, remembering that $\mathrm{d}^2x/\mathrm{d}t^2 = a$, then we get $a_2\hat{\mathbf{j}} + a_3\hat{\mathbf{j}} = -2a_2\hat{\mathbf{j}}$, and so

$$a_1 + a_3 = -2a_2 \qquad (4)$$

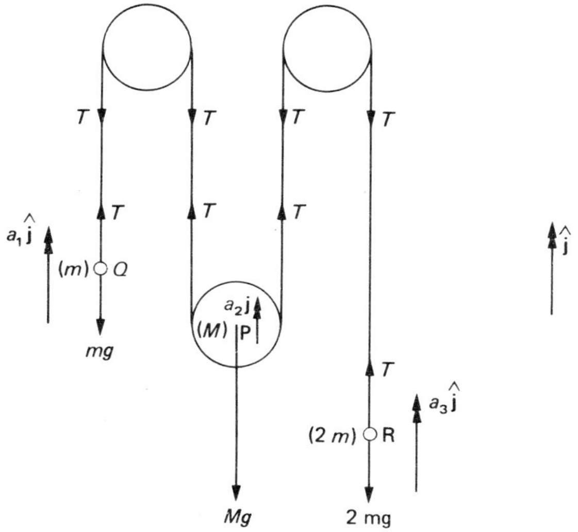


**Fig. 8.12.**

We may now solve Equations 1 to 4 to find the four unknowns, namely the three accelerations and the tension.

Substitute in Equ. 4 from Equations 1, 2, and 3:

$$\frac{T - mg}{m} + \frac{T - 2mg}{2m} = -2\,\frac{2T - Mg}{M}$$

Multiply by $2mM$:

$$2MT - 2mMg + MT - 2mMg = -8mT + 8mMg$$

thus

$$T = \frac{8mMg}{8m + 3M}$$

Therefore

$$a_1 = \frac{T - mg}{m} = \frac{8Mg}{8m + 3M} - \frac{8mg + 3Mg}{8m + 3M} = \frac{(5M - 8m)g}{8m + 3M}$$

and

$$a_2 = \frac{2T - Mg}{M} = \frac{16mg}{8m + 3M} - \frac{8mg + 3Mg}{8m + 3M} = \frac{(8m - 3M)g}{8m + 3M}$$

and

$$a_3 = \frac{T - 2mg}{2m} = \frac{4Mg}{8m + 3M} - \frac{8mg + 3Mg}{8m + 3M} = \frac{(M - 8m)g}{8m + 3M}$$

Now the pulley will move downwards if $a_2 < 0$, that is if $3M > 8m$. The particle $m$ will move upwards if $a_1 > 0$, that is if $5M > 8m$. The particle $2m$ will move upwards if $a_3 > 0$, that is if $M > 8m$.

Clearly, various combinations of these are possible for different values of the masses $m$ and $M$. The reader is advised to clarify for himself what happens in different cases, such as, for example, $8m = \frac{1}{2}M, 2M, 4M, 6M$.

**Exercise 8c**

(Answers may be left as multiples of $g$ in questions 1 to 3.)

1. Two equal pulleys have fixed axles in the same horizontal plane. A light inextensible string passes over the pulleys and under a third pulley of mass 20 kg, which hangs between them with the portions of the string vertical. Masses of 15 kg and $M$ are attached to the other ends of the string, and hang vertically. Discuss the motion of the system when it is released from rest, paying particular attention to $M$.
2. A pulley is attached by a string to a ceiling. Around this pulley passes a light inextensible string, to one end of which is attached a pulley P of mass 8 kg. To the other end is attached a particle Q of mass 16 kg. Around pulley P passes another light inextensible string, with masses R of 2 kg and S of 4 kg attached to its ends. Find the tension in each string and the acceleration of each part of the system when it is released from rest.
3. A smooth wedge of mass $M$ stands on a smooth horizontal table. One face of the wedge makes an angle $\alpha$ with the horizontal, and has a particle of mass $m$ placed on it. Find the resulting accelerations of the wedge and the particle.

## 8.7 Miscellaneous exercises 8

1. A mass 10 kg is to be accelerated at $5 \times 10^{-2}$ m s$^{-2}$ in a direction 060° (N 60° E). If it is known that a constant force of 5 N acts in a direction due south, determine the forces acting in the directions due east, and due north, which will produce the required acceleration. (MEI)
2. A breakdown lorry is to tow a car along a horizontal road by means of an inextensible horizontal bar. The mass of the car is 1000 kg, and that of the lorry and its driver is 2000 kg. Assuming that the resistances to motion can be taken as equivalent to 500 N acting horizontally on the lorry, and 100 N acting horizontally on the car, and that the horizontal tractive force exerted by the lorry engine is 2100 N, calculate the acceleration of the two vehicles. Find also the tension in the bar during the period of acceleration. (MEI)
3. A crane can lift a load of 1000 kg by means of a single vertical cable which can withstand a maximum tension of $10^4$ N. What is the greatest possible upward vertical acceleration that can be given to the load?

   To speed the process, two such cranes are used, but in this case the two cables lie each at 30° on either side of the vertical. If the tensions are now not to exceed 7500 N for safety reasons, what is the maximum upward vertical acceleration that can be given to the load? (Give your answers correct to two significant figures.) (MEI)
4. A hot-air balloon is rising vertically with an acceleration of 0·2 m s$^{-2}$. A man, mass 80 kg, stands in the cage of the balloon carrying in his hand a telescope, which, to him, appears to weight 15 N. Calculate the force that the floor of the cage exerts on the man, and the mass of the telescope. (MEI)

5. A particle Q, of mass 10 kg, is placed on a rough plane inclined to the horizontal at an angle whose tangent is 0·75. A light inextensible string, lying along a line of greatest slope, is tied to *Q*, passes over a light frictionless pulley at the top of the plane and is then tied to a second particle P which hangs freely.

When P is of mass 5 kg, Q is about to slide down the inclined plane. If $\mu$ is the coefficient of friction between Q and the inclined plane, calculate the value of $\mu$. What mass must P have if Q is about to slide up the plane? (L)

6. A particle A, of mass 10 kg, rests on a smooth horizontal bench. It is connected by two fine strings, passing over light smooth pulleys at opposite edges of the bench, to two particles B and C, of masses 2 kg and 6 kg respectively, hanging freely. The system starts from rest with the strings taut and in the same straight line between the pulleys. Calculate (L)

(a) the acceleration of A;
(b) the tensions in the two strings;
(c) the distance moved by A in the first 1·5 s. (L)

7. An object of unit mass is moving in a plane and its position vector from O is **r** and its coordinates $(r, \theta)$. If

$$\mathbf{r} = \frac{\cos\theta}{2 + \cos\theta}\mathbf{i} + \frac{\sin\theta}{2 + \cos\theta}\mathbf{j}$$

obtain an expression for $r$ in terms of $\theta$.

By differentiating find $\dot{\mathbf{r}}$ in terms of $\dot{\theta}$, $\theta$, **i** and **j**, and if $r^2\dot{\theta} = a$, where $a$ is a constant, prove that

$$\dot{\mathbf{r}} = -2a\sin\theta\,\mathbf{i} + a(2\cos\theta + 1)\mathbf{j}$$

Hence, by differentiating again, prove that the resultant force acting on the object is of magnitude $2a^2/r^2$ and directed towards 0. (SMP)

8. A light inextensible string passes over a smooth fixed pulley and has a particle of mass $5m$ attached to one end and a second smooth pulley of mass $m$ attached to the other end. Another light inextensible string passes over this second pulley and carries a mass $3m$ at one end and a mass $m$ at the other end. If the system moves freely under gravity, find the acceleration of the heaviest particle and the tension in each string. (L)

# 9
# Projectiles

## 9.1 Velocity and acceleration

Suppose a particle moves in space so that its position at time $t$ is given by the vector function $\mathbf{x}(t)$, which may be expressed in Cartesian component form either as

$$\mathbf{x}(t) = x(t)\hat{\mathbf{i}} + y(t)\hat{\mathbf{j}} + z(t)\hat{\mathbf{k}}$$

or as

$$\mathbf{x}(t) = \begin{pmatrix} x(t) \\ y(t) \\ z(t) \end{pmatrix}$$

Then $\dot{\mathbf{x}}(t) = \mathrm{d}\mathbf{x}/\mathrm{d}t$ gives the velocity $\mathbf{v}(t)$ of the particle at time $t$. We showed in Chapter 3 that

$$\mathbf{v} = \dot{\mathbf{x}} = \begin{pmatrix} \dot{x} \\ \dot{y} \\ \dot{z} \end{pmatrix};$$

in other words, the components of the velocity may be evaluated individually from the components of the displacement. The velocity vector at time $t$ is in the direction of the tangent to the path of the particle at the point with position vector $\mathbf{x}(t)$.

Similarly, the acceleration is given by

$$\mathbf{a}(t) = \ddot{\mathbf{x}} = \begin{pmatrix} \ddot{x} \\ \ddot{y} \\ \ddot{z} \end{pmatrix}.$$

**Worked Example 9.1**

A particle moves so that its position vector at time $t$ has components

$$\begin{pmatrix} 2t^2 \\ t^3 \\ 3 - t \end{pmatrix}$$

Find its velocity and acceleration at time $t$, and their magnitudes after 3 seconds.

*Solution*

$$\mathbf{x}(t) = \begin{pmatrix} 2t^2 \\ t^3 \\ 3 - t \end{pmatrix} \quad \text{gives}$$

$$\mathbf{v}(t) = \begin{pmatrix} 4t \\ 3t^2 \\ -1 \end{pmatrix} \text{ and } \mathbf{a}(t) = \begin{pmatrix} 4 \\ 6t \\ 0 \end{pmatrix}$$

Therefore

$$\mathbf{v}(3) = \begin{pmatrix} 12 \\ 12 \\ -1 \end{pmatrix} \text{ m s}^{-1} \text{ and } \mathbf{a}(3) = \begin{pmatrix} 4 \\ 18 \\ 0 \end{pmatrix} \text{ m s}^{-2}$$

Hence

$$|\mathbf{v}(3)| = \sqrt{12^2 + 12^2 + (-1)^2} = \sqrt{289} = 17 \text{ m s}^{-1},$$

and

$$|\mathbf{a}(3)| = \sqrt{4^2 + 18^2} = \sqrt{340} \approx 18{\cdot}4 \text{ m s}^{-2}$$

**Worked Example 9.2**

A particle moves in a plane so that its position at time $t$ is given by the component vector

$$\begin{pmatrix} 2 - t \\ 3t^2 \end{pmatrix}$$

Find its velocity and acceleration at time $t$. What is its path?

*Solution*

We have

$$\mathbf{r}(t) = \begin{pmatrix} x(t) \\ y(t) \end{pmatrix} = \begin{pmatrix} 2 - t \\ 3t^2 \end{pmatrix}$$

Therefore $3t^2 = y = 3(2 - x)^2$. Therefore the path of the particle is the parabola with equation $y = 3(2 - x)^2$, which is sketched in Fig. 9.1.

From the diagram, we see that part of the curve corresponds to negative values of $t$.

The velocity and acceleration are found as follows:

$$\mathbf{r}(t) = \begin{pmatrix} 2 - t \\ 3t^2 \end{pmatrix}$$

thus

$$\mathbf{v}(t) = \begin{pmatrix} -1 \\ 6t \end{pmatrix} \text{ and } \mathbf{a}(t) = \begin{pmatrix} 0 \\ 6 \end{pmatrix}$$

The important point to note about these is that the components may be regarded

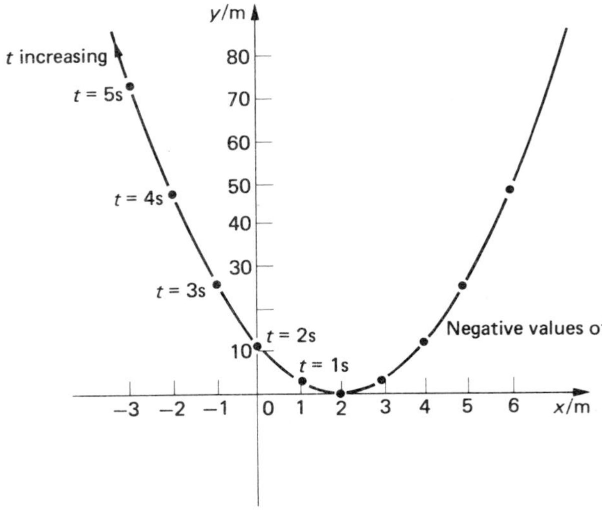


**Fig. 9.1.** Worked example 9.2.

completely separately, even though we have here treated pairs of components as vectors. Thus, if we consider a particle moving along the $x$-axis with displacement $x(t) = 2 - t$ at time $t$, its velocity and acceleration are $v(t) = -1$ and $a(t) = 0$—the $x$-components of the column vectors above. Similarly, a particle moving along the $y$-axis with displacement $y(t) = 3t^2$ at time $t$ has velocity $6t$ and acceleration 6 at time $t$.

This will be particularly important, for example, in the case of a projectile, where we may be concerned only with the horizontal displacement of a body thrown into the air. We may investigate this by considering only the horizontal components of the vectors in the subsequent motion.

The reader will be presumed familiar with the calculus results quoted in Chapter 3, and is also advised to re-read the worked examples of Section 3.8 at this stage. Exercise 9*a* is intended to revise these results.

## Exercise 9*a*

1. A particle moves in space so that its position at time $t$ is given by the column vector

$$\begin{pmatrix} \cos t \\ \sin t \\ t \end{pmatrix}$$

Find its velocity and acceleration at time $t$, and find expressions for their magnitudes at time $t$. Comment on these expressions.

2. A particle moves in space so that its position at time $t$ is given by the component vector

$$\begin{pmatrix} 4 \\ 5 - 10t \\ 5 - 10t \end{pmatrix}$$

Find its position, velocity and acceleration: (a) when $t = 0$ s; (b) when $t = 3$ s; (c) when it is in the horizontal plane $z = 0$.

3. A particle moves in a plane subject to the acceleration

$$\begin{pmatrix} 2 \\ 3 \end{pmatrix} \text{ m s}^{-2}$$

At time $t = 0$ s, it has position vector $\mathbf{x}_0$ and velocity $\mathbf{u}$. Find $\mathbf{x}(t)$ and $\mathbf{v}(t)$, its position and velocity at time $t$.

4. A particle moves in space subject to the acceleration

$$\begin{pmatrix} 10 \\ 10 \\ -10 \end{pmatrix} \text{ m s}^{-2}$$

where the axes are, respectively, eastwards, northwards and upwards. Suggest an idealized physical situation in which this acceleration might occur. Find the position and velocity of the particle at time $t$, given that it is moving through the origin with velocity

$$\begin{pmatrix} v \cos \alpha \\ 0 \\ v \sin \alpha \end{pmatrix}$$

at time $t = 0$ s.

## 9.2 Projectiles

We will begin our more detailed study of motion by considering projectiles—things which are thrown into the air with a known velocity. Then they are subjected only to the acceleration of gravity, if we neglect air resistance for the time being. We may justify our neglect of air resistance since, experimentally, it is known to be small in comparison with gravity and we will use a model in which gravity is the only acceleration present.

Suppose, then, that an object is thrown from the origin at time $t = 0$ s, with speed $u$ at an elevation of $\alpha$. Then its displacement and velocity at this time may be written in component form as

$$\mathbf{x}(0) = \begin{pmatrix} 0 \\ 0 \end{pmatrix}$$

and

$$\mathbf{v}(0) = \begin{pmatrix} u \cos \alpha \\ u \sin \alpha \end{pmatrix}$$

where we have taken $Ox$ horizontally and $Oy$ vertically. Further, the acceleration at any time is

$$\mathbf{g} = \begin{pmatrix} 0 \\ -g \end{pmatrix}$$

Suppose the position vector of the particle at time $t$ is $\mathbf{x}(t)$, and its velocity at time $t$ is $\mathbf{v}(t)$, which we know will be tangential to its path at the point P with position

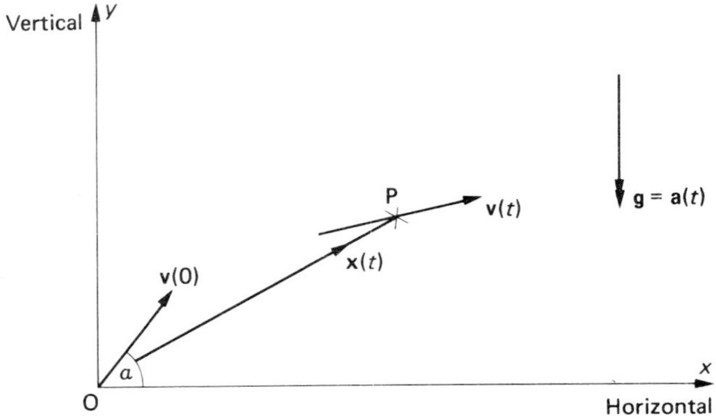


**Fig. 9.2.** The motion of a projectile.

vector $\mathbf{x}(t)$. Then we have

$$\mathbf{a}(t) = \mathbf{g} \quad \text{where} \quad \mathbf{g} = \begin{pmatrix} 0 \\ -g \end{pmatrix} \tag{1}$$

Integrating gives

$$\mathbf{v}(t) - \mathbf{v}(0) = \int_0^t \mathbf{g}\, dt$$

Therefore

$$\mathbf{v}(t) = \mathbf{v}(0) + \mathbf{g}t = \begin{pmatrix} u\cos\alpha \\ u\sin\alpha - gt \end{pmatrix} \tag{2}$$

Integrating again gives

$$\mathbf{x}(t) - \mathbf{x}(0) = \int_0^t (\mathbf{v}(0) + \mathbf{g}t)\, dt$$
$$= \mathbf{v}(0)t + \tfrac{1}{2}\mathbf{g}t^2$$

Therefore

$$\mathbf{x}(t) = \mathbf{v}(0)t + \tfrac{1}{2}t^2\mathbf{g} = \begin{pmatrix} u\cos\alpha t \\ u\sin\alpha t - \tfrac{1}{2}t^2 g \end{pmatrix} = \begin{pmatrix} x \\ y \end{pmatrix}, \tag{3}$$

where $(x, y)$ are the coordinates of the point P.

We may find the equation of the path of the projectile from Equ. 3: we have

$$x = u\cos\alpha t \quad \text{and} \quad y = u\sin\alpha t - \tfrac{1}{2}t^2 g$$

Therefore

$$t = \frac{x}{u\cos\alpha} \quad \text{and so} \quad y = \frac{u\sin\alpha x}{u\cos\alpha} - \tfrac{1}{2}g\left(\frac{x}{u\cos\alpha}\right)^2$$

Therefore

$$y = x\tan\alpha - \frac{gx^2}{2u^2}\sec^2\alpha \tag{4}$$

This equation represents a parabola, and so the path of a projectile is parabolic if we neglect air resistance. It will be seen later that the actual path, taking air resistance into account, only approximates to a parabola. We may sketch this path by considering some details of the motion. The particle returns to its original level when $y = 0$ m. If $y = 0$ m, then

$$t = 0 \text{ s} \quad \text{or} \quad t = 2u\sin\alpha/g \tag{5}$$

and

$$x = 0 \text{ m} \quad \text{or} \quad x = \frac{2u^2\sin\alpha\cos\alpha}{g} = \frac{u^2\sin 2\alpha}{g} \tag{6}$$

This value of $x$ is called the *range R* of the projectile—the horizontal displacement when the particle has returned to its original height.

The greatest height is achieved when the velocity is instantaneously horizontal, i.e. when $u\sin\alpha - gt = 0$. Then

$$t = u\sin\alpha/g \text{ and } y = h \text{ (say)} = u^2\sin^2\alpha/2g \tag{7}$$

This is the greatest height, which is reached in half the time taken to cover the range; the path is symmetric about the line $x = \frac{1}{2}R$. Since $R = u^2\sin\alpha/g$, the range $R$ is greatest for $\sin 2\alpha = 1$ since $u$ is constant. Therefore the greatest range is obtained with an angle of projection of 45°.

## 9.3 Worked examples

Further results concerning projectiles are demonstrated in these examples. We shall quote, without further explanation, Equations 1 to 7 of the previous section; and shall use Fig. 9.3, if appropriate, to demonstrate certain points. In a full solution, we should establish such results as are needed.

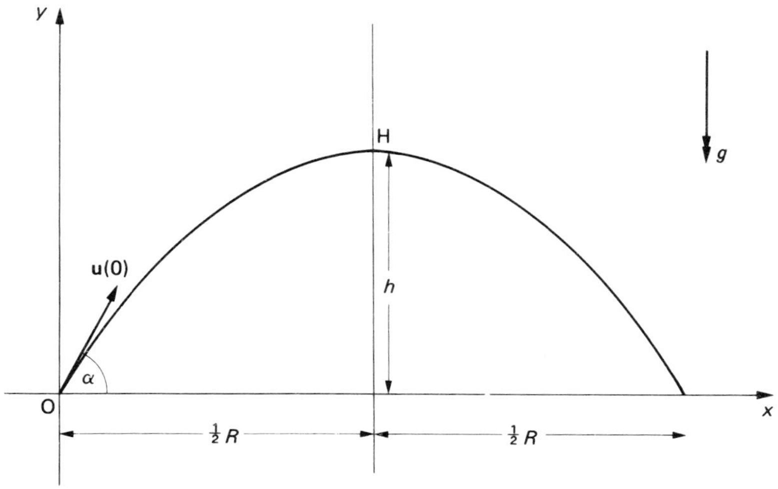


**Fig. 9.3.** The path of a projectile.

**Worked Example 9.3**

A particle is projected from the origin O with speed $11\sqrt{\frac{5}{3}}$ m s$^{-1}$ at an angle $\alpha$ to the horizontal ground. Find the possible values of $\alpha$ that allow it to clear a wall whose top is at (11, 3). Take $g = 10\,\text{m}\,\text{s}^{-2}$.

*Solution*

From Equ. 4,

$$y = x\tan\alpha - \frac{gx^2}{2u^2}\sec^2\alpha,$$

where $u^2 = 121 \times 5/3$, $g = 10$. Therefore

$$y = x\tan\alpha - \frac{3x^2}{121}(1 + \tan^2\alpha).$$

When $x = 11$ m, we must have $y > 3$ m for the projectile to clear the wall. Therefore

$$11\tan\alpha - 3(1 + \tan^2\alpha) > 3$$

thus

$$3\tan^2\alpha - 11\tan\alpha + 6 < 0$$

therefore

$$(3\tan\alpha - 2)(\tan\alpha - 3) < 0$$

thus

$$\tfrac{2}{3} < \tan\alpha < 3$$

therefore

$$33{\cdot}7° < \alpha < 71{\cdot}6°$$

Fig. 9.4 shows the two limiting values of $\alpha$, and the corresponding paths. We may

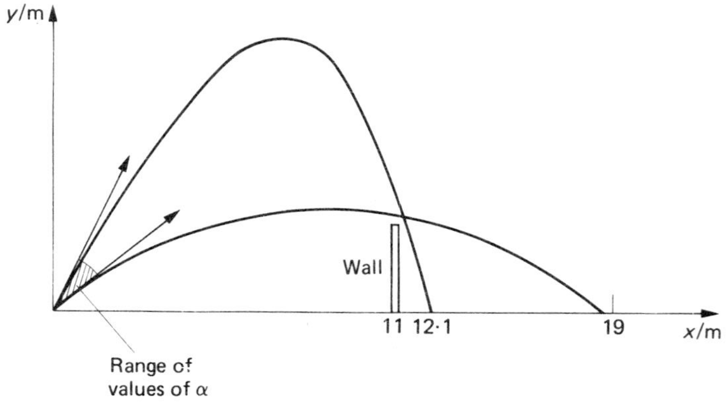


**Fig. 9.4.** Worked example 9.3.

locate the paths by noting their ranges. From Equ. 6

$$R = \frac{u^2 \sin 2\alpha}{g} = \frac{u^2 \times 2\tan\alpha}{g(1+\tan^2\alpha)}$$

where $\frac{u^2}{g} = \frac{121 \times 5}{3 \times 10}$. Hence, if $\tan\alpha = \frac{2}{3}$, then

$$R = \frac{121 \times 5}{3 \times 10} \times 2 \times \frac{2}{3} \times \frac{9}{13} = \frac{242}{13} \approx 19\,\text{m}$$

If $\tan\alpha = 3$, then

$$R = \frac{121 \times 5}{3 \times 10} \times \frac{2 \times 3}{10} = 12{\cdot}1\,\text{m}$$

In each case, the projectile reaches its highest point before passing over the wall.

**Worked Example 9.4**

A particle is projected up a slope so that its path lies in the vertical plane containing the line of greatest slope. Investigate the subsequent motion.

*Solution*

This is a re-statement of the problem considered in Section 9.2, where the ground was horizontal. The motion takes place entirely in the plane containing the line of greatest slope, so all our diagrams are of this plane. If the motion is not in this plane, the problem is different again (see Exercise 9*b*, question 8).

Let $\mathbf{x}(0) = 0$ and

$$\mathbf{v}(0) = \begin{pmatrix} u\cos\alpha \\ u\sin\alpha \end{pmatrix}$$

using the usual notation for displacement and velocity, where we have taken O$x$ in the plane and O$y$ perpendicular to the plane. Then the acceleration at time $t$ is

$$\mathbf{a}(t) = \begin{pmatrix} -g\sin\beta \\ -g\cos\beta \end{pmatrix}$$ where the plane is inclined at the angle $\beta$ to the horizontal.

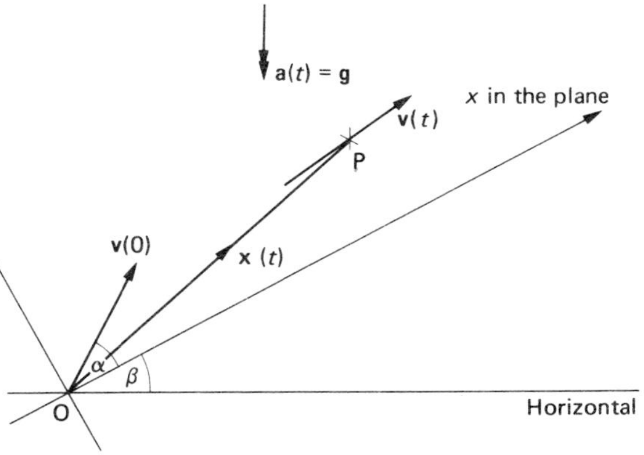


**Fig. 9.5.** A particle projected up an inclined plane.

Thus we have

$$\mathbf{a}(t) = \mathbf{g} \text{ where } \mathbf{g} = -g\begin{pmatrix}\sin\beta\\ \cos\beta\end{pmatrix} \tag{1}$$

Integrating gives

$$\mathbf{v}(t) - \mathbf{v}(0) = \int_0^t \mathbf{g}\,\mathrm{d}t$$

Therefore

$$\mathbf{v}(t) = \mathbf{v}(0) + \mathbf{g}t = \begin{pmatrix}u\cos\alpha - gt\sin\beta\\ u\sin\alpha - gt\cos\beta\end{pmatrix} \tag{2}$$

Integrating again gives

$$\mathbf{x}(t) - \mathbf{x}(0) = \int_0^t (\mathbf{v}(0) + \mathbf{g}t)\,\mathrm{d}t$$
$$= \mathbf{v}(0)t + \tfrac{1}{2}t^2\mathbf{g}$$

Therefore

$$\mathbf{x}(t) = \mathbf{v}(0)t + \tfrac{1}{2}t^2\mathbf{g} = \begin{pmatrix}u\cos\alpha t - \frac{1}{2}gt^2\sin\beta\\ u\sin\alpha t - \frac{1}{2}gt^2\cos\beta\end{pmatrix} = \begin{pmatrix}x\\ y\end{pmatrix} \tag{3}$$

where $(x, y)$ are the coordinates of the point P.

It is not easy to find the equation of the path from Eqn. 3, but this is relatively unimportant since the information we will usually require can be deduced from Equations 2 and 3.

We could have said that the problem is the same as that of Section 9.2; we could have taken axes $OX$ horizontally and $OY$ vertically and deduced that, *referred to those axes*, the equation of the path is

$$Y = X\tan(\alpha + \beta) - \frac{gX^2}{2u^2}\sec^2(\alpha + \beta) \text{ (from Equ. 4, p. 142)}$$

From Equ. 3, the particle returns to the plane when $y = 0$, i.e. when $t = 2u\sin\alpha/g\cos\beta = T$, say. Then, from Equ. 3,

$$x = \frac{2u^2\sin\alpha\cos\alpha}{g\cos\beta} - \frac{g\sin\beta}{2}\left(\frac{2u\sin\alpha}{g\cos\beta}\right)^2$$
$$= \frac{2u^2\sin\alpha}{g\cos^2\beta}\left(\cos\alpha\cos\beta - \sin\alpha\sin\beta\right)$$

Therefore

$$x = R = \frac{2u^2\sin\alpha\cos(\alpha + \beta)}{g\cos^2\beta}$$

gives the distance up the plane from the launching point, i.e. the range.

For a given slope and speed of projection, i.e. given $\beta$ and $u$, the range is greatest when $\sin\alpha\cos(\alpha + \beta)$ is greatest. Now

$$\sin\alpha\cos(\alpha + \beta) = \tfrac{1}{2}[\sin(2\alpha + \beta) - \sin\beta]$$

which has its greatest value of $\frac{1}{2}(1 - \sin\beta)$ when $2\alpha + \beta = \frac{1}{2}\pi$. Thus the range is greatest when $\alpha = \frac{1}{4}\pi - \frac{1}{2}\beta$, and the greatest range is

$$\frac{u^2(1 - \sin\beta)}{g\cos^2\beta} = \frac{u^2}{g(1 + \sin\beta)}$$

The greatest height above the plane (i.e. the greatest value of $y$) occurs when $\dot{y} = 0$, i.e. when

$$t = \frac{u\sin\alpha}{g\sin\beta} = \tfrac{1}{2}T = \tfrac{1}{2}(\text{time for range})$$

This greatest height is therefore $u^2\sin^2\alpha/2g\cos\beta$, from Equ. 3.

The greatest *vertical* height may be given by Equ. 7 on page 143, and is $u^2\sin^2(\alpha + \beta)/2g$ at time $u\sin(\alpha + \beta)/g$. This statement is not valid if the particle has hit the plane by this time. In that case, the greatest height is

$$R\sin\beta = \frac{2u^2\sin\alpha\sin\beta\cos(\alpha + \beta)}{g\cos^2\beta} \quad \text{at time} \quad \frac{2u\sin\alpha}{g\cos\beta}$$

The greatest vertical height is $R\sin\beta$ if

$$\frac{2u\sin\alpha}{g\cos\beta} \leqq \frac{u\sin(\alpha + \beta)}{g}$$

**Worked Example 9.5**

A point O on horizontal ground is taken as origin, and axes O$x$, O$y$, O$z$ are taken eastwards, northwards and upwards respectively. A target is fired into the air from the point (50, 0, 0) with velocity

$$\begin{pmatrix} 0 \\ 10 \\ 30 \end{pmatrix} \text{m s}^{-1}$$

A rifleman is at the origin. Find the velocity of the shot as it leaves the rifle if it is fired at the same time as the target and hits the target at the target's highest point. Take $g = 10$ m s$^{-2}$.

*Solution*

For the target,

$$\mathbf{a}(t) = \mathbf{g} = \begin{pmatrix} 0 \\ 0 \\ -10 \end{pmatrix} \text{m s}^{-2}$$

Therefore

$$\mathbf{v}(t) - \mathbf{v}(0) = \int_0^t \begin{pmatrix} 0 \\ 0 \\ -10 \end{pmatrix} dt = \begin{pmatrix} 0 \\ 0 \\ -10t \end{pmatrix}$$

Therefore

$$\mathbf{v}(t) = \begin{pmatrix} 0 \\ 10 \\ 30 - 10t \end{pmatrix}$$

Therefore

$$\mathbf{x}(t) - \mathbf{x}(0) = \int_0^t \begin{pmatrix} 0 \\ 10 \\ 30 - 10t \end{pmatrix} dt$$

$$= \begin{pmatrix} 0 \\ 10t \\ 30t - 5t^2 \end{pmatrix}$$

Therefore the position of the target at time $t$ is $\mathbf{x}(t)$, where

$$\mathbf{x}(t) = \begin{pmatrix} 50 \\ 10t \\ 30t - 5t^2 \end{pmatrix}$$

The target reaches its greatest height when $z = 30t - 5t^2$ is greatest. But $z = 45 - 5(t - 3)^2$, and is therefore greatest when $t = 3$ s.

Therefore

$$\mathbf{x}(3) = \begin{pmatrix} 50 \\ 30 \\ 45 \end{pmatrix} \text{m}$$

for the target. For the shot, suppose the initial velocity is

$$\mathbf{v}(0) = \begin{pmatrix} v_1 \\ v_2 \\ v_3 \end{pmatrix}$$

We also have

$$\mathbf{a}(t) = \mathbf{g} = \begin{pmatrix} 0 \\ 0 \\ -10 \end{pmatrix} \text{m s}^{-2}$$

Therefore

$$\mathbf{v}(t) - \mathbf{v}(0) = \begin{pmatrix} 0 \\ 0 \\ -10t \end{pmatrix}$$

as above, and so

$$\mathbf{v}(t) = \begin{pmatrix} v_1 \\ v_2 \\ v_3 - 10t \end{pmatrix}$$

Therefore

$$\mathbf{x}(3) - \mathbf{x}(0) = \int_0^3 \begin{pmatrix} v_1 \\ v_2 \\ v_3 - 10t \end{pmatrix} dt$$

$$= \left[ \begin{pmatrix} v_1 t \\ v_2 t \\ v_3 t - 5t^2 \end{pmatrix} \right]_0^3$$

That is,

$$\mathbf{x}(3) = \begin{pmatrix} 3v_1 \\ 3v_2 \\ 3v_3 - 45 \end{pmatrix}$$

for the shot. But the shot hits the target at this instant. So

$$\begin{pmatrix} 3v_1 \\ 3v_2 \\ 3v_3 - 45 \end{pmatrix} = \begin{pmatrix} 50 \\ 30 \\ 45 \end{pmatrix}$$

Therefore

$$\mathbf{v}(0) = \begin{pmatrix} v_1 \\ v_2 \\ v_3 \end{pmatrix} = \begin{pmatrix} 50/3 \\ 10 \\ 30 \end{pmatrix} \text{ m s}^{-1}$$

**Exercise 9*b***

Take $g = 9{\cdot}81$ m s$^{-2}$, unless specified otherwise. In questions 1 and 2, concerning projectiles on horizontal ground:

$\mathbf{u}$ is the initial velocity, magnitude $u$, elevation $\beta$;
$\mathbf{v}(t)$ is the velocity at time $t$;
$R$ is the range, and $T$ the time taken to cover it;
$(x, y)$ is the point on the trajectory corresponding to time $t$, referred to axes O$x$ horizontally and O$y$ vertically;
$h$ is the maximum height attained.

1. $\mathbf{u} = \begin{pmatrix} 3 \\ 4 \end{pmatrix}$ m s$^{-1}$. Find $u$, $\beta$, $R$, $T$ and $h$.
2. $u = 6$ m s$^{-1}$, $\beta = 27°$. Find $\mathbf{u}$, $R$, $T$ and $h$.
3. A particle is projected with speed 10 m s$^{-1}$ at an angle of 40° to the horizontal up a slope of angle 20°. If the particle is projected so that its path lies in a vertical plane through the line of greatest slope, find where and when it lands.
4. A particle is projected with speed 25 m s$^{-1}$ at an angle of 44° to the horizontal up a slope of angle 20°. If the particle is projected so that its path lies in a vertical plane through a line of greatest slope, find where and when it lands, and where and when it reaches its greatest vertical height.
5. A particle is moving under gravity in a vertical plane O$x$O$y$, O$y$ being vertically upwards and O$x$ horizontal. The particle is projected from O with velocity $V$ in a direction making an angle $\alpha$ with O$x$. If the particle passes through the point $(R\cos\beta, R\sin\beta)$, find an expression for $R$ in terms of $V$, $\alpha$, $\beta$ and show that for given $V$ and $\beta$, the maximum value of $R$ for varying $\alpha$ is $V^2/[g(1 + \sin\beta)]$.

A vertical wall of height $2a$ stands on horizontal ground. P is a point on the ground, the least distance from P to the foot of the wall being $h$. A particle is projected from a point O distant $a$ vertically above P, the motion being in a plane perpendicular to the wall. Find the least velocity of projection in order that the particle may: (i) clear the wall; (ii) reach the wall.

Prove that the corresponding angles of projection are complementary. (C)

## 9.4 Miscellaneous exercises 9

1. A particle is projected with speed 20 m $s^{-1}$ at an angle 40° to the horizontal, up a slope of angle 25°, so that its path lies in a vertical plane making an angle of 10° with the line of greatest slope. Find where and when it lands.

2. (a) The position, velocity and acceleration of a particle, with respect to a given origin, are expressed by the vectors **r**, **v**, **a**. If gravity is a constant vector **g**, state under what conditions each of the following equations would hold for the particle:

$$\text{(i) } \mathbf{a} = \mathbf{g} \quad \text{(ii) } \mathbf{a} = \mathbf{g} - k\mathbf{v}$$

Show that (i) implies also equations of the following forms:

$$\mathbf{v} = \mathbf{u} + t\mathbf{g}; \quad \mathbf{r} = \mathbf{r}_0 + t\mathbf{u} + \tfrac{1}{2}t^2\mathbf{g}$$

(b) A projectile is fired from a point O with a velocity of 150 m $s^{-1}$ at an angle $\alpha$ to the horizontal. Taking O as origin and axes O$x$, O$y$ horizontally and vertically, show that if air resistance can be neglected and $g$ is taken as 10 m $s^{-2}$ the equation of the path is

$$y = x\tan\alpha - \frac{x^2}{4500}(\tan^2\alpha + 1)$$

Find the possible values of $\alpha$ if the projectile is to strike the point with coordinates (1500, 500).

Show on a sketch the likely effect of air resistance on each of these paths and comment briefly on whether one would generally expect to have a choice of angles of projection in order to hit a given target under such conditions.

3. A long-jumper at the instant of leaving the ground has a horizontal velocity $u$ (due to his run), together with a velocity $\lambda u$ inclined at $\theta$ to the horizontal (due to his jump). Find an expression for the horizontal length $l$ of his jump and show that if $\lambda = 1$ and $\theta$ is chosen to make $l$ a maximum then his greatest height during the jump is about equal to $\frac{1}{7}l$. (MEI)

4. A shell is fired from a gun with muzzle velocity $V$ so as to hit a helicopter hovering at a height $b$ ($< V^2/2g$) and at a horizontal distance $a$ from the gun. If the angle of projection of the shell to the horizontal is $\theta$ show that

$$ga^2\tan^2\theta - 2V^2a\tan\theta + ga^2 + 2V^2b = 0$$

By considering this equation as a quadratic equation for $\tan\theta$ deduce the farthest horizontal distance at which the helicopter can be hit if the height $b$ and the muzzle velocity $V$ are given. (JMB)

5. A projectile is projected from a point A on a horizontal plane so as to strike a target on a vertical wall. The motion of the projectile is in a vertical plane perpendicular to the wall. The distance of the wall from A is $l$, and the speed of projection is $(2gl)^{\frac{1}{2}}$.

If $\alpha$ is the angle of projection to the horizontal and $h$ is the height of the target, show that $h = l(\tan\alpha - \frac{1}{4}\sec^2\alpha)$. When the angle of projection is $\pi/4$ show that $h = \frac{1}{2}l$.

If a small error of 0·001 rad were made in this angle of projection find, as a percentage of $h$, the consequent small distance on the wall by which the target would be missed. (JMB)

6. A particle is projected with velocity $V$ at an angle $\alpha$ to the horizontal. Find its range $R$ on the horizontal plane through the point of projection.

If the distance apart of the two points on the trajectory at which the velocity of the particle makes an angle $\frac{1}{2}\alpha$ with the hozirontal is equal to $3R/8$, find the angle $\alpha$ to the nearest minute. (L)

7. The two points A and B, of which A is the lower, lie upon a line of greatest slope of a plane inclined to the horizontal at an angle $\alpha$. Shots with initial velocity $V$ can be fired from either A or B in a vertical plane through AB.. If the distance AB is the maximum range for a shot up the plane from A, show that the distance AB is $(V^2/g)(1 + \sin\alpha)^{-1}$ and that it is possible for a shot from B to over-shoot A by the distance $2(V^2/g)\sec\alpha\tan\alpha$ at the most. (MEI)

8. A particle starts from a point A whose position vector is **a** with velocity **u** under a constant acceleration **g**. Obtain an expression for the position vector of the particle after time $t$.

Two particles move freely under gravity; show that their relative velocity remains constant.

Two boys stand on level ground, $b$ metres apart. One throws a stone vertically upwards with velocity $u$ metres per second, the other waits until this stone is at its highest point then throws a stone directly at it with speed $v$ metres per second. Show that the stones will collide provided $v$ is big enough and find the lower limit for $v$. Find $u$ to make this lower limit least.

List the assumptions you are making. (MEI)

# 10
# The Scalar Product

## 10.1 Work and power

In this chapter, we shall define and demonstrate one possible way of 'multiplying' two vectors. The other common multiplication will be defined in Chapter 12, on vector products.

We first consider an example. Suppose we have a railway truck on a straight level track. Suppose that it is pulled along the track by an engine in front of it, which pulls it with a force of constant magnitude $F$. The pull of the engine may be represented by a vector $\mathbf{F}$, and the consequent displacement of the truck by a vector $\mathbf{x}$. Since the pull and the movement are both along the track, $\mathbf{F}$ and $\mathbf{x}$ will have the same direction and sense.

Suppose the displacement of the truck has magnitude $x$. Then in this example the *work* done by the engine pulling the truck is defined as $Fx$, i.e. magnitude of force times distance. The unit of work is 1 N m which is called 1 *joule*, written 1 J.

We define the *power* of the engine to be the rate at which it does work. Thus, if the work done is $W$, then the power $P$ is given by

$$\begin{aligned} P &= \mathrm{d}W/\mathrm{d}t, && \text{where } t \text{ represents time} \\ &= \mathrm{d}(Fx)/\mathrm{d}t && \text{in this case} \\ &= F\,\mathrm{d}x/\mathrm{d}t && \text{since the force } F \text{ is constant} \end{aligned}$$

and so

$$P = Fv \qquad \text{where } v \text{ is the speed of the truck and engine.}$$

The unit of power is 1 *watt*, written 1 W, where 1 W = 1 J s$^{-1}$.

Both work and power are *scalar* quantities—this will become clearer in our next example.

Now suppose that the truck, instead of being pulled by the engine, is pulled by a horizontal rope which is kept at a constant angle $\theta$ to the track. Again, suppose that the force has constant magnitude $F$ and is represented by the vector $\mathbf{F}$, and that the displacement is represented by the vector $\mathbf{x}$ (see Fig. 10.1*a*).

We find it convenient to consider a slightly different but equivalent problem. We imagine that the force $\mathbf{F}$ is produced by combining the pulls of two ropes, one along the track and one at right angles to the track (see Fig. 10.1b). Suppose the forces in these two ropes are $\mathbf{B}$ and $\mathbf{A}$ respectively, where $\mathbf{B}$ and $\mathbf{A}$ are the *components* of $\mathbf{F}$ in their respective directions. Then $\mathbf{A} + \mathbf{B} = \mathbf{F}$. From the diagram, we see that the magnitudes of the forces are connected by $B = F\cos\theta$ and $A = F\sin\theta$.

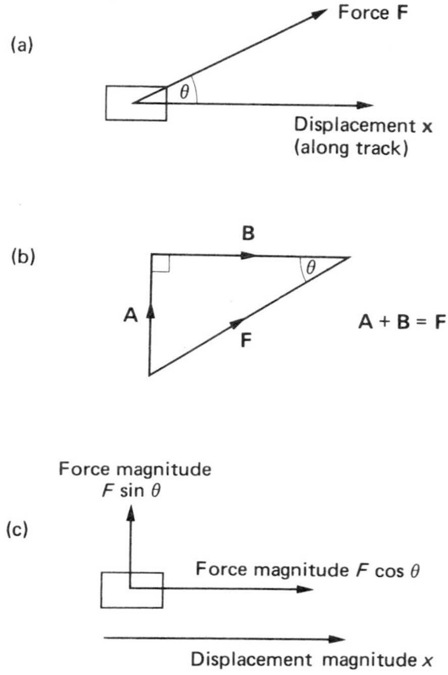


**Fig. 10.1.** (a) The truck being pulled by a rope at an angle to the track. (b) Replacing the force **F** by the equivalent set {**A**, **B**}. (c) The truck being moved by forces $F\sin\theta$ and $F\cos\theta$.

Hence the pull in the single rope can be represented by two separate forces, $F\cos\theta$ along the track and $F\sin\theta$ at right angles to the track (see Fig. 10.1 (c)). Now these forces clearly serve two entirely different purposes. The force $F\sin\theta$ on its own could not move the truck along the track. At best, it could tilt it about the near wheels. Thus it does no work towards moving the truck.

On the other hand, the force $F\cos\theta$ is like the force $F$ in the first example—it moves the truck along the track, and is the sole cause of the movement. It does work $(F\cos\theta)x$ in doing so. Therefore the work done on the truck in this case is $Fx\cos\theta$. Therefore we may conclude that the work done by a constant force **F** in moving the truck through a displacement **x** is $Fx\cos\theta$, where $\theta$ is the angle between **F** and **x**.

The power is

$$P = \mathrm{d}(Fx\cos\theta)/\mathrm{d}t$$

$$= F\cos\theta\,\mathrm{d}x/\mathrm{d}t \qquad \text{since } F \text{ and } \theta \text{ are constants}$$

and so

$$P = Fv\cos\theta$$

Thus we have expressions for work $(Fx\cos\theta)$ and power $(Fv\cos\theta)$ which take the same form—product of the magnitudes of the two vectors and the angle between them. We use this to define the *scalar product* of two vectors **a** and **b** as $ab\cos\theta$, where $a$ and $b$ are the respective magnitudes, and $\theta$ is the angle between the vectors. This is a scalar quantity, whence the name scalar product. We will repeat and clarify this definition in the next section.

## 10.2 Scalar product of two vectors

Choose an origin O, and two position vectors **a** and **b**. Then the *angle $\theta$ between* **a** *and* **b** will mean the smaller angle between the positive directions of **a** and **b**. In other words, $\theta \leqq 2\pi - \theta$, which is an inequality between the two possible choices. This is essential when we consider certain trigonometric ratios—the cosines of the two angles are equal, but the sines are not, for example.

Suppose the magnitudes of **a** and **b** are $a$ and $b$ respectively. Then we define the *scalar product* $\mathbf{a}\cdot\mathbf{b}$ of **a** and **b** to be the scalar quantity $ab\cos\theta$. The quantity $\mathbf{a}\cdot\mathbf{b}$ is also called the *inner product* or *dot product* of the two vectors, and is conventionally pronounced '*a* dot *b*'. Thus

$$\mathbf{a}\cdot\mathbf{b} = ab\cos\theta$$

Thus, from Section 10.1, we see that the work done by a constant force **F** in causing a displacement **x** is $\mathbf{F}\cdot\mathbf{x}$, and the power of that force is $\mathbf{F}\cdot\mathbf{v}$. If the force is not constant, we have to resort to integration of functions involving vectors.

The use of scalar products is not restricted to work and power. We will show a geometric property before going on to consider how we can use algebraic expressions involving these products.

Take a fixed unit vector $\hat{\mathbf{a}}$ to define the initial line for polar coordinates, and take a vector $\mathbf{r} = \overrightarrow{\mathrm{OR}}$ such that the point R has polar coordinates $(r, \theta)$. Then the *projection of* **r** *onto the initial line* is defined to be $\mathbf{r}\cdot\hat{\mathbf{a}} = r \times 1 \times \cos\theta = r\cos\theta$. We see that this is just the length of ON, together with a sign + or − according as N is on the positive or negative part of the initial line. Then $\mathbf{n} = (r\cos\theta)\hat{\mathbf{a}}$ is the position vector for N.

The projection of **r** onto *any* line determined by a unit vector $\hat{\mathbf{a}}$ is defined in the same way, and will be $\mathbf{r}\cdot\hat{\mathbf{a}} = r\cos\theta$. Now we know from our definition that

$$\mathbf{r}\cdot\mathbf{a} = ra\cos\theta = a(\mathbf{r}\cdot\hat{\mathbf{a}})$$

Thus $\mathbf{r}\cdot\mathbf{a}$ is equal to the projection of **r** onto the line of **a**, multiplied by the magnitude of **a**. This will be important in proving some properties later in this chapter.

Throughout this work, we have assumed that the vectors considered lie in a plane. This does not, however, restrict us to plane vectors. Throughout, we have only con-

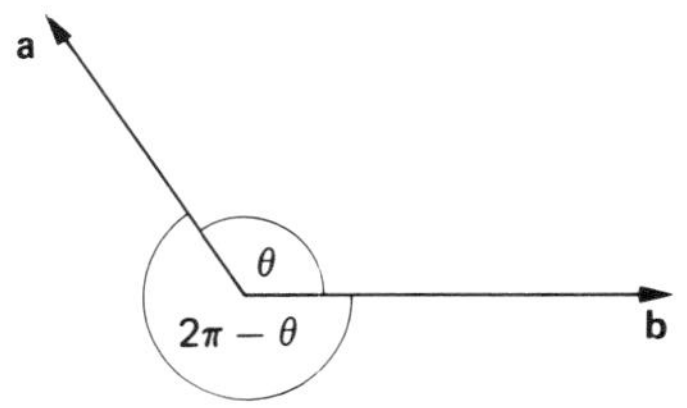


**Fig. 10.2.** The angles between the vectors **a** and **b**.

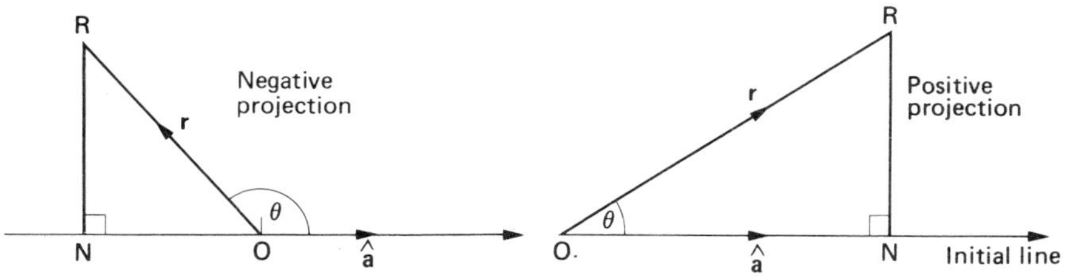


**Fig. 10.3.** The projection of **r** onto the initial line.

sidered two position vectors **a** and **b** at a time. These define a plane in space, so that if we are considering a scalar product, we only need consider the plane defined by the vectors. This is why we have not considered three-dimensional space. Our definition of scalar product holds for three-dimensional vectors as well as for two-dimensional ones.

## 10.3 Other types of vector

We may use our definition to evaluate scalar products of pairs of free vectors and pairs of localized line vectors.

In each case, we choose an origin O and select position vectors **p** and **q** equivalent to the given vectors. We then evaluate $\mathbf{p} \cdot \mathbf{q} = pq\cos\theta$ as before.

Thus we may talk of the scalar product of the two vectors **p** and **q** as $\mathbf{p} \cdot \mathbf{q} = pq\cos\theta$ without specifying which type of vector we are dealing with.

The exception is the case of column vectors, i.e. members of $R^3$. We define the scalar product **a . b** of

$$\mathbf{a} = \begin{pmatrix} a_1 \\ a_2 \\ a_3 \end{pmatrix} \text{and } \mathbf{b} = \begin{pmatrix} b_1 \\ b_2 \\ b_3 \end{pmatrix}$$

by the equation

$$\mathbf{a} \cdot \mathbf{b} = a_1 b_1 + a_2 b_2 + a_3 b_3.$$

This will be discussed in more detail in Section 10.7 and in Chapter 13.

## 10.4 Examples using scalar products

### Worked Example 10.1

Two position vectors **p** and **q** have the same length 2, and their scalar product is $-1$. Find the angle between them.

*Solution*

$\mathbf{p} \cdot \mathbf{q} = -1$, thus $pq\cos\theta = -1$, where $\theta$ is the required angle. Thus $4\cos\theta = -1$ since $p = q = 2$. Thus, $\cos\theta = -\frac{1}{4}$ and so $\theta = 104{\cdot}5°$ since $0 \leq \theta \leq 180°$.

**Worked Example 10.2**

Two position vectors **p** and **q** have the same length. The angle between them is 30°, and their scalar product is 3. Find their length.

*Solution*

Suppose the vectors each have length $p$.
Then $\mathbf{p}\cdot\mathbf{q} = pq\cos\theta$ gives $3 = p^2\cos 30°$, therefore $p = \sqrt{(3/\cos 30°)}$ since $p \geq 0$ and so $p = 1{\cdot}86$ (3S).

**Worked Example 10.3**

Find the work done by a force of 30 000 N in moving an object through a distance of 45 m when: (a) the force is in the direction of motion; and (b) the force makes an angle of 40° to the direction of motion. Find the rate at which the force is working at the time when the velocity is 2 m s$^{-1}$. Why is the power not constant?

*Solution*

(a) The work is given by

$$W = 30\,000\text{ N} \times 45\text{ m} = 1{\cdot}35 \times 10^6\text{ J}$$

The power is given by

$$P = 30\,000\text{ N} \times 2\text{ m s}^{-1} = 6 \times 10^4\text{ W}$$

(b) The work done is given by

$$W = \mathbf{F}\cdot\mathbf{x} = 30\,000\text{ N} \times 45\text{ m} \times \cos 40° = 1{\cdot}03 \times 10^6\text{ J}$$

The power is given by

$$P = 30\,000\text{ N} \times 2\text{ m s}^{-1} \times \cos 40° = 4{\cdot}60 \times 10^4\text{ W}$$

The power is not constant since the velocity is not constant.

**Exercise 10a**

1. Find the angle between **a** and **b** in the following cases:
(a) $\mathbf{a}\cdot\mathbf{b} = 2$ and $|\mathbf{a}| = 2|\mathbf{b}| = 3$;
(b) $\mathbf{a}\cdot\mathbf{b} = -\frac{1}{4}$ and $|\mathbf{a}| = 3|\mathbf{b}| = 2$.

2. The angle between **a** and **b** is 120°, and $a = 2b$. Is it possible to find $b$ if: (a) $\mathbf{a}\cdot\mathbf{b} = 4$; and (b) $\mathbf{a}\cdot\mathbf{b} = -4$?

3. Two vectors are such that $\mathbf{a}\cdot\mathbf{b} = 5$.
(a) Find the angle between them if they both have length 6.
(b) Find their lengths if the angle between them is 35° and their lengths are equal.

4. A railway truck is pulled by two ropes, making angles of 30° and 40° with the straight level track. The forces in the ropes are respectively $5 \times 10^5$ N and $4 \times 10^5$ N. Find the work done by each rope separately, and hence the total work done, in moving the truck 1 m.

5. A sledge slides down a frictionless slope (i.e. the only force on the sledge is its weight). If the slope makes an angle of 15° with the horizontal, and the mass of the sledge is 12 kg, find the work done in moving 15 m. Find the power deve-

loped when the sledge is moving at 9 m s$^{-1}$. Assume that $g = 9{\cdot}8$ N kg$^{-1}$, so that the weight of the sledge is $12 \times 9{\cdot}8$ N.

6. Points A and B have polar coordinates (2, 30°) and (−3, 45°). Find the scalar product of their position vectors **a** and **b** referred to the origin of polar coordinates.

## 10.5 Properties of the scalar product

We will now establish a number of properties which hold for the scalar product we have defined. They also hold for the scalar product we define in $R^3$, and form the basis of an abstract algebraic concept known as an *inner product space.* We will find the laws essential when we come to deal with expressions like $(2\mathbf{x} + 3\mathbf{y}).(\mathbf{x} - \mathbf{y})$, i.e. when we come to perform algebra with scalar products.

We have the definition $\mathbf{a}.\mathbf{b} = ab\cos\theta$, where $\theta$ is the smaller angle between the positive directions of **a** and **b**. This expression is symmetrical in $a$ and $b$—$\theta$ is also the angle between **b** and **a**. Hence also $\mathbf{b}.\mathbf{a} = ab\cos\theta$. Thus

$$\mathbf{a}.\mathbf{b} = \mathbf{b}.\mathbf{a} \qquad \text{(I1)}$$

i.e. scalar products are commutative.

How consider $(\alpha\mathbf{x}).\mathbf{y}$, where $\alpha$ is any real number. Suppose the angle between **x** and **y** is $\theta$. Then the diagram shows that the angle between $-\mathbf{x}$ and **y** is $\pi - \theta$, and the angle between **x** and $-\mathbf{y}$ is also $\pi - \theta$. Thus the angle between $(\alpha\mathbf{x})$ and **y** is

$$\begin{cases} \theta \text{ if } \alpha > 0 \\ \text{unspecified if } \alpha = 0 \\ \pi - \theta \text{ if } \alpha < 0 \end{cases}$$

Also

$$|\alpha\mathbf{x}| = |\alpha|\,|\mathbf{x}| = \begin{cases} \alpha x \text{ if } \alpha > 0 \\ 0 \quad \text{if } \alpha = 0 \\ -\alpha x \text{ if } \alpha < 0 \end{cases}$$

Therefore

$$\begin{aligned} (\alpha\mathbf{x}).\mathbf{y} &= |\alpha\mathbf{x}| \times |\mathbf{y}| \times \cos(\text{angle between } \alpha\mathbf{x} \text{ and } \mathbf{y}) \\ &= \begin{cases} (\alpha x)(y)(\cos\theta) & \text{if } \alpha > 0 \\ 0 & \text{if } \alpha = 0 \\ (-\alpha x)(y)\cos(\pi - \theta) & \text{if } \alpha < 0 \end{cases} \\ &= \alpha(xy\cos\theta) \text{ for all values of } \alpha \\ &= \alpha(\mathbf{x}.\mathbf{y}) \end{aligned}$$

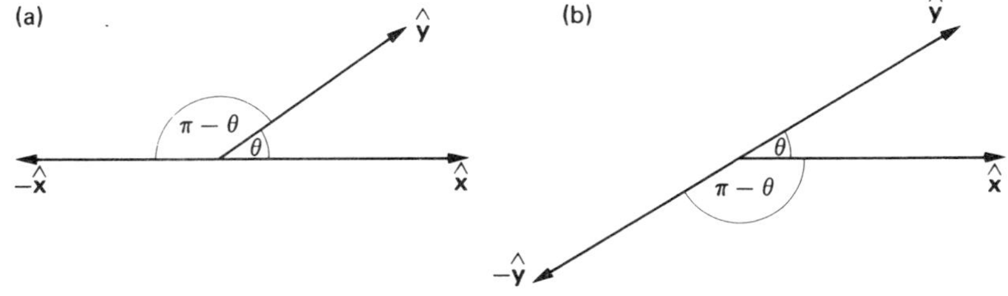


**Fig. 10.4.** The angles between: (a) **x** and $-\mathbf{y}$; and (b) **y** and $-\mathbf{x}$.

Similarly

$$\begin{aligned}\mathbf{x}\cdot(\alpha\mathbf{y}) &= (\alpha\mathbf{y})\cdot\mathbf{x} && \text{by Equ. I1}\\ &= \alpha(\mathbf{y}\cdot\mathbf{x}) && \text{from above}\\ &= \alpha(\mathbf{x}\cdot\mathbf{y}) && \text{by Equ. I1}\end{aligned}$$

Hence we have proved that

$$(\alpha\mathbf{x})\cdot\mathbf{y} = \mathbf{x}\cdot(\alpha\mathbf{y}) = \alpha(\mathbf{x}\cdot\mathbf{y}) \tag{I2}$$

and that brackets are unnecessary. Thus, for example, $(3\mathbf{y})\cdot(4\mathbf{x}) = 12\mathbf{x}\cdot\mathbf{y}$.

Now consider $\mathbf{a}\cdot(\mathbf{b}+\mathbf{c})$. We will demonstrate the result of this multiplication by using our geometrical interpretation of scalar products by projections.

Now $\mathbf{a}\cdot(\mathbf{b}+\mathbf{c})$ is equal to the projection of $(\mathbf{b}+\mathbf{c})$ onto $\mathbf{a}$, multiplied by the length $a$ of $\mathbf{a}$. From the diagram, this is equal to $a$ OB′. Now OB′ is equal to OC′ + C′B′, where OC′ is the projection of **c** onto **a**, and B′C′ is the projection onto **a** of a vector equivalent to **b**, and therefore has the same length as the projection of **b** onto **a**.

Hence

$$\begin{aligned}a\,\mathrm{OB'} &= a(\mathrm{OC'} + \mathrm{C'B'})\\ &= a\mathrm{OC'} + a\mathrm{C'B'}\\ &= \text{length of } \mathbf{a} \text{ multiplied by projection of } \mathbf{c} \text{ onto } \mathbf{a}\\ &\quad + \text{length of } \mathbf{a} \text{ multiplied by projection of } \mathbf{b} \text{ onto } \mathbf{a}\\ &= \mathbf{a}\cdot\mathbf{c} + \mathbf{a}\cdot\mathbf{b}\end{aligned}$$

Therefore

$$\mathbf{a}\cdot(\mathbf{b}+\mathbf{c}) = \mathbf{a}\cdot\mathbf{b} + \mathbf{a}\cdot\mathbf{c} \tag{I3}$$

This is a distributive law, of . over +. The reader is advised to re-draw Fig. 10.5 for a different initial configuration of vectors. Note that this is a demonstration, not a proof.

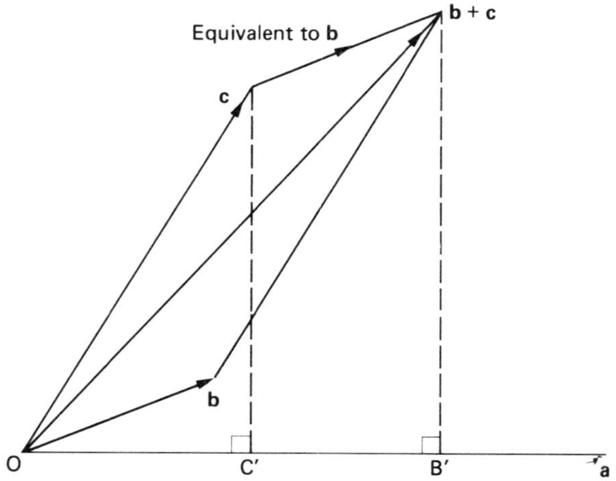


Fig. 10.5. $\mathbf{a}\cdot(\mathbf{b}+\mathbf{c}) = \mathbf{a}\cdot\mathbf{b} + \mathbf{a}\cdot\mathbf{c}$.

We could, if we wished, combine Equations I2 and I3 with a single law of the scalar product of a vector with any linear combination:

$$\mathbf{a}\cdot(\alpha\mathbf{b} + \beta\mathbf{c}) = \mathbf{a}\cdot(\alpha\mathbf{b}) + \mathbf{a}\cdot(\beta\mathbf{c}) \quad \text{by distributive law (I3)}$$

and so

$$\mathbf{a}\cdot(\alpha\mathbf{b} + \beta\mathbf{c}) = \alpha(\mathbf{a}\cdot\mathbf{b}) + \beta(\mathbf{a}\cdot\mathbf{c}) \quad \text{by commutative law (I2)}$$

We could extend this law further to give the product of two linear combinations:

$$\begin{aligned}(\alpha\mathbf{a} + \beta\mathbf{b})\cdot(\gamma\mathbf{c} + \delta\mathbf{d}) &= (\alpha\mathbf{a} + \beta\mathbf{b})\cdot(\gamma\mathbf{c}) + (\alpha\mathbf{a} + \beta\mathbf{b})\cdot(\delta\mathbf{d}) && \text{from above}\\ &= (\gamma\mathbf{c})\cdot(\alpha\mathbf{a} + \beta\mathbf{b}) + (\delta\mathbf{d})\cdot(\alpha\mathbf{a} + \beta\mathbf{b}) && \text{by (I1)}\\ &= (\alpha\gamma)\mathbf{a}\cdot\mathbf{c} + (\beta\gamma)\mathbf{b}\cdot\mathbf{c} + (\alpha\delta)\mathbf{a}\cdot\mathbf{d} + (\beta\delta)\mathbf{b}\cdot\mathbf{d}\end{aligned}$$

which works just as the multiplication of brackets in real algebra.

It will be left to the reader (see Exercise 11*b*) to prove that *any* finite linear combinations can be multiplied together in this way.

We are now able to say that

$$(2\mathbf{x} + 3\mathbf{y})\cdot(4\mathbf{x} - \mathbf{y}) = 8\mathbf{x}\cdot\mathbf{x} + 10\mathbf{x}\cdot\mathbf{y} - 3\mathbf{y}\cdot\mathbf{y}$$

The expression $\mathbf{x}\cdot\mathbf{x}$ lends itself to further simplification. The angle between $\mathbf{x}$ and $\mathbf{x}$ is 0, which has cosine 1. Therefore $\mathbf{x}\cdot\mathbf{x} = x \times x \times 1$, i.e. $\mathbf{x}\cdot\mathbf{x} = x^2$, or the scalar product of a vector with itself is the square of its length. We may also write $\mathbf{x}\cdot\mathbf{x} = \mathbf{x}^2$. This fact will prove useful later in two contexts: finding the length of a vector by using its scalar product with itself; and, in more abstract work, using this property to define the length of a vector where such a definition might have no geometrical significance.

From this, we deduce that $\mathbf{x}\cdot\mathbf{x} \geq 0$, since $x^2 \geq 0$. Furthermore, $\mathbf{x}\cdot\mathbf{x}$, will be zero if and only if $x = 0$, i.e. $\mathbf{x} = \mathbf{0}$. This is another important result:

$$\mathbf{x}\cdot\mathbf{x} \geq 0, \text{ with equality if and only if } \mathbf{x} = \mathbf{0} \qquad \text{(I4)}$$

The numbered properties, namely Equations I1 to I4 are of significance in abstract work connected with inner product spaces.

**Worked Example 10.4**

Evaluate the scalar product $(3\mathbf{x} - 5\mathbf{y})\cdot(2\mathbf{x} + 7\mathbf{y})$

*Solution*

$$\begin{aligned}(3\mathbf{x} - 5\mathbf{y})\cdot(2\mathbf{x} + 7\mathbf{y}) &= 6\mathbf{x}\cdot\mathbf{x} + 21\mathbf{x}\cdot\mathbf{y} - 10\mathbf{y}\cdot\mathbf{x} - 35\mathbf{y}\cdot\mathbf{y}\\ &= 6x^2 + 11\mathbf{x}\cdot\mathbf{y} - 35y^2\end{aligned}$$

**Worked Example 10.5**

(a) Give a geometrical interpretation to the scalar product $(\mathbf{a} + \mathbf{b})\cdot(\mathbf{a} - \mathbf{b})$.
(b) If $a = b$, evaluate this scalar product and explain the significance of the result.
(c) If it is given that $a = 2b$, and the scalar product is 12, find $a$ and $b$.

*Solution*

(a) Take an origin O, and suppose that $\mathbf{a}$ and $\mathbf{b}$ are the position vectors of points A and B. Then $\mathbf{a} + \mathbf{b}$ and $\mathbf{a} - \mathbf{b}$ represent the diagonals **OC** and **BA** of the

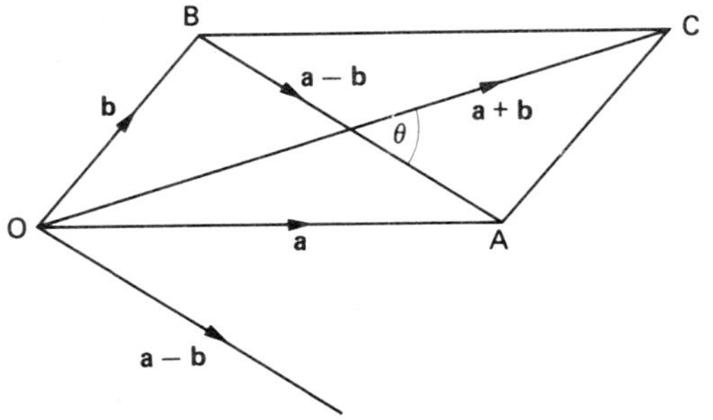


**Fig. 10.6.** Worked example 10.5.

parallelogram OACB (see Fig. 10.6). The scalar product is then equal to $|\mathbf{a} + \mathbf{b}| \times |\mathbf{a} - \mathbf{b}| \times \cos\theta$, where $\theta$ is the angle between the diagonals.

(b) $(\mathbf{a} + \mathbf{b}).(\mathbf{a} - \mathbf{b}) = a^2 - b^2 = 0$ if $a = b$. Thus the diagonals of a rhombus are perpendicular, since the sides of a rhombus are equal ($a = b$), and the scalar product is zero.

(c) $(\mathbf{a} + \mathbf{b}).(\mathbf{a} - \mathbf{b}) = a^2 - b^2 = 12$, and $a = 2b$. Therefore $4b^2 - b^2 = 3b^2 = 12$, and so $b = 2$ since it cannot be negative. Therefore $a = 4$ and $b = 2$.

**Exercise 10*b***

1. Under what circumstances will $(2\mathbf{x} - 3\mathbf{y}).(2\mathbf{x} - 3\mathbf{y})$ be zero?
2. (a) If $\hat{\mathbf{a}}$ is a unit vector, and $(\mathbf{x} - \hat{\mathbf{a}}).(\mathbf{x} + \hat{\mathbf{a}}) = 8$, find $|\mathbf{x}|$.
   (b) If also $\mathbf{x}.\hat{\mathbf{a}} = 2$, find $|\mathbf{x} - \hat{\mathbf{a}}|$ and $|\mathbf{x} + \hat{\mathbf{a}}|$, leaving your answer as square roots.
   (c) Hence find the cosine of the angle between $\mathbf{x} - \hat{\mathbf{a}}$ and $\mathbf{x} + \hat{\mathbf{a}}$.
3. The vectors **a** and **b** are such that $|\mathbf{a}| = 2|\mathbf{b}| = 4$, and the angle between them is 60°. Evaluate the scalar products $\mathbf{a}.\mathbf{b}$ and $(\mathbf{a} + \mathbf{b}).(\mathbf{a} + \mathbf{b})$. Hence find $|\mathbf{a} + \mathbf{b}|$.

## 10.6 Orthogonality

Suppose we have two perpendicular vectors **a** and **b**. Then $\mathbf{a}.\mathbf{b} = ab\cos 90° = 0$, i.e. the scalar product of two perpendicular vectors is zero.

Suppose, conversely, that we have two non-zero vectors **a** and **b** whose scalar product is zero. Then $ab\cos\theta = 0$, where $\theta$ is the angle between **a** and **b**. $a$ and $b$ are non-zero, and so $\cos\theta = 0$, and hence $\theta = 90°$, i.e. the vectors are perpendicular.

We have shown that two non-zero vectors **a** and **b** are perpendicular if and only if their scalar product is zero. We call such vectors *orthogonal.*

Thus, if **a** and **b** are non-zero,

$$\mathbf{a} \text{ and } \mathbf{b} \text{ are orthogonal} \iff \mathbf{a}.\mathbf{b} = 0.$$

For example, the unit vector $\hat{\mathbf{i}}$ and $\hat{\mathbf{j}}$ in the directions of the coordinate axes O$x$ and O$y$ are orthogonal, and $\hat{\mathbf{i}}.\hat{\mathbf{j}} = 0$. Similarly, in the three-dimensional case, $\hat{\mathbf{i}}.\hat{\mathbf{j}} = \hat{\mathbf{j}}.\hat{\mathbf{k}} = \hat{\mathbf{k}}.\hat{\mathbf{i}} = 0$. The three vectors $\hat{\mathbf{i}}$, $\hat{\mathbf{j}}$ and $\hat{\mathbf{k}}$ are called *mutually orthogonal,* because every pair is orthogonal.

Actually, these vectors are not just orthogonal — they are also unit vectors, since $\hat{\mathbf{i}}.\hat{\mathbf{i}} = \hat{\mathbf{j}}.\hat{\mathbf{j}} = \hat{\mathbf{k}}.\hat{\mathbf{k}} = 1$. A pair of orthogonal unit vectors is called *orthonormal.* A set, such as $\{\hat{\mathbf{i}}, \hat{\mathbf{j}}, \hat{\mathbf{k}}\}$, of mutually orthonormal vectors is called an *orthonormal set.*

## 10.7 Scalar products in $R^3$

We combine the various properties of scalar products of position vectors to justify the definition of $\mathbf{a}.\mathbf{b}$ for $\mathbf{a}, \mathbf{b} \in R^3$ that we gave in Section 10.3. Recall that we use

$$\mathbf{a} = \begin{pmatrix} a_1 \\ a_2 \\ a_3 \end{pmatrix}$$

as an alternative notation for $\mathbf{a} = a_1\hat{\mathbf{i}} + a_2\hat{\mathbf{j}} + a_3\hat{\mathbf{k}}$. Suppose $\mathbf{b} = b_1\hat{\mathbf{i}} + b_2\hat{\mathbf{j}} + b_3\hat{\mathbf{k}}$, with column vector

$$\mathbf{b} = \begin{pmatrix} b_1 \\ b_2 \\ b_3 \end{pmatrix}$$

Then

$$\begin{aligned} \mathbf{a}.\mathbf{b} &= (a_1\hat{\mathbf{i}} + a_2\hat{\mathbf{j}} + a_3\hat{\mathbf{k}}).(b_1\hat{\mathbf{i}} + b_2\hat{\mathbf{j}} + b_3\hat{\mathbf{k}}) \\ &= a_1b_1\hat{\mathbf{i}}.\hat{\mathbf{i}} + a_1b_2\hat{\mathbf{i}}.\hat{\mathbf{j}} + a_1b_3\hat{\mathbf{i}}.\hat{\mathbf{k}} \\ &\quad + a_2b_1\hat{\mathbf{j}}.\hat{\mathbf{i}} + a_2b_2\hat{\mathbf{j}}.\hat{\mathbf{j}} + a_2b_3\hat{\mathbf{j}}.\hat{\mathbf{k}} \\ &\quad + a_3b_1\hat{\mathbf{k}}.\hat{\mathbf{i}} + a_3b_2\hat{\mathbf{k}}.\hat{\mathbf{i}} + a_3b_2\hat{\mathbf{k}}.\hat{\mathbf{k}} && \text{using the laws of Section 10.5} \\ &= a_1b_1 + a_2b_2 + a_3b_3, && \text{using the orthogonality properties of Section 10.6} \end{aligned}$$

Hence, also, $\mathbf{a}.\mathbf{a} = a_1^2 + a_2^2 + a_3^2 = |\mathbf{a}|^2$, in agreement with our earlier definition of $|\mathbf{a}|$.

This expression for $\mathbf{a}.\mathbf{b}$ was our earlier definition for the scalar product of two column vectors. Further details will be found in worked example 10.7 (briefly) and in Chapter 13 (at greater length).

## 10.8 Worked examples

**Worked Example 10.6**

A, B and C are the points with Cartesian coordinates (2, 3, 4), (3, 5, 1) and (3, −2, −1) respectively. Find angle $\theta = \mathrm{B\hat{A}C}$.

*Solution*

The column vector $\mathbf{u}$ for $\mathbf{AB}$ is

$$\mathbf{u} = \mathbf{b} - \mathbf{a} = \begin{pmatrix} 1 \\ 2 \\ -3 \end{pmatrix} \text{ of length } \sqrt{14}$$

The column vector **v** for **AC** is

$$\mathbf{v} = \mathbf{c} - \mathbf{a} = \begin{pmatrix} 1 \\ -5 \\ -5 \end{pmatrix} \text{ of length } \sqrt{51}$$

$$\mathbf{u} \cdot \mathbf{v} = uv \cos\theta$$

thus

$$1 \times 1 + 2 \times (-5) + (-3) \times (-5) = \sqrt{14} \times \sqrt{51} \times \cos\theta$$

therefore

$$\cos\theta = 6/\sqrt{14 \times 51} \text{ and so } \theta = \widehat{BAC} = 77{\cdot}0°.$$

**Worked Example 10.7**

Prove that $2\hat{\mathbf{i}} + 3\hat{\mathbf{j}} + \hat{\mathbf{k}}$ and $3\hat{\mathbf{i}} - 2\hat{\mathbf{j}}$ are orthogonal, and find orthonormal vectors in their directions.

*Solution*

$$(2\hat{\mathbf{i}} + 3\hat{\mathbf{j}} + \hat{\mathbf{k}}) \cdot (3\hat{\mathbf{i}} - 2\hat{\mathbf{j}}) = 6 + (-6) + 0 = 0$$

Hence the vectors are orthogonal. The length of $2\hat{\mathbf{i}} + 3\hat{\mathbf{j}} + \hat{\mathbf{k}}$ is $\sqrt{2^2 + 3^2 + 1^2} = \sqrt{14}$. Similarly, $|3\hat{\mathbf{i}} - 2\hat{\mathbf{j}}| = \sqrt{13}$. Hence orthonormal vectors in the directions of the given vectors are

$$\frac{2}{\sqrt{14}}\hat{\mathbf{i}} + \frac{3}{\sqrt{14}}\hat{\mathbf{j}} + \frac{1}{\sqrt{14}}\hat{\mathbf{k}} \quad \text{and} \quad \frac{3}{\sqrt{13}}\hat{\mathbf{i}} - \frac{2}{\sqrt{13}}\hat{\mathbf{j}}.$$

The negatives of these are also orthonormal—in any given direction, we have two unit vectors, one in each sense.

**Worked Example 10.8**

Two vectors **a** and **b** are such that $|\mathbf{a}| = 2$, $|\mathbf{b}| = 3$, and $\mathbf{a} \cdot \mathbf{b} = 4$. Find the length $\mathbf{a} - \mathbf{b}$.

*Solution*

$$\begin{aligned} |\mathbf{a} - \mathbf{b}| &= \sqrt{(\mathbf{a} - \mathbf{b}) \cdot (\mathbf{a} - \mathbf{b})} \\ &= \sqrt{a^2 - 2\mathbf{a} \cdot \mathbf{b} + b^2} \\ &= \sqrt{4 - 8 + 9} \\ &= \sqrt{5} \approx 2{\cdot}24 \end{aligned}$$

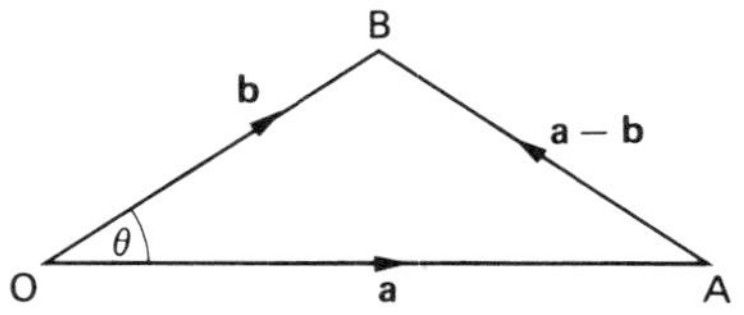


**Fig. 10.7.** $AB^2 = OA^2 + OB^2 - 2 \times OA \times OB \times \cos\theta$.

Notice that this result may be written as

$$|\mathbf{a} - \mathbf{b}|^2 = a^2 + b^2 - 2\mathbf{a}.\mathbf{b} = a^2 + b^2 - 2ab\cos\theta$$

which is the cosine rule and has just been proved, since $\mathbf{a} - \mathbf{b}$ represents the third side of the triangle formed by **a** and **b**, (see Fig. 10.7).

**Exercise 10*c***

1. Which of the following pairs of vectors are prependicular? Find the angle between any pair that is not perpendicular. (a) $\hat{\imath} + \hat{\jmath}$ and $\hat{\jmath} + \hat{k}$; (b) $\hat{\imath} - \hat{\jmath}$ and $\hat{\imath} + \hat{\jmath}$; (c) $\hat{\imath} + 2\hat{\jmath} + 2\hat{k}$ and $3\hat{\imath} - \hat{\jmath} - \hat{k}$; (d) $3\hat{\imath} - 2\hat{\jmath} - \hat{k}$ and $\hat{\imath} + 2\hat{\jmath} - \hat{k}$.

2. Find unit vectors in the same direction and sense as the following: (a) $\hat{\imath} - \hat{\jmath}$; (b) $\hat{\imath} + \hat{\jmath} + 3\hat{k}$; (c) $2\hat{\imath} - 3\hat{\jmath} + 7\hat{k}$.

3. Two vectors **a** and **b** are such that $|\mathbf{a}| = 3$, $|\mathbf{b}| = 4$, and $\mathbf{a}.\mathbf{b} = -5$. Find:
   (a) the angle between **a** and **b**;
   (b) the lengths of $\mathbf{a} + \mathbf{b}$ and $\mathbf{a} - \mathbf{b}$;
   (c) the angle between $\mathbf{a} + \mathbf{b}$ and $\mathbf{a} - \mathbf{b}$.

4. OACB is a parallelogram, and Y is a point on the side BC such that the line OY is perpendicular to the diagonal AB. $\overrightarrow{OA} = \mathbf{a}$, $\overrightarrow{OB} = \mathbf{b}$ and $BY = hBC$.
   (i) Prove that $h(\mathbf{a}^2 - \mathbf{a}.\mathbf{b}) = \mathbf{b}^2 - \mathbf{a}.\mathbf{b}$.
   (ii) If OA = 5 m, OB = 4 m, and $A\hat{O}B = 60°$, find the lengths of BY and OY.
   (MME)

5. Given that $\mathbf{a} = -\mathbf{i} + \mathbf{j}$ and $\mathbf{b} = \mathbf{i} + 2\mathbf{j}$, find the vectors $\mathbf{a} + 3\mathbf{b}$ and $5\mathbf{b} - 16\mathbf{a}$, and calculate the numerical value of the three scalar products $(\mathbf{a} + 3\mathbf{b})^2$, $(5\mathbf{b} - 16\mathbf{a})^2$ and $(\mathbf{a} + 3\mathbf{b}).(5\mathbf{b} - 16\mathbf{a})$. In the triangle OPQ, $\overrightarrow{OP} = \mathbf{a} + 3\mathbf{b}$, and $\overrightarrow{OQ} = 5\mathbf{b} - 16\mathbf{a}$. Prove that the angle POQ is a right angle, and calculate the area of the triangle OPQ. (MME)

## 10.9 Miscellaneous Exercises 10

1. A sledge is pulled on level ice by two ropes. The forces in the ropes are 3 000 N and 4 000 N respectively, and the angle between them is 60°. By scale drawing, find the resultant of these two forces, giving its magnitude and the angle it makes with the smaller force. Find the work done by this force in moving the sledge a distance of 4 m.

2. A and B are points with polar coordinates (2, 30°) and (3, 60°), respectively, referred to the origin O. **a** and **b** are the position vectors of A and B relative to O.
   (a) Evaluate the scalar products $\mathbf{a}.\mathbf{a}$, $\mathbf{a}.\mathbf{b}$ and $\mathbf{b}.\mathbf{b}$.
   (b) Expand the scalar product $(\mathbf{a} + \mathbf{b}).(\mathbf{a} - 2\mathbf{b})$, and hence find its value.

3. (a) If $\hat{\mathbf{a}}$ is a unit vector, and $(\hat{\mathbf{a}} - \mathbf{b}).(\hat{\mathbf{a}} + \mathbf{b}) = \frac{1}{4}$, find $|\mathbf{b}|$. (b) If also $\mathbf{b}.\hat{\mathbf{a}} = \frac{1}{2}$, find the angle between $\hat{\mathbf{a}}$ and **b**. (c) Evaluate the scalar products $(\hat{\mathbf{a}} - \mathbf{b})^2$ and $(\hat{\mathbf{a}} + \mathbf{b})^2$. (d) Find the angle between $\hat{\mathbf{a}} - \mathbf{b}$ and $\hat{\mathbf{a}} + \mathbf{b}$.

4. For this question, $\mathbf{a} = 2\hat{\imath} + 3\hat{\jmath} - \hat{k}$ and $\mathbf{b} = \hat{\imath} - 2\hat{\jmath} + \hat{k}$, in the usual notation.
   (a) Is the angle between **a** and **b** acute or obtuse?
   (b) If **a** and $\mathbf{a} + \alpha\mathbf{b}$ are orthogonal, find the value of $\alpha$.
   (c) Find a unit vector in the same direction and sense as $2\mathbf{a} - 3\mathbf{b}$.

5. Define the scalar product $\mathbf{a}.\mathbf{b}$ of the two vectors **a** and **b**. If **a**, **b**, **c** are given vectors, in what circumstances is it true that $\mathbf{a}.\mathbf{b} = \mathbf{a}.\mathbf{c}$?

A straight line L is parallel to a vector **a** and passes through a point B whose position vector is **b**. The point C has position vector **c** and **p** is the vector from C to

L, perpendicular to L, with terminus on L. Prove that

$$\mathbf{p} = \mathbf{b} - \mathbf{c} - \frac{(\mathbf{b} - \mathbf{c}) \cdot \mathbf{a}}{|\mathbf{a}|^2} \mathbf{a}$$ (MEI)

6. If $\mathbf{a} = 5\hat{\mathbf{i}} - \hat{\mathbf{j}} - 3\hat{\mathbf{k}}$, and $\mathbf{b} = \hat{\mathbf{i}} + 3\hat{\mathbf{j}} - 5\hat{\mathbf{k}}$, show that the vectors $\mathbf{a} + \mathbf{b}$ and $\mathbf{a} - \mathbf{b}$ are orthogonal, and find the angle between the vectors $2\mathbf{a} + \mathbf{b}$ and $\mathbf{a} + 2\mathbf{b}$. (MEI part)

7. If $\mathbf{u} = a\mathbf{i} + b\mathbf{j} + c\mathbf{k}$, where $\mathbf{i}, \mathbf{j}, \mathbf{k}$ are mutually perpendicular unit vectors, show that $a = \mathbf{u} \cdot \mathbf{i}$, $b = \mathbf{u} \cdot \mathbf{j}$ and $c = \mathbf{u} \cdot \mathbf{k}$. If $\mathbf{u} = (\mathbf{i} + \mathbf{j} + \mathbf{k})/\sqrt{3}$, $\mathbf{v} = \sqrt{(\frac{2}{3})}(\mathbf{i} - \frac{1}{2}\mathbf{j} - \frac{1}{2}\mathbf{k})$ and $\mathbf{w} = (\mathbf{j} - \mathbf{k})/\sqrt{2}$ show that $\mathbf{u}$, $\mathbf{v}$ and $\mathbf{w}$ are mutually perpendicular unit vectors and express $\mathbf{i}$ in the form $p\mathbf{u} + q\mathbf{v} + r\mathbf{w}$. (JMB part)

8. Define the sum $\mathbf{a} + \mathbf{b}$ and the scalar product $\mathbf{a} \cdot \mathbf{b}$ of two vectors $\mathbf{a}$ and $\mathbf{b}$ and, from your definitions, prove that $\mathbf{a} \cdot (\mathbf{b} + \mathbf{c}) = \mathbf{a} \cdot \mathbf{b} + \mathbf{a} \cdot \mathbf{c}$.

If $\mathbf{i}$ and $\mathbf{j}$ are perpendicular unit vectors and $x_1, x_2, y_1, y_2$ are scalars, prove that $(x_1\mathbf{i} + y_1\mathbf{j}) \cdot (x_2\mathbf{i} + y_2\mathbf{j}) = x_1x_2 + y_1y_2$.

A particle moving in a plane is acted on by a constant force in that plane such that, when the particle is given a displacement $-3\mathbf{i} + 4\mathbf{j}$ m, the work done by the force is $-100$ J and, when it is given a displacement $4\mathbf{i} + 3\mathbf{j}$ m, the work done by the force is 50 J. Find the force, and the work done by it when the particle is given a displacement $\mathbf{i} + 2\mathbf{j}$ m. (O)

# 11
# Impulse and Momentum

## 11.1 The impulse–momentum integral

We are now able to consider one of the three important ways of integrating the equation of Newton's second law. Another will follow in Chapter 14.

Suppose the force $\mathbf{F} = \mathbf{F}(t)$ is a function of time $t$, and acts on a particle of mass $m$, which has velocity $\mathbf{v} = \mathbf{v}(t)$ at time $t$. Suppose also that $\mathbf{v}(t_1) = \mathbf{v}_1$ and $\mathbf{v}(t_2) = \mathbf{v}_2$. Then Newton's second law states that

$$\mathbf{F} = \frac{\mathrm{d}}{\mathrm{d}t}(m\mathbf{v})$$

Integrate each side with respect to $t$, between the limits $t_1$ and $t_2$. Then

$$\int_{t_1}^{t_2} \mathbf{F}\,\mathrm{d}t = \int_{t=t_1}^{t_2} \frac{\mathrm{d}}{\mathrm{d}t}(m\mathbf{v})\,\mathrm{d}t$$

$$= \big[m\mathbf{v}\big]_{t=t_1}^{t_2}$$

Therefore

$$\int_{t_1}^{t_2} \mathbf{F}\,\mathrm{d}t = \text{final momentum} - \text{initial momentum}$$

$$= \text{change in momentum} \qquad (1)$$

Newton's first law says that the momentum of a particle will change if and only if a force $F$ acts on it. Equ. 1 quantifies this law.

In particular, if the force $\mathbf{F}$ is constant, then Equ. 1 gives

$$\mathbf{F}(t_2 - t_1) = \text{change in momentum} \qquad (2)$$

The change in momentum caused by a force acting over a period of time is called the *impulse* of the force, and has units N s. Impulse is a vector quantity, and may be evaluated as $\mathbf{F}t$, if $\mathbf{F}$ is constant and $t$ is the time for which the force acts; or as $\int_{t=t_1}^{t_2} \mathbf{F}\,\mathrm{d}t$, as above.

**Worked Example 11.1**

Find the impulse of the force $\mathbf{F} = (1 - t)\hat{\mathbf{i}} + t^2\hat{\mathbf{j}} - \hat{\mathbf{k}}$ between times $t = 0$ s and $t = 2$ s, and the final velocity if this impulse is applied to a particle of mass 4 kg initially at rest.

*Solution*

The impulse is

$$\mathbf{I} = \int_0^2 \left[(1 - t)\hat{\mathbf{i}} + t^2\,\hat{\mathbf{j}} - \hat{\mathbf{k}}\right]\mathrm{d}t$$

$$= \left[(t - \tfrac{1}{2}t^2)\hat{\mathbf{i}} + \tfrac{1}{3}t^3\hat{\mathbf{j}} - t\hat{\mathbf{k}}\right]_0^2$$

$$= \tfrac{8}{3}\,\hat{\mathbf{j}} - 2\hat{\mathbf{k}}\ \text{N s}$$

The change in momentum of the particle is $m\mathbf{v}_2 - m\mathbf{v}_1$, where $\mathbf{v}_1 = \mathbf{0}$ m s$^{-1}$ and $m = 4$ kg. Therefore

$$\tfrac{8}{3}\hat{\mathbf{j}} - 2\hat{\mathbf{k}} = 4\mathbf{v}_2 \text{ and so } \mathbf{v}_2 = \tfrac{2}{3}\hat{\mathbf{j}} - \tfrac{1}{2}\hat{\mathbf{k}}\ \text{m s}^{-1}$$

## 11.2 Conservation of momentum

It follows directly from Equ. 1 that if no external force acts on a particle over a period of time, then its momentum remains constant over that period. This is the *principle of conservation of linear momentum* (PCLM), and may also be applied to bodies and systems of particles under the same conditions. Further, it may be applied in any direction in which the resultant external force acting on the particle has no component, even if the momentum of the particle is changing in other directions.

**Worked Example 11.2**

A gun of mass 1000 kg is mounted on a smooth horizontal surface, and has a horizontal barrel. It can fire a shell of mass 40 kg with a speed of 300 m s$^{-1}$. What is the speed of the gun when the shot has been fired?

*Solution*

We refer to Fig. 11.1. We shall assume that the shell is propelled by a charge so that the forces acting on the shell have equal and opposite reactions on the gun. Select the horizontal as the $\hat{\mathbf{i}}$ direction. Since there are no external forces in this direction, we may apply PCLM in the $\hat{\mathbf{i}}$ direction, to give

$$1000\ v_2\hat{\mathbf{i}} + 300 \times 40\hat{\mathbf{i}} = 0$$

where $v_2\hat{\mathbf{i}}$ is the velocity of the gun. Therefore $1000\ v_2\hat{\mathbf{i}} + 12\,000\hat{\mathbf{i}} = \mathbf{0}$ and so $v_2\hat{\mathbf{i}} = -12\hat{\mathbf{i}}$ m s$^{-1}$, the negative sign indicates that the gun, as expected, travels in the opposite sense to the shell.

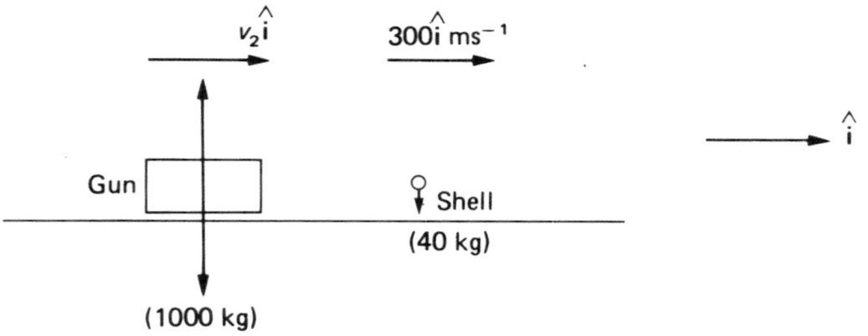


**Fig. 11.1.** Gun and shell after firing.

In this solution, we have made two assumptions which should be carefully noted.

Firstly, we assumed that a charge projected the shell (it is not a rocket). Whether the charge is considered to have given up its energy virtually instantaneously, or gradually during the passage of the shell through the barrel, does not matter.

Secondly, we assumed that the effect of the charge was to exert equal and opposite forces on the gun and the shell in the $\hat{\mathbf{i}}$ direction. These forces need not be considered further as they are internal to the system.

## 11.3 Worked examples

Equations 1 and 2 of Section 11.1 enable us to solve certain problems that we considered in Chapter 8 in a different, and sometimes more convenient, way. The methods must be essentially the same, since they both are derived from Newton's second law.

### Worked Example 11.3

A particle of mass $m$ is placed on a rough plane with coefficient of friction $\mu$ and inclined at an angle $\alpha$ to the horizontal. Find the velocity of the particle after time $t$, assuming that it slides when released.

*Solution*

We refer to Fig. 11.2. Using the notation of the diagram, we have: when the particle slides, friction is limiting, and so

$$F = \mu R \tag{1}$$

Apply Newton's second law in the $\hat{\mathbf{j}}$ direction:

$$mg\cos\alpha - R = 0 \text{ and so } R = mg\cos\alpha. \tag{2}$$

Therefore $F = \mu\, mg \cos\alpha$, from Equations 1 and 2.

Apply the second impulse–momentum equation (Eq. 2, §11.1) in the $\hat{\mathbf{i}}$ direction to give

$$mg(\sin\alpha - \mu\cos\alpha)t = mv$$

where $v$ is the speed after time $t$. Therefore

$$v = g(\sin\alpha - \mu\cos\alpha)t$$

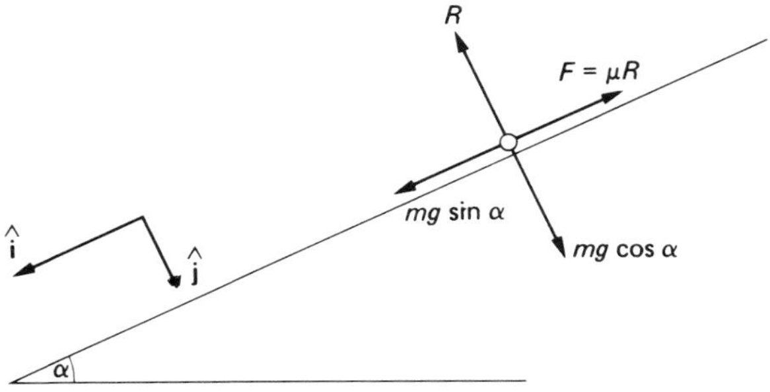


Fig. 11.2.

We may connect this method with the method of Chapter 8 as follows: a particle of constant mass $m$, acted on by a constant force $\mathbf{F}$ has constant acceleration $\mathbf{a}$ and obeys the laws $\mathbf{F} = m\mathbf{a}$ and $\mathbf{F}t = m\mathbf{v} - m\mathbf{u}$. Therefore $\mathbf{F} = m(\mathbf{v} - \mathbf{u})/t = m\mathbf{a}$ and so $\mathbf{v} = \mathbf{u} + \mathbf{a}t$, which is a result used in Chapter 8.

**Worked Example 11.4**

A particle of mass 2 kg is at rest on a smooth horizontal plane, and is subjected to an impulse of 20 N s at an angle of 60° to the plane. Find the final speed of the particle.

*Solution*

In this example, the total momentum change is not in a direction in which no external forces act. Select $\hat{\mathbf{i}}$ parallel to the plane, and $\hat{\mathbf{j}}$ perpendicular to the plane, as in Fig. 11.3. Then the impulse $\mathbf{I}$ may be written as

$$\mathbf{I} = 20\cos 60°\,\hat{\mathbf{i}} - 20\sin 60°\,\hat{\mathbf{j}}\ \text{N s}.$$

The $\hat{\mathbf{j}}$-component of $\mathbf{I}$ is opposed by an impulsive reaction of the plane which is equal in magnitude and opposite in sense. Also, external forces act in this direction.

However, no external forces act in the $\hat{\mathbf{i}}$ direction, and so we have a change in momentum in the $\hat{\mathbf{i}}$ direction of 20 cos 60° and so the final momentum of the particle is $20 \times \frac{1}{2} = 10$ N s. Therefore the final speed of the particle is 5 m s$^{-1}$.

**Exercise 11*a***

1. Find the impulse of the force $t^2\hat{\mathbf{i}} - 2t\hat{\mathbf{j}} + (t^3 - 1)\hat{\mathbf{k}}$ (a) between times $t = 0$ s and $t = 2$ s, and (b) between times $t = 2$ s and $t = 4$ s. If this force is applied to a particle of mass 3 kg between the times $t = 0$ s and $t = 4$ s, and if the particle is at rest at $t = 2$ s, find its velocity at $t = 0$ s and at $t = 4$ s.

2. A car of mass 900 kg with its brakes on is just prevented from sliding down a slope of angle 30° by the combined efforts of six men, each pulling on a rope parallel to the slope with a force of 650 N. Find the frictional force on the car. If one of the men lets go, find the speed of the car after 4 s, assuming that the frictional force does not change.

3. A gun of mass 1200 kg is mounted on a smooth horizontal rail, which is taken as the $\hat{\mathbf{i}}$ direction, and has a horizontal barrel. It can fire a shell of mass 45 kg with a speed of 350 ms$^{-1}$. What is the speed of the gun, (a) when the shot is fired in the $\hat{\mathbf{i}}$ direction, and (b) when the shot is fired in the direction of $\hat{\mathbf{i}} + \hat{\mathbf{j}}$?

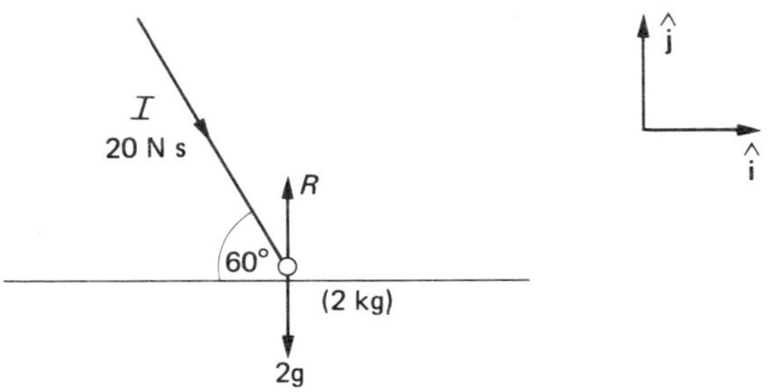


Fig. 11.3.

In case (a), a braking force of 52 500 N is applied after the shot has been fired. Find how long it takes to stop the gun.

4. A body of mass 6 kg is dropped vertically through a liquid which offers a resistance of 1·5 N kg$^{-1}$. Find the time taken for the body to acquire a speed of 12 ms$^{-1}$. Find the time taken to acquire the same *speed* if, in addition, there is a horizontal current which exerts a force of 2 N kg$^{-1}$.

## 11.4 Coalescence of particles on impact

If two particles travelling on the same surface collide, then they will either join together (coalesce), and continue moving together; or they will bounce off one another and continue their separate ways. We consider the two possibilities separately, starting with coalescence.

Suppose that two particles of masses $m$ and $m'$ respectively move in the same straight line on a smooth horizontal table, and that they have velocities $u\hat{\mathbf{i}}$ and $u'\hat{\mathbf{i}}$ respectively, where we assume $0 < u < u'$. Suppose that eventually the mass $m'$ collides with the mass $m$, and that they coalesce and move on together with velocity $v\hat{\mathbf{i}}$.

The momentum of the particle of mass $m$ changes from $mu\hat{\mathbf{i}}$ to $mv\hat{\mathbf{i}}$, and so it has been given an impulse $\mathbf{I}$ by a force $\mathbf{F}$ acting for a time $t_2 - t_1$, where

$$\mathbf{I} = \int_{t_1}^{t_2} \mathbf{F}\,dt = m(v - u)\hat{\mathbf{i}}$$

and the impact lasts from time $t_1$ to time $t_2$. This force $\mathbf{F}$ must be due to the impact, and must give rise to a force $-\mathbf{F}$ on the other particle, by Newton's third law. If we view the system as a whole, the forces $\mathbf{F}$ and $-\mathbf{F}$ are internal, and equal and opposite.

In the $\hat{\mathbf{i}}$ direction, there are no external forces on the system as a whole, so we may apply PCLM to get

$$(m + m')v\hat{\mathbf{i}} = mu\hat{\mathbf{i}} + m'u'\hat{\mathbf{i}}$$

thus

$$v\hat{\mathbf{i}} = \frac{mu + m'u'}{m + m'}\hat{\mathbf{i}}$$

The impulse $\mathbf{I}$ given to the mass $m$ in the impact is

$$\mathbf{I} = m(v - u)\hat{\mathbf{i}} = \int_{t_1}^{t_2} \mathbf{F}\,dt.$$

That is

$$|\mathbf{I}| = \frac{m}{m + m'}(mu + m'u' - mu - m'u) = \frac{mm'(u' - u)}{m + m'}$$

It is usual to consider such changes in momentum caused by impact to be instantaneous, that is, the force $\mathbf{F}$ generated by the impact is considered to be a force of extremely large magnitude acting for a very short time.

Suppose a constant force has magnitude $nF$ and acts for a time $t/n$. Then, for all $n$, the magnitude of the impulse is $nF \times t/n = Ft$, a constant. The limiting case as $n \to \infty$ is a model of the situation envisaged in an impact where the changes in momentum of the particles involved take place instantaneously. This is a useful model for impacts in many real situations, and will be used frequently. The reader should note carefully the following conclusions concerning such impacts:

(1) Since the changes in momentum are instantaneous, the particles will not change their positions during the impulse.

(2) Other forces of finite size in the direction of the impulse may be neglected as having no effect on the momentum change at the moment of impact. For instance, a frictional force entirely in the direction of an impulse has a limiting value and so the impulse of this force acting for an infinitesimal time is effectively zero.

**Worked Example 11.5**

Two ice skaters of masses 44 kg and 48 kg have speeds of 6 m s$^{-1}$ and 8 m s$^{-1}$ respectively at an angle of 45° to each other just before they collide. On impact they cling to each other. Find their velocity and speed immediately after the collision.

*Solution*

Select directions $\hat{\mathbf{i}}$ parallel to the 44 kg skater, and $\hat{\mathbf{j}}$ perpendicular to $\hat{\mathbf{i}}$, as shown in Fig. 11.4. Then the skaters' velocities are

$$\begin{pmatrix} 6 \\ 0 \end{pmatrix} \text{m s}^{-1} \text{ and } \begin{pmatrix} 8\cos 45° \\ 8\cos 45° \end{pmatrix} = \begin{pmatrix} 4\sqrt{2} \\ 4\sqrt{2} \end{pmatrix} \text{m s}^{-1}$$

respectively. Suppose their velocity after impact is

$$\begin{pmatrix} u \\ v \end{pmatrix}$$

At the moment of impact, no external impulsive forces act. Therefore we may use PCLM to give

$$44\begin{pmatrix} 6 \\ 0 \end{pmatrix} + 48\begin{pmatrix} 4\sqrt{2} \\ 4\sqrt{2} \end{pmatrix} = 92\begin{pmatrix} u \\ v \end{pmatrix}$$

thus

$$\begin{pmatrix} 92u \\ 92v \end{pmatrix} = \begin{pmatrix} 264 + 192\sqrt{2} \\ 192\sqrt{2} \end{pmatrix}$$

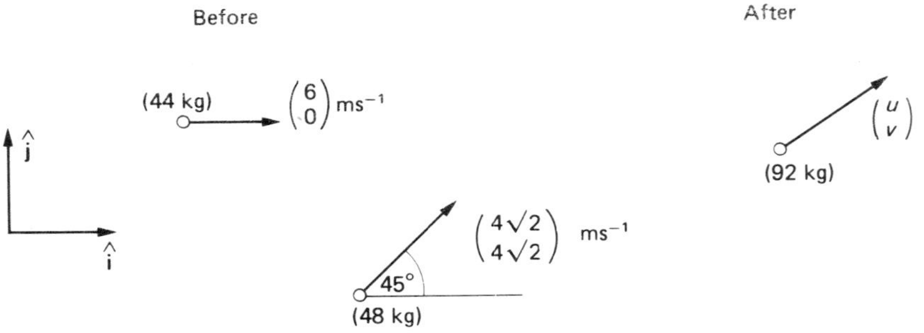


**Fig. 11.4.**

and so

$$\begin{pmatrix} u \\ v \end{pmatrix} = \begin{pmatrix} 5{\cdot}82 \\ 2{\cdot}95 \end{pmatrix} \text{ m s}^{-1}$$

is their final velocity. Their final speed is $\sqrt{u^2 + v^2} = 6{\cdot}53$ m s$^{-1}$

**Worked Example 11.6**

A particle of mass $m$ is attached to the end O of an unstretched light spring of stiffness $k$ which is at rest on a horizontal table, the coefficient of friction between the particle and the table being $\mu$. The other end of the spring is fixed to the table. A second particle of mass $m'$ is travelling in the line of the spring and towards it. When it is travelling at speed $u$, it strikes the first particle and coalesces with it. Find the distance travelled before the coalesced particles first come to rest, and state a condition for the particles to stay at rest, thus keeping the spring in compression.

*Solution*

We refer to Fig. 11.5. Select the direction and sense of motion of the particle $m'$ as the $\hat{\mathbf{i}}$ direction, so that its velocity just before the impact is $u\hat{\mathbf{i}}$, and suppose that the velocity of the coalesced particles immediately after the impact is $V\hat{\mathbf{i}}$. The frictional forces $-F\hat{\mathbf{i}}$ on the particle $m'$ before the impact, and $-F\hat{\mathbf{i}}$ on the combined particles after the impact may be neglected when considering the impulse on contact. Apply PCLM in the $\hat{\mathbf{i}}$ direction:

$$(m + m')\, V\hat{\mathbf{i}} = \mathbf{0} + m'u\hat{\mathbf{i}}$$

Therefore $V = m'u/(m + m')$ is the speed of the coalesced particles immediately after the impact, at which time they may be considered to be in the position of the impact. That is, the spring is not yet in compression, and the combined particles are at O.

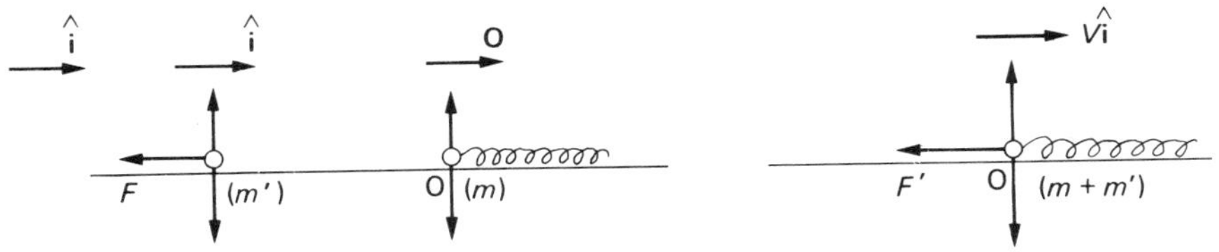


**Fig. 11.5.**

Now consider the system when the spring has been compressed by a distance $x$, as in Fig. 11.6. Apply Newton's second law:

$$\begin{pmatrix} T - F \\ R - (m + m')g \end{pmatrix} = (m + m') \begin{pmatrix} \ddot{x} \\ 0 \end{pmatrix}$$

Further, friction is limiting, so that $F = \mu R$, and HL can be applied to give $T = kx$. Therefore

$$\begin{pmatrix} -kx - \mu R \\ R - (m + m')g \end{pmatrix} = (m + m') \begin{pmatrix} \ddot{x} \\ 0 \end{pmatrix}$$

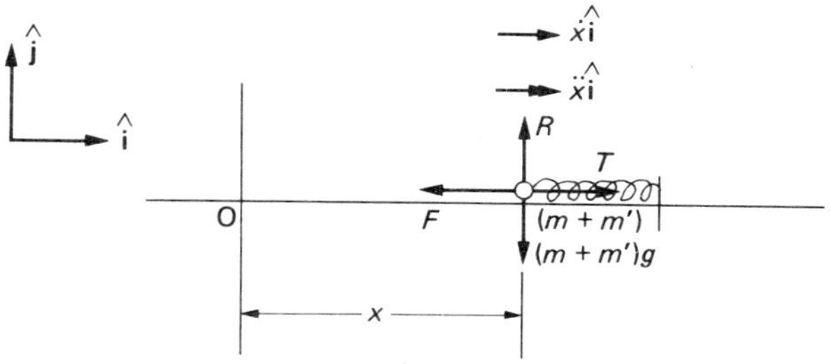


**Fig. 11.6.**

Therefore $R = (m + m')g$, and so $-kx - \mu(m + m')g = (m + m')\ddot{x}$. Now we may write $\dot{x} = v$ and $\ddot{x} = v(\mathrm{d}v/\mathrm{d}x)$. Therefore

$$-kx - \mu(m + m')g = (m + m')v\frac{\mathrm{d}v}{\mathrm{d}x}$$

Therefore

$$\int_0^X [-kx - \mu(m + m')g]\,\mathrm{d}x = (m + m')\int_V^0 v\,\mathrm{d}v$$

since $v = V$ when $x = 0$, and where $x = X$ when $v = 0$. Therefore

$$\left[-\tfrac{1}{2}kx^2 - \mu(m + m')gx\right]_0^X = (m + m')\left[\tfrac{1}{2}v^2\right]_v^0$$

Therefore

$$-\tfrac{1}{2}kX^2 - \mu(m + m')gX = -\tfrac{1}{2}(m + m')\,V^2$$

Now $V^2 = (m'u/(m + m'))^2$ and so

$$\frac{kX^2}{2} + \mu(m + m')gX - \frac{1}{2}\frac{m'^2u^2}{m + m'} = 0$$

Therefore

$$X = \frac{-\mu(m + m')g \pm \sqrt{\mu^2(m + m')^2g^2 + [km'^2u^2/(m + m')]}}{k}$$

Now $X > 0$, and so

$$X = \frac{-\mu(m + m')g}{k} + \sqrt{\frac{\mu^2(m + m')^3g^2 + km'^2u^2}{k^2(m + m')}}$$

An alternative method of solution will be given in Chapter 14.

After the particle comes to rest, the frictional force, which has limiting value $\mu(m + m')g$, opposes the tension $kX$, and the coalesced particles will move again if $kX > \mu(m + m')g$, from which it may be shown that

$$u^2 > \frac{3\mu^2(m + m')^3g^2}{km'^2}$$

The proof of this is left to the reader.

**Exercise 11*b***

1. Three particles, A of mass 2 kg, B of mass 4 kg, and C of mass 6 kg, lie in a straight line, with B at the midpoint of AC and 2 m from each of A and C. They are free to move along the line, which offers no resistance to motion. A is projected towards B with speed $0{\cdot}4\,\mathrm{m\,s^{-1}}$. When it reaches B, the particles coalesce and move on together to coalesce with C. Find the total time taken until the final contact, and the speed with which the final particle of mass 12 kg moves off.

2. A particle P of mass 2 kg has velocity $3\hat{\mathbf{i}} + 4\hat{\mathbf{j}}\,\mathrm{m\,s^{-1}}$. It meets a second particle Q, of mass 3 kg and velocity $\hat{\mathbf{i}} - \hat{\mathbf{j}}\,\mathrm{m\,s^{-1}}$, and the two particles coalesce and move on together. Find the velocity of the combined particle after impact. The combined particle then meets a third particle R, of mass 5 kg, coalesces with it and moves off with velocity $3\hat{\mathbf{i}}\,\mathrm{m\,s^{-1}}$. Find the velocity of R before the impact.

3. Two particles, P of mass $m$ and Q of mass $2m$, are connected by a light inextensible string which passes over a fixed smooth pulley. They are released from rest at the same instant as a third particle R, of mass $3m$, is dropped vertically towards P. R and P meet after 2 s, and coalesse. Show that, if we take $g = 10\,\mathrm{m\,s^{-2}}$:
(a) Just before the collision, R has speed $20\,\mathrm{m\,s^{-1}}$ and P has speed $20/3\,\mathrm{m\,s^{-1}}$.
(b) Just after the collision, the particles move with speed $20/3\,\mathrm{m\,s^{-1}}$, in a direction and sense to be stated.
(c) The subsequent acceleration of the system is $10/3\,\mathrm{m\,s^{-2}}$.

4. Two particles, P of mass $3m$ and Q of mass $m$ are connected by a light inextensible string passing over a smooth pulley. Initially, P is at rest on a table, and Q is held with the string loose. Q is released from rest, and the string becomes taut after Q has dropped $0{\cdot}8$ m, with both portions of the string vertical. Find when the system is next momentarily at rest. Assume that momentum is conserved when the string tightens. (Take $g = 10\,\mathrm{m\,s^{-2}}$.)

## 11.5 Particles rebounding on impact

We now consider the impact of bodies which do not coalesce. The previous discussion on instantaneous impulses is still valid, but we must now consider how the particles bounce off each other. In order to quantify this we use an experimental law accredited to Newton. At the moment of collision of two bodies, we assume that they have a common tangent plane at their point of contact. Suppose $\hat{\mathbf{n}}$ is a unit vector perpendicular to this plane. *Newton's experimental law* (NEL) states that change of momentum will take place only in the $\hat{\mathbf{n}}$ direction, and that the relative velocity of the bodies in the $\hat{\mathbf{n}}$ direction after impact is equal to $(-e)$ times their relative velocity in the $\hat{\mathbf{n}}$ direction before impact, where $e$ is a constant called the coefficient of *restitution*. That is,

$$v_2 - v_1 = -e(u_2 - u_1)$$

where the bodies have $\hat{\mathbf{n}}$-components of velocity $u_1$ and $u_2$ before the impact, and $v_1$ and $v_2$ after the impact.

Alternatively, we may state NEL as

$$(\mathbf{v}_2 - \mathbf{v}_1)\cdot\hat{\mathbf{n}} = -e(\mathbf{u}_2 - \mathbf{u}_1)\cdot\hat{\mathbf{n}}$$

where $\mathbf{u}_1$ and $\mathbf{u}_2$ are the velocities before the impact, and $\mathbf{v}_1$ and $\mathbf{v}_2$ the velocities after the impact, since, for example $(\mathbf{u}_2 - \mathbf{u}_1) . \hat{\mathbf{n}}$ is the component of $\mathbf{u}_2 - \mathbf{u}_1$ in the $\hat{\mathbf{n}}$ direction.

The coefficient of restitution $e$ depends on the material, of *each* body in the collision. If $e = 1$, then the collision is called *perfectly elastic*. In all collisions, we assume that only bouncing takes place, and, in particular, that the colliding bodies do not roll on contact. A collision may be between a moving body, and a fixed object, for example, in the case of a ball thrown against a wall.

### Worked Example 11.7

A particle of mass 2 kg is moving in a straight line with speed 3 m s$^{-1}$ when it collides with a mass of 3 kg moving in the same direction and sense with a speed of 1 m s$^{-1}$. Find their speeds after collision, if the coefficient of restitution between the particles is $\frac{1}{2}$.

*Solution*

Suppose the speeds after the impact are $u$ and $v$ respectively, as shown in Fig. 11.7. Using PCLM,

$$2 \times 3 + 3 \times 1 = 2u + 3v \text{ and so } 2u + 3v = 9 \tag{1}$$

Using NEL,

$$v - u = -\tfrac{1}{2}(1 - 3) = 1 \quad \text{and so} \quad v - u = 1 \tag{2}$$

Multiplying Equ. 2 by 2 and adding to Equ. 1 gives $5v = 11$ and so $v = 2{\cdot}2$ m s$^{-1}$ and $u = 1{\cdot}2$ m s$^{-1}$.

Fig. 11.7.

### Worked Example 11.8

A particle of mass 2 kg and velocity

$$\begin{pmatrix} 3 \\ 4 \end{pmatrix} \text{m s}^{-1}$$

collides with a stationary particle of mass 3 kg. The vector

$$\begin{pmatrix} 0 \\ 1 \end{pmatrix}$$

is perpendicular to the tangent plane at their point of contact. Find their velocities after collision, if the coefficient of restitution between the particles is $\frac{1}{2}$.

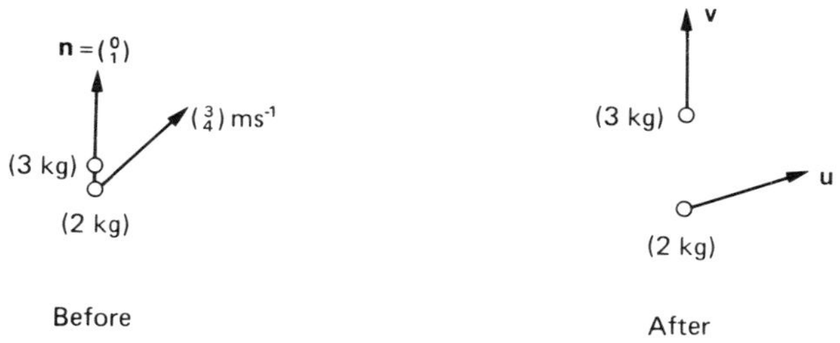


**Fig. 11.8.**

*Solution*

Suppose the velocities after impact are **u** and **v** respectively, as shown in Fig. 11.8, and where

$$\mathbf{u} = \begin{pmatrix} u_1 \\ u_2 \end{pmatrix} \quad \text{and} \quad \mathbf{v} = \begin{pmatrix} v_1 \\ v_2 \end{pmatrix}$$

Momentum can only change in the direction of

$$\mathbf{n} = \begin{pmatrix} 0 \\ 1 \end{pmatrix}$$

Therefore $u_1 = 3 \text{ m s}^{-1}$ and $v_1 = 0 \text{ m s}^{-1}$. Using PCLM

$$2\begin{pmatrix} 3 \\ 4 \end{pmatrix} + \begin{pmatrix} 0 \\ 0 \end{pmatrix} = 2\begin{pmatrix} 3 \\ u_2 \end{pmatrix} + 3\begin{pmatrix} 0 \\ v_2 \end{pmatrix}$$

and so

$$2u_2 + 3v_2 = 8$$

Using NEL in the **n** direction:

$$v_2 - u_2 = -\tfrac{1}{2}(0 - 4) = 2$$

and so

$$v_2 - u_2 = 2$$

Therefore $5v_2 = 12$ and so $v_2 = 2{\cdot}4 \text{ m s}^{-1}$ and $u_2 = 0{\cdot}4 \text{ m s}^{-1}$. Therefore the final velocities are

$$\mathbf{u} = \begin{pmatrix} 3 \\ 0{\cdot}4 \end{pmatrix} \text{m s}^{-1} \quad \text{and} \quad \mathbf{v} = \begin{pmatrix} 0 \\ 2{\cdot}4 \end{pmatrix} \text{m s}^{-1}$$

**Worked Example 11.9**

Two spheres collide with their line of centres parallel to

$$\mathbf{n} = \begin{pmatrix} 1 \\ -1 \\ 1 \end{pmatrix}$$

and coefficient of restitution $\frac{3}{4}$. If one sphere has mass 2 kg, and the other mass 1 kg, and if their respective velocities before the collision are

$$\begin{pmatrix} 1 \\ 2 \\ 3 \end{pmatrix} \text{m s}^{-1} \quad \text{and} \quad \begin{pmatrix} 2 \\ 1 \\ -3 \end{pmatrix} \text{m s}^{-1}$$

find their velocities after the impact.

*Solution*

Suppose the velocities after the impact are

$$\mathbf{u} = \begin{pmatrix} u_1 \\ u_2 \\ u_3 \end{pmatrix} \quad \text{and} \quad \mathbf{v} = \begin{pmatrix} v_1 \\ v_2 \\ v_3 \end{pmatrix}$$

respectively. Using PCLM

$$2\begin{pmatrix} 1 \\ 2 \\ 3 \end{pmatrix} + 1\begin{pmatrix} 2 \\ 1 \\ -3 \end{pmatrix} = 2\begin{pmatrix} u_1 \\ u_2 \\ u_3 \end{pmatrix} + 1\begin{pmatrix} v_1 \\ v_2 \\ v_3 \end{pmatrix}$$

and so

$$2u_1 + v_1 = 4 \tag{1}$$

$$2u_2 + v_2 = 5 \tag{2}$$

$$2u_3 + v_3 = 3 \tag{3}$$

Using NEL,

$$(\mathbf{v} - \mathbf{u}) \cdot \mathbf{n} = -\tfrac{3}{4}\left[\begin{pmatrix} 2 \\ 1 \\ -3 \end{pmatrix} - \begin{pmatrix} 1 \\ 2 \\ 3 \end{pmatrix}\right] \cdot \mathbf{n}$$

thus $(v_1 - u_1) - (v_2 - u_2) + (v_3 - u_3) = -\frac{3}{4}(1 + 1 - 6) = 3$ (4)

The impulse on collision is in the $\mathbf{n}$ direction. Therefore

$$\mathbf{v} - \begin{pmatrix} 2 \\ 1 \\ -3 \end{pmatrix} = k\begin{pmatrix} 1 \\ -1 \\ 1 \end{pmatrix}$$

and so

$$k = v_1 - 2 \quad \text{and} \quad v_2 = 3 - v_1 \tag{5}$$

$$v_3 = v_1 - 5 \tag{6}$$

Hence Equ. 1 gives

$$u_1 = 2 - \tfrac{1}{2}v_1$$

Equations 2 and 5 give

$$u_2 = \tfrac{5}{2} - \tfrac{1}{2}v_2 = \tfrac{5}{2} - \tfrac{3}{2} + \tfrac{1}{2}v_1 = 1 + \tfrac{1}{2}v_1$$

Equations 3 and 6 give

$$u_3 = \tfrac{3}{2} - \tfrac{1}{2}v_3 = \tfrac{3}{2} - \tfrac{1}{2}v_1 + \tfrac{5}{2} = 4 - \tfrac{1}{2}v_1$$

Equ. 4 now gives

$$v_1 - 2 + \tfrac{1}{2}v_1 - 3 + v_1 + 1 + \tfrac{1}{2}v_1 + v_1 - 5 - 4 + \tfrac{1}{2}v_1 = 3$$

Therefore

$$9v_1/2 = 16 \quad \text{and so} \quad v_1 = 32/9 \text{ m s}^{-1}$$

Hence

$$\mathbf{v} = \tfrac{1}{9}\begin{pmatrix} 32 \\ -5 \\ -13 \end{pmatrix} \text{m s}^{-1} \quad \text{and} \quad \mathbf{u} = \tfrac{1}{9}\begin{pmatrix} 2 \\ 25 \\ 20 \end{pmatrix} \text{m s}^{-1}$$

**Exercise 11*c***

1. A particle is dropped from a height of 12 m onto a plane surface. The coefficient of restitution between the particle and the surface is $\sqrt{\tfrac{3}{4}}$. Find the height to which the particle rises after bouncing, and the ratio of the times for the fall and the rise.

2. A particle is projected horizontally with a speed of 5 m s$^{-1}$ from a point 6 m above a horizontal plane. Find where it first hits the plane. If the coefficient of restitution between the plane and the particle is $\tfrac{1}{2}$, find where it next meets the plane.

3. A sphere of mass $m$ moving with speed $u$ on a smooth horizontal surface collides with a second sphere, of the same radius, but of mass $2m$, moving in the same direction with speed $\tfrac{3}{4}u$.

(a) Find the speeds of each of the spheres after impact if the coefficient of restitution between them is $\tfrac{3}{4}$.

(b) Show that there is no value of $e$ for which either of the spheres can be halted by the impact.

4. A particle of mass 3 kg and velocity

$$\begin{pmatrix} 5 \\ -1 \end{pmatrix} \text{m s}^{-1}$$

collides with a particle of mass 1 kg moving with velocity

$$\begin{pmatrix} 2 \\ 2 \end{pmatrix} \text{m s}^{-1}$$

thus exerting an impulse in the direction of

$$\begin{pmatrix} 1 \\ -2 \end{pmatrix}$$

Find the velocities of the particles after the collision, if the coefficient of restitution between the particles is $\tfrac{2}{3}$.

5. A smooth sphere A of mass 3 kg and velocity

$$\begin{pmatrix} 1 \\ -1 \\ 2 \end{pmatrix} \text{m s}^{-1}$$

collides with a smooth sphere B of mass 4 kg and velocity

$$\begin{pmatrix} 2 \\ 4 \\ 0 \end{pmatrix} \text{m s}^{-1}.$$

If the velocity of A after the impact is

$$\begin{pmatrix} -1 \\ 1 \\ 2 \end{pmatrix} \text{m s}^{-1},$$

find the velocity of B after the impact.

Find the impulse exerted by B on A, and hence find the direction of the line of centres at the moment of impact. Use this to deduce the coefficient of restitution $e$ between the two spheres.

## 11.6 Continuous change of momentum

Newton's second law states that $\mathbf{F} = \mathrm{d}(m\mathbf{v})/\mathrm{d}t$, that is, that the applied force is equivalent to the rate of change of linear momentum. Up to now, we have considered only the changes in momentum caused by applying a force or an impulse. We now look at situations where a force is being applied because there has been a momentum change.

Suppose, for example, that a hose directs a horizontal stream of water against a vertical wall, and that after impact the water runs down the wall.

Select the direction of the stream of water as the $\hat{\mathbf{i}}$ direction. The momentum of the water changes in the $\hat{\mathbf{i}}$ direction, and so, by Newton's second law, this must be equivalent to a force acting on the wall and an equal and opposite reaction acting on the water. Suppose that the velocity of the water is $v\hat{\mathbf{i}}$, and that the mass of water delivered each second is $m$. Then the rate of change of momentum in the $\hat{\mathbf{i}}$ direction is $\mathbf{0} - mv\hat{\mathbf{i}}$. Thus the effective force on the water is $-mv\hat{\mathbf{i}}$, and the effective force on the wall is $+mv\hat{\mathbf{i}}$.

**Worked Example 11.11**

A smooth wedge of mass 10 kg is on a smooth horizontal plane. The inclined face of the wedge makes an angle of 60° with the horizontal. 2 kg of water is projected each second onto the inclined face of the wedge with speed 3 m s$^{-1}$ and at an angle of 45° to the vertical. The water then runs down the face of the wedge at 3 m s$^{-1}$. Neglecting the mass of the water on the wedge, find the acceleration of the wedge.

*Solution*

Select $\hat{\mathbf{i}}$ parallel to the plane, and $\hat{\mathbf{j}}$ vertically upwards, as shown in Fig. 11.9. The rate of change of linear momentum in the $\hat{\mathbf{i}}$ direction is

$$(-2 \times 3 \times \cos 60^\circ - 2 \times 3 \times \cos 45^\circ)\ \text{N s s}^{-1} \approx -7{\cdot}24\ \text{N s s}^{-1}$$

since this is numerically the actual change of momentum in 1 s. Hence the horizontal force on the wedge is 7·24 N, and the acceleration of the wedge is in the $\hat{\mathbf{i}}$ direction and given by $7{\cdot}24 = 10\,a$, that is $a = 0{\cdot}724$ m s$^{-2}$.

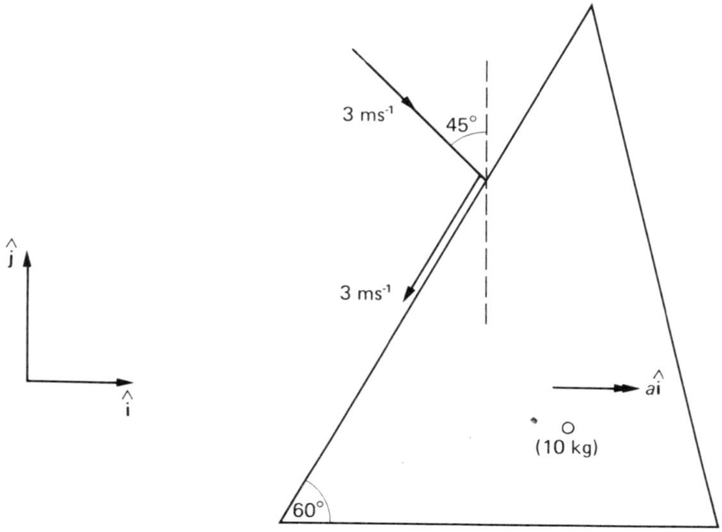


Fig. 11.9.

**Worked Example 11.12**

Show that a body with a plane face perpendicular to its direction of motion experiences an air resistance proportional to the square of its speed.

*Solution*

Suppose the plane face has area $A$ and velocity $v\mathbf{\hat{i}}$, and that air has density $\rho$. Then, in time $\delta t$ the body displaces a volume of air $Av\delta t$, that is, a mass of air $\rho Av\delta t$. If we assume that the air moves perpendicular to the $\hat{i}$ direction after being displaced, then the momentum change in time $\delta t$ in the $\mathbf{\hat{i}}$ direction is given by $\rho vA\delta t[0 - (-v)]\mathbf{\hat{i}} = \rho v^2 A\delta t\mathbf{\hat{i}}$. Hence the rate of change of linear momentum is $\rho v^2 A\mathbf{\hat{i}}$. By Newton's second law, the effective force on the air is $+\rho v^2 A\mathbf{\hat{i}}$, and the equal and opposite reaction on the body is $-\rho Av^2\mathbf{\hat{i}}$. Thus the body experiences air resistance $-kv^2\mathbf{\hat{i}}$, where $k = \rho A$.

**Exercise 11*d***

1. Waves strike a vertical sea wall with a speed of 15 m s$^{-1}$. If the density of sea water is 1020 kg m$^{-3}$, find the force on 1 m$^2$ of the wall due to the destruction of the momentum of the waves.

2. A machine gun fires 300 bullets per minute horizontally against a vertical steel plate. The bullets each have mass 30 g, strike the plates with a speed of 300 m s$^{-1}$, and rebound with a speed of 10 m s$^{-1}$. Find the force per unit area on the plate, assuming the stream of bullets to be continuous.

3. A jet of water is fired vertically at a speed of 10 m s$^{-1}$ from a nozzle of area 60 mm$^2$, and supports a ball of mass 450 g. Find the height of the ball above the nozzle.

4. A smooth wedge of mass 10 kg is on a smooth horizontal plane. The inclined

face of the wedge makes an angle of 30° with the horizontal. 3 kg of water is projected each second onto the inclined face of the wedge with speed 4 m $s^{-1}$ at right angles to the face of the wedge. Two-thirds of the water runs down the face of the wedge with speed 4 m $s^{-1}$, and the remainder rebounds horizontally with speed 2 m $s^{-1}$. Neglecting the mass of the water on the wedge, find the acceleration of the wedge.

5. A rocket moving in space has total mass $m$ and speed $v$ at time $t$ after its motor has fired. At time $t + \delta t$, it has speed $v + \delta v$ and mass $m + \delta m$, where $\delta m < 0$. Gravitational attractions may be neglected, and the rocket ejects fuel with a constant speed $u$ relative to itself. Show that $m\delta v + \delta v \delta m + u\delta m = 0$, and hence deduce that $m\,\mathrm{d}v/\mathrm{d}t = -u\,\mathrm{d}m/\mathrm{d}t$.

If the rocket had speed $U$ and total mass $M$ when the rocket was fired, find its speed at the end of firing if its total mass is then $kM$. Show that this does not depend on the rate at which the fuel is consumed.

## 11.7 Miscellaneous exercises 11

1. A mass of 2 kg is placed on a smooth plane inclined to the horizintal at an angle $\theta$, where $\sin\theta = 7/25$. Determine the force which, when acting up the line of greatest slope will hold the mass at rest.

If this force is removed find the momentum of the mass after 5 seconds, and hence its velocity at that time.

After the initial 5 seconds motion the mass enters a rough portion of the inclined plane, and during the next 10 seconds a constant frictional force resisting motion produces a 25% decrease in the velocity of the mass. Calculate the magnitude of this force. (MEI)

2. A force P, magnitude 5 N, direction 090°, acts on a mass of 2 kg initially at rest. What is the momentum of the mass after 6 seconds? Hence determine the velocity of the mass at that instant.

An *additional* force Q, magnitude 30 N, direction 180°, acts on the mass during the next 4 seconds. What is the magnitude of the velocity of the mass at the end of the 10-second period? (MEI)

3. A lifeboat is launched from rest down a slipway which is inclined at 20° to the horizontal. The resistance to motion (assumed constant) amount to $4 \times 10^4$ N. If the mass of the lifeboat is $2 \times 10^4$ kg, and the boat reaches the bottom of the slipway with a velocity of 8 m $s^{-1}$, calculate the time that the boat takes to travel down the slipway.

Immediately after entering the water at the bottom of the slipway, the boat moves horizontally with a velocity of 4 m $s^{-1}$. Use an accurate diagram to find the magnitude of the impulse given to the boat by the water. (MEI)

4. A smooth sphere A of mass 4 units and velocity $(\mathbf{i} - \mathbf{j} + 2\mathbf{k})$ units collides with a smooth sphere B of mass 2 units and velocity $(\mathbf{i} + 5\mathbf{j} - \mathbf{k})$. If the subsequent velocity of A is $(2\mathbf{i} + \mathbf{j} + \mathbf{k})$ find the subsequent velocity of B.

If $\alpha$ is the angle through which the direction of motion of A is turned by the collision, and $\beta$ the corresponding angle for B, show that $2\cos\alpha = 3\cos\beta$.

Find the impulse exerted by B on A and deduce the direction of the line of centres at the moment of impact.

Hence show that the components of relative velocity in the direction of the line of centres before and after impact are in the ratio $5:-1$. (JMB)

5. A rocket of mass 40 tonne ($=4 \times 10^4$ kg) is mounted rigidly on a trolley of mass 10 tonne which is free to move horizontally. The rocket ejects mass 1 tonne horizontally in a burst lasting 5 seconds, giving the ejected matter a speed which may be taken as 2 km/s relative to the ground. Calculate the velocity of the rocket just after the ejection (a) neglecting resistances, and (b) assuming resistance of $4 \times 10^4$ newton.

If the same operation were carried out with the rocket mounted vertically and free to lift off its mounting show that, for a lift-off to occur, the duration of the burst (assumed uniform) must not exceed a certain critical time, and calculate this time. (The question of resistance does not arise in this calculation. Explain why.) (Take $g = 10$ m s$^{-2}$.) (MEI)

6. A small ball of mass $m$ is dropped from a point at height $H$ above a horizontal table. After falling a distance $h$ the ball strikes an inclined plate and leaves it horizontally with its speed reduced to a fraction $f$ of its value just before the impact. Show that the impulse on the ball due to the plate is inclined at an angle arctan$(f)$ to the vertical. Determine the magnitude of the impulse and show its direction clearly on a diagram. (Air resistance may be neglected.)

The ball strikes the table after moving though a horizontal distance $d$. Find an expression for $d$ in terms of $H$, $h$, $f$ and $g$ and show that for given $f$ and variable $h$ the maximum value of $d$ is $fH$. (MEI)

7. A smooth sphere A of mass 1 kg moves with speed 5 m s$^{-1}$ in a smooth horizontal plane directly towards a vertical wall. Before it hits the wall it is struck from behind by a smooth sphere B with the same radius as A but of mass 2 kg moving towards the wall along the same line as A with speed 10 m s$^{-1}$. Given that the coefficient of restitution between the spheres is $\frac{1}{2}$ find their new velocities.

The sphere A later strikes the wall and rebounds, the coefficient of restitution being $\frac{1}{4}$. It then collides again with B which has been following it towards the wall. Show that, after this collision, both A and B are again moving towards the wall, the speed of A being three times that of B. (MEI)

8. Two stones, each of mass $5m$, are moving across a sheet of smooth ice at equal speeds of $10v$ in opposite directions on parallel paths, so that no collision is involved. A frog of mass $m$, travelling on one of the stones, leaps across to the other one, and in so doing deflects the stone he leaves through 30° and changes its speed to $8v$.

Find, by drawing and measurement or by calculation: (i) through what angle the other stone is deflected and its subsequent speed; (ii) the (vector) impulse the frog exerts on the stone on which he lands. (SMP)

9. A sphere of mass $m$ moving with speed $2u$ on a smooth horizontal plane collides directly with a second sphere, of the same radius but of mass $3m$, moving in the same direction with speed $u$.

(a) Find the speeds of the two spheres after the impact if they are perfectly elastic.

(b) Find the coefficient of restitution between the spheres if after the impact the speed of the second sphere is twice that of the first. (L)

10. A red ball is stationary on a rectangular billiard table OABC. It is then struck by a white ball of equal mass and equal radius with velocity $u(-2\mathbf{i} + 11\mathbf{j})$, where $\mathbf{i}$ and $\mathbf{j}$ are unit vectors along OA and OC respectively. After impact the red and white balls have velocities parallel to the vectors $-3\mathbf{i} + 4\mathbf{j}$, $2\mathbf{i} + 4\mathbf{j}$ respectively. Prove that the coefficient of restitution between the two balls is $\frac{1}{2}$. (L)

# 12
# The Vector Product

## 12.1 Vector product of two vectors

In Chapter 10, we met a product of two vectors which was a scalar; we now find a need for another product of two vectors, which will be a vector. We have met the situation already, in connection with forces and moments.

Suppose a force is represented by the vector **F**, where the point X with position vector **x** is on the line of action of the force. (see Fig. 12.1). We have defined the moment of the force **F** about the origin to have magnitude

$$|\mathbf{F}| \times (\text{perpendicular distance from X to line of action of } \mathbf{F})$$

that is $|\mathbf{F}| \times |\mathbf{x}| \times \sin\theta = Fx\sin\theta$, where $\theta$ is the angle between **F** and **x**. In the diagram, the moment is anticlockwise, which we conventionally designate as positive. We represent this moment as a vector as follows: $\hat{\mathbf{n}}$ is a unit vector perpendicular to **F** and **x**, and in the sense determined by a right-handed screw turning from **x** to **F**. The moment of **F** about O is then represented by $(F \times \sin\theta)\hat{\mathbf{n}}$. It follows that $-\hat{\mathbf{n}}$ corresponds to a clockwise moment. Thus we may regard moments as vector quantities.

We generalize this definition into that of the vector product of two vectors. We define the *vector product* $\mathbf{a} \wedge \mathbf{b}$ or $\mathbf{a} \times \mathbf{b}$ (pronounced '*a* cross *b*') of the two vectors **a** and **b** to be the vector $\mathbf{a} \wedge \mathbf{b} = ab\sin\theta\hat{\mathbf{n}}$, where $a = |\mathbf{a}|$, $b = |\mathbf{b}|$, $\theta$ is the smaller angle between the positive senses of **a** and **b**, i.e. $\theta \leqq 2\pi - \theta$, and $\hat{\mathbf{n}}$ is a unit vector

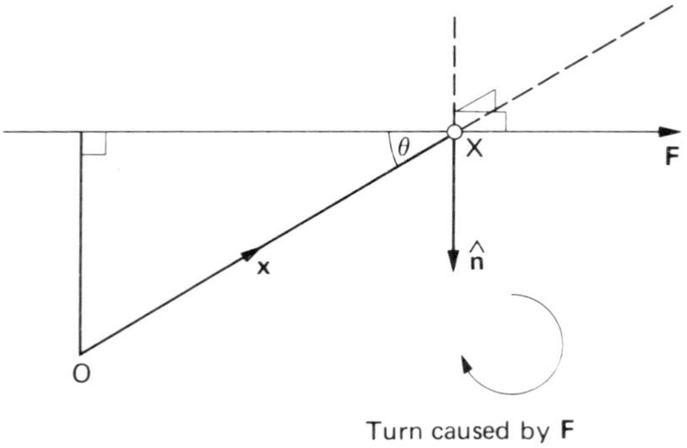


**Fig. 12.1.** Moment of **F** about O $= \mathbf{x} \wedge \mathbf{F} = Fx\sin\theta\hat{\mathbf{n}}$.

perpendicular to both **a** and **b**, and in the sense determined by a right-handed screw turning from **a** to **b**.

This is in contrast to the scalar product of **a** and **b**, where the resulting product was a scalar rather than a vector.

Thus the *moment of the force* **F** *about the point* O is $\mathbf{x} \wedge \mathbf{F}$, where **x** is the position vector of any point X on the line of action of **F**. We may also say that the moment of the vector **b** about O is $\mathbf{a} \wedge \mathbf{b}$, where **b** passes through A. We use this latter definition to produce an alternative geometrical interpretation. In Fig. 12.2, the length of BD is $b \sin \theta$, and so the quantity $ab \sin \theta$ is the area of the parallelogram OACB with **a** and **b** as adjacent sides. That is, the area of this parallelogram is $|\mathbf{a} \wedge \mathbf{b}|$. We will see much later that we may define the area of this parallelogram to be the vector $\mathbf{a} \wedge \mathbf{b}$, thus claiming that *area is a vector quantity*. You may have met so-called 'negative areas' in connection with matrix transformations, or in calculus; the choice between $\hat{\mathbf{n}}$ and $-\hat{\mathbf{n}}$ merely attaches a sign to the magnitude of the area.

## 12.2 Properties of the vector product

Suppose **a** and **b** are position vectors, as in Fig. 12.2, and that $\mathbf{a} \wedge \mathbf{b} = ab \sin \theta \hat{\mathbf{n}}$. Then a right-handed screw turning from **b** to **a** defines the unit vector $-\hat{\mathbf{n}}$; and the magnitude of $\mathbf{b} \wedge \mathbf{a}$ is $ba \sin \theta$. Therefore

$$\begin{aligned} \mathbf{b} \wedge \mathbf{a} &= (ba \sin \theta)(-\hat{\mathbf{n}}) \\ &= -(ab \sin \theta)\hat{\mathbf{n}} \end{aligned}$$

Hence

$$\mathbf{b} \wedge \mathbf{a} = -\mathbf{a} \wedge \mathbf{b},$$

i.e. vector multiplication is *not* commutative.

To establish the *distributive law*

$$\mathbf{a} \wedge (\mathbf{b} + \mathbf{c}) = \mathbf{a} \wedge \mathbf{b} + \mathbf{a} \wedge \mathbf{c},$$

we use Fig. 12.3. We define the *orthogonal projection* $\mathbf{b}'$ of **b** onto the plane through O perpendicular to **a** as follows: $\mathbf{b}'$ is in the plane of **a** and **b**; $\mathbf{b}'$ is in the plane through O, perpendicular to **a**; the length of $\mathbf{b}'$ is $b \sin \theta$. The orthogonal projections

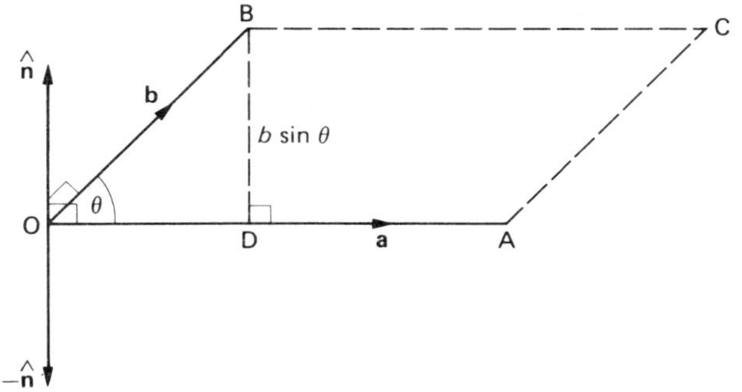


**Fig. 12.2.** $|\mathbf{a} \wedge \mathbf{b}|$ = area of parallelogram OACB.

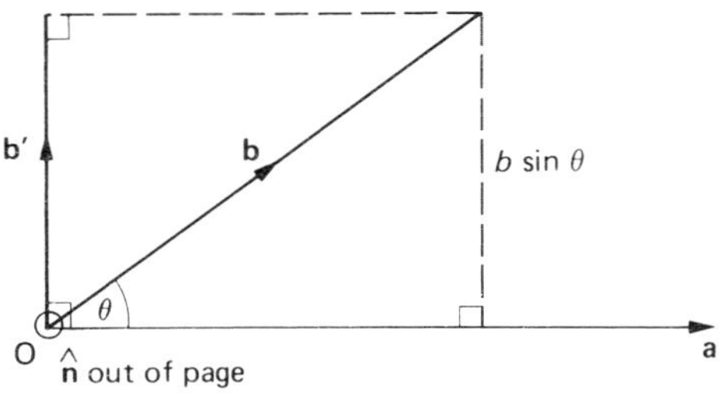


**Fig. 12.3.** $\mathbf{a} \wedge \mathbf{b} = \mathbf{a} \wedge \mathbf{b}'$.

$\mathbf{c}'$ of $\mathbf{c}$ and $\mathbf{d}'$ of $\mathbf{d} = \mathbf{b} + \mathbf{c}$ are similarly defined. Then

$$\mathbf{a} \wedge \mathbf{b} = ab\sin\theta\hat{\mathbf{n}},$$

where $\hat{\mathbf{n}}$ is perpendicular to the plane of $\mathbf{a}$, $\mathbf{b}$ and $\mathbf{b}'$. Thus

$$\begin{aligned}\mathbf{a} \wedge \mathbf{b} &= (a \times b\sin\theta \times \sin\tfrac{1}{2}\pi)\hat{\mathbf{n}} \\ &= (|\mathbf{a}| \times |\mathbf{b}'| \times \sin\tfrac{1}{2}\pi)\hat{\mathbf{n}}\end{aligned}$$

Hence $\mathbf{a} \wedge \mathbf{b} = \mathbf{a} \wedge \mathbf{b}'$, since $\frac{1}{2}\pi$ is the angle between $\mathbf{a}$ and $\mathbf{b}'$. Also $\mathbf{a} \wedge \mathbf{c} = \mathbf{a} \wedge \mathbf{c}'$ and $\mathbf{a} \wedge \mathbf{d} = \mathbf{a} \wedge \mathbf{d}'$.

Now transform $\mathbf{b}'$ to $\mathbf{b}''$ as follows: rotate $\mathbf{b}'$ through one right angle about $\mathbf{a}$, and enlarge by scale factor $a = |\mathbf{a}|$. Then $\mathbf{b}''$ is orthogonal to $\mathbf{a}$ and to $\mathbf{b}$ and $\mathbf{b}'$, and has magnitude $|\mathbf{b}'| \times |\mathbf{a}| = ab\sin\theta$. Thus $\mathbf{b}'' = \mathbf{a} \wedge \mathbf{b}$.

Similarly, transform $\mathbf{c}'$ to $\mathbf{c}'' = \mathbf{a} \wedge \mathbf{c}$ and $\mathbf{d}'$ to $\mathbf{d}'' = \mathbf{a} \wedge \mathbf{d}$. Now, the transformations of orthogonal projection, rotation, and enlargement all preserve, among other things, vector sums. Now

$$\mathbf{d} = \mathbf{b} + \mathbf{c}$$

thus

$$\mathbf{d}' = \mathbf{b}' + \mathbf{c}', \quad \text{by the first transformation}$$

and so

$$\mathbf{d}'' = \mathbf{b}'' + \mathbf{c}'', \quad \text{by the second transformation}$$

hence

$$\mathbf{a} \wedge \mathbf{d} = \mathbf{a} \wedge \mathbf{b} + \mathbf{a} \wedge \mathbf{c}$$

and

$$\mathbf{a} \wedge (\mathbf{b} + \mathbf{c}) = \mathbf{a} \wedge \mathbf{b} + \mathbf{a} \wedge \mathbf{c}$$

as required. Therefore

$$\begin{aligned}(\mathbf{b} + \mathbf{c}) \wedge \mathbf{a} &= -\mathbf{a} \wedge (\mathbf{b} + \mathbf{c}) \\ &= -(\mathbf{a} \wedge \mathbf{b} + \mathbf{a} \wedge \mathbf{c}) \\ &= -\mathbf{a} \wedge \mathbf{b} - \mathbf{a} \wedge \mathbf{c} \\ &= \mathbf{b} \wedge \mathbf{a} + \mathbf{c} \wedge \mathbf{a}.\end{aligned}$$

We may extend this to justify multiplying out brackets of any size, but, since the multiplication is not commutative, we must always beware the order in which the products are taken.

The reader is given the opportunity to establish some further results for himself in Exercise 12*a*, before they are formally stated and proved in subsequent sections.

**Exercise 12*a***

All these properties will be expanded in subsequent sections.

1. $\{\hat{\mathbf{i}}, \hat{\mathbf{j}}, \hat{\mathbf{k}}\}$ is the standard basis for three-dimensional space. Complete the following table for vector products, where the element on the side of the table specifies the left-hand element in the product, i.e. the entry shown is for $\hat{\mathbf{i}} \wedge \hat{\mathbf{j}}$.

| | $\hat{\mathbf{i}}$ | $\hat{\mathbf{j}}$ | $\hat{\mathbf{k}}$ |
|---|---|---|---|
| $\hat{\mathbf{i}}$ | | $\hat{\mathbf{k}}$ | |
| $\hat{\mathbf{j}}$ | | | |
| $\hat{\mathbf{k}}$ | | | |

Hence find an expression for $(a_1\hat{\mathbf{i}} + a_2\hat{\mathbf{j}} + a_3\hat{\mathbf{k}}) \wedge (b_1\hat{\mathbf{i}} + b_2\hat{\mathbf{j}} + b_3\hat{\mathbf{k}})$.

2. $\mathbf{a}$ is a fixed position vector, and $\hat{\mathbf{b}}$ a fixed unit position vector, and they determine fixed points A and B respectively. Find the locus of points R whose position vectors satisfy the equation $(\mathbf{r} - \mathbf{a}) \wedge \hat{\mathbf{b}} = \mathbf{0}$. What significance has the quantity $|(\mathbf{p} - \mathbf{a}) \wedge \hat{\mathbf{b}}|$ where $\mathbf{p}$ is the position vector of a point P *not* on the locus?

3. E and F are forces, and X is a fixed point. What mechanical significance have the vector product $\mathbf{x} \wedge \mathbf{F}$ and the equation $\mathbf{x} \wedge \mathbf{E} + \mathbf{x} \wedge \mathbf{F} = \mathbf{x} \wedge (\mathbf{E} + \mathbf{F})$?

## 12.3 Further properties of the vector product

We have already established the following properties:

non-commutativity: $\mathbf{a} \wedge \mathbf{b} = -\mathbf{b} \wedge \mathbf{a}$ (1)

distributive laws:
$$\begin{cases} \mathbf{a} \wedge (\mathbf{b} + \mathbf{c}) = \mathbf{a} \wedge \mathbf{b} + \mathbf{a} \wedge \mathbf{c} & \text{(2a)} \\ (\mathbf{a} + \mathbf{b}) \wedge \mathbf{c} = \mathbf{a} \wedge \mathbf{c} + \mathbf{b} \wedge \mathbf{c} & \text{(2b)} \end{cases}$$

Further properties were investigated by the reader in Exercise 12*a*; and we will give more details of some of these in this and subsequent sections.

Consider first $\mathbf{a} \wedge (\beta\mathbf{b})$, assuming that $\mathbf{a} \wedge \mathbf{b} = ab\sin\theta\hat{\mathbf{n}}$. The angle between $\mathbf{a}$ and $\beta\mathbf{b}$ is either $\theta$ or $\pi - \theta$, where $\theta$ is the angle between $\mathbf{a}$ and $\mathbf{b}$; and $\sin\theta = \sin(\pi - \theta)$. The modulus of $\beta\mathbf{b}$ is $|\beta\mathbf{b}| = |\beta||\mathbf{b}| = |\beta| \times b$. Therefore

$$\mathbf{a} \wedge (\beta\mathbf{b}) = |\mathbf{a}| \times |\beta\mathbf{b}| \times \sin\theta \times \hat{\mathbf{m}}$$

$$\text{where } \hat{\mathbf{m}} = \begin{cases} \hat{\mathbf{n}} & (\beta \geqq 0) \\ -\hat{\mathbf{n}} & (\beta < 0) \end{cases}$$

$$\begin{aligned} &= a \times |\beta| \times b \times \sin\theta \times \hat{\mathbf{m}} \\ &= (ab\sin\theta)(|\beta|\hat{\mathbf{m}}) \\ &= \beta(ab\sin\theta\,\hat{\mathbf{n}}) \\ &= \beta(\mathbf{a} \wedge \mathbf{b}) \end{aligned}$$

since $|\beta|\hat{\mathbf{m}} = \beta\hat{\mathbf{n}}$ for all values of $\beta$. Similarly, we may show that

$$\mathbf{a} \wedge (\beta\mathbf{b}) = (\beta\mathbf{a}) \wedge \mathbf{b}$$

Therefore

$$\mathbf{a} \wedge (\beta\mathbf{b}) = (\beta\mathbf{a}) \wedge \mathbf{b} = \beta(\mathbf{a} \wedge \mathbf{b}) \tag{3}$$

More alternatives may be obtained using the anti-commutative property of Equ. 1.

Now consider $\mathbf{a} \wedge \mathbf{a}$. The angle between $\mathbf{a}$ and itself is zero, and $\sin 0 = 0$. Therefore

$$\mathbf{a} \wedge \mathbf{a} = \mathbf{0} \quad \text{for all vectors } \mathbf{a} \tag{4}$$

Also, we have

$$\mathbf{a} \wedge \mathbf{0} = \mathbf{0}$$

since $|\mathbf{0}| = 0$.

Now we can ask, more generally, what the condition is for a vector product to be zero, knowing already the particular cases of Equations 4 and 5. Suppose $\mathbf{a} \wedge \mathbf{b} = \mathbf{0}$. Then

$$ab\sin\theta\hat{\mathbf{n}} = \mathbf{0} \quad \text{and so} \quad |ab\sin\theta\hat{\mathbf{n}}| = 0 \quad \text{thus} \quad ab\sin\theta = 0.$$

This means that $a = 0$ or $b = 0$ or $\sin\theta = 0$, or any two or more of these are zero, which implies that $\mathbf{a} = \mathbf{0}$ or $\mathbf{b} = \mathbf{0}$ or $\mathbf{a}$ and $\mathbf{b}$ have the same direction. Hence $\alpha\mathbf{a} = \beta\mathbf{b}$ for some $\alpha$, $\beta$, with at least one of $\alpha$ and $\beta$ non-zero.

Conversely, suppose that $\alpha\mathbf{a} = \beta\mathbf{b}$, with at least one of $\alpha$ and $\beta$ non-zero. If $\alpha = 0$, then $\beta\mathbf{b} = \mathbf{0}$ and so $\mathbf{b} = \mathbf{0}$, in which case

$$\mathbf{a} \wedge \mathbf{b} = \mathbf{a} \wedge \mathbf{0} = \mathbf{0}$$

Similary, $\beta = 0$ implies that $\mathbf{a} = \mathbf{0}$ which implies that $\mathbf{a} \wedge \mathbf{b} = \mathbf{0} \wedge \mathbf{b} = \mathbf{0}$. Now, suppose $\alpha\mathbf{a} = \beta\mathbf{b}$, with $\alpha$, $\beta$ non-zero. Then

$$\begin{aligned}
\mathbf{a} \wedge \mathbf{b} &= \left(\frac{1}{\alpha}\alpha\mathbf{a}\right) \wedge \left(\frac{1}{\beta}\beta\mathbf{b}\right) && \text{since } \alpha \neq 0 \text{ and } \beta \neq 0\\
&= \frac{1}{\alpha\beta}(\alpha\mathbf{a} \wedge \beta\mathbf{b}) && \text{using Equ. 3}\\
&= \frac{1}{\alpha\beta}(\alpha\mathbf{a} \wedge \alpha\mathbf{a}) && \text{since } \alpha\mathbf{a} = \beta\mathbf{b}\\
&= \mathbf{0} && \text{using Equ. 4}
\end{aligned}$$

Thus we have proved that

$$\mathbf{a} \wedge \mathbf{b} = \mathbf{0} \iff \alpha\mathbf{a} = \beta\mathbf{b} \tag{6}$$

Geometrically, this says that the non-zero vectors $\mathbf{a}$ and $\mathbf{b}$ are parallel if and only if their vector product $\mathbf{a} \wedge \mathbf{b}$ is zero.

That is, $\mathbf{a} \neq \mathbf{0}, \mathbf{b} \neq \mathbf{0}, \mathbf{a} \wedge \mathbf{b} = \mathbf{0} \iff \mathbf{a}$ and $\mathbf{b}$ are parallel.

An immediate application of this helps us to answer part of question 4 of Exercise 12*a*. We have fixed points A and B, and their position vectors $\mathbf{a}$ and $\hat{\mathbf{b}}$. We also have a variable point R, satisfying $(\mathbf{r} - \mathbf{a}) \wedge \hat{\mathbf{b}} = \mathbf{0}$. By the condition above, $\mathbf{r} - \mathbf{a}$ is parallel to $\hat{\mathbf{b}}$, i.e. **AR** is parallel to $\hat{\mathbf{b}}$ for all positions of R. Therefore R lies

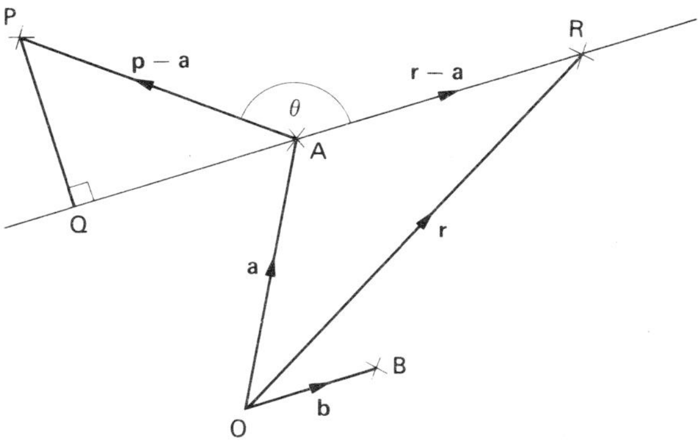


Fig. 12.4.

on the straight line through A parallel to $\hat{\mathbf{b}}$, and the equation $(\mathbf{r} - \mathbf{a}) \wedge \hat{\mathbf{b}} = \mathbf{0}$ is an alternative form for the equation of this straight line. This equation was given in Chapter 4 as $\mathbf{r} = \mathbf{a} + t\hat{\mathbf{b}}$, and we see that the two are compatible, since, if $\mathbf{r} = \mathbf{a} + t\hat{\mathbf{b}}$, then $\mathbf{r} - \mathbf{a} = t\hat{\mathbf{b}}$ and $(\mathbf{r} - \mathbf{a}) \wedge \hat{\mathbf{b}} = (t\hat{\mathbf{b}}) \wedge \hat{\mathbf{b}} = \mathbf{0}$.

Now take a point P, with position vector **p**, *not* on the line. The angle between $\mathbf{p} - \mathbf{a}$ and $\hat{\mathbf{b}}$ is the angle $\theta$ between the straight line $\overleftrightarrow{\mathrm{AR}}$ and **AP**. Therefore

$$\begin{aligned}(\mathbf{p} - \mathbf{a}) \wedge \hat{\mathbf{b}} &= |\mathbf{p} - \hat{\mathbf{a}}| \times |\hat{\mathbf{b}}| \times \sin\theta \times \hat{\mathbf{n}} \\ &= |\mathbf{AP}| \times 1 \times \sin\theta \times \hat{\mathbf{n}} \\ &= |\mathbf{PQ}| \times \hat{\mathbf{n}},\end{aligned}$$

where Q is the point on $\overleftrightarrow{\mathrm{AR}}$ such that **PQ** is perpendicular to $\overleftrightarrow{\mathrm{AR}}$. Therefore $|(\mathbf{p} - \mathbf{a}) \wedge \hat{\mathbf{b}}| = |\mathbf{PQ}|$, i.e. $|(\mathbf{p} - \mathbf{a}) \wedge \hat{\mathbf{b}}|$ is the perpendicular distance from the point P to the line $\overleftrightarrow{\mathrm{AR}}$. Uses of this property will be seen in Chapter 13, in connection with coordinates.

## 12.4 Coordinate form of the vector product

Question 3 of Exercise 12*a* should have produced the following vector products of the standard unit vectors $\hat{\mathbf{i}}, \hat{\mathbf{j}}, \hat{\mathbf{k}}$:

$$\hat{\mathbf{i}} \wedge \hat{\mathbf{i}} = \hat{\mathbf{j}} \wedge \hat{\mathbf{j}} = \hat{\mathbf{k}} \wedge \hat{\mathbf{k}} = \mathbf{0}$$

$$\left.\begin{aligned}\hat{\mathbf{i}} \wedge \hat{\mathbf{j}} &= -\hat{\mathbf{j}} \wedge \hat{\mathbf{i}} = \hat{\mathbf{k}} \\ \hat{\mathbf{j}} \wedge \hat{\mathbf{k}} &= -\hat{\mathbf{k}} \wedge \hat{\mathbf{j}} = \hat{\mathbf{i}} \\ \hat{\mathbf{k}} \wedge \hat{\mathbf{i}} &= -\hat{\mathbf{i}} \wedge \hat{\mathbf{k}} = \hat{\mathbf{j}}\end{aligned}\right\} \quad \text{i.e. cyclic permutations of the line above}$$

We may now use the laws of the previous paragraphs to expand the brackets given in the question:

$$\begin{aligned}(a_1\hat{\mathbf{i}} + a_2\hat{\mathbf{j}} + a_3\hat{\mathbf{k}}) \wedge (b_1\hat{\mathbf{i}} + b_2\hat{\mathbf{j}} + b_3\hat{\mathbf{k}}) = {} & a_1b_1\hat{\mathbf{i}} \wedge \hat{\mathbf{i}} + a_1b_2\hat{\mathbf{i}} \wedge \hat{\mathbf{j}} + a_1b_3\hat{\mathbf{i}} \wedge \hat{\mathbf{k}} \\ & + a_2b_1\hat{\mathbf{j}} \wedge \hat{\mathbf{i}} + a_2b_2\hat{\mathbf{j}} \wedge \hat{\mathbf{j}} + a_2b_3\hat{\mathbf{j}} \wedge \hat{\mathbf{k}} \\ & + a_3b_1\hat{\mathbf{k}} \wedge \hat{\mathbf{i}} + a_3b_2\hat{\mathbf{k}} \wedge \hat{\mathbf{j}} + a_3b_3\hat{\mathbf{k}} \wedge \hat{\mathbf{k}}\end{aligned}$$

$$= \mathbf{0} + a_1b_2\hat{\mathbf{k}} - a_1b_3\hat{\mathbf{j}} - a_2b_1\hat{\mathbf{k}} + \mathbf{0} + a_2b_3\hat{\mathbf{i}} + a_3b_1\hat{\mathbf{j}} - a_3b_2\hat{\mathbf{i}} + \mathbf{0}$$

$$= (a_2b_3 - a_3b_2)\hat{\mathbf{i}} + (a_3b_1 - a_1b_3)\hat{\mathbf{j}} + (a_1b_2 - a_2b_1)\hat{\mathbf{k}}$$

$$= \begin{vmatrix} \hat{\mathbf{i}} & a_1 & b_1 \\ \hat{\mathbf{j}} & a_2 & b_2 \\ \hat{\mathbf{k}} & a_3 & b_3 \end{vmatrix}$$

We use this determinant to define the vector product of the corresponding column vectors

$$\mathbf{a} = \begin{pmatrix} a_1 \\ a_2 \\ a_3 \end{pmatrix} \quad \text{and} \quad \mathbf{b} = \begin{pmatrix} b_1 \\ b_2 \\ b_3 \end{pmatrix}$$

by

$$\mathbf{a} \wedge \mathbf{b} = \begin{vmatrix} \hat{\mathbf{i}} & a_1 & b_1 \\ \hat{\mathbf{j}} & a_2 & b_2 \\ \hat{\mathbf{k}} & a_3 & b_3 \end{vmatrix}$$

**Worked example 12.1**

$$\begin{pmatrix} 1 \\ 2 \\ 3 \end{pmatrix} \wedge \begin{pmatrix} 3 \\ -2 \\ 1 \end{pmatrix} = \begin{vmatrix} \hat{\mathbf{i}} & 1 & 3 \\ \hat{\mathbf{j}} & 2 & -2 \\ \hat{\mathbf{k}} & 3 & 1 \end{vmatrix} = \begin{pmatrix} 2 + 6 \\ -(1 - 9) \\ -2 - 6 \end{pmatrix} = \begin{pmatrix} 8 \\ 8 \\ -8 \end{pmatrix}$$

**Worked example 12.2**

To find a unit vector perpendicular to both

$$\mathbf{a} = \begin{pmatrix} 1 \\ 2 \\ 3 \end{pmatrix} \quad \text{and} \quad \mathbf{b} = \begin{pmatrix} 3 \\ 2 \\ 1 \end{pmatrix}$$

*Solution*

$\mathbf{a} \wedge \mathbf{b}$ is a vector perpendicular to both **a** and **b**. A unit vector perpendicular to both therefore has as components the direction cosines of $\mathbf{a} \wedge \mathbf{b}$. Now

$$\mathbf{a} \wedge \mathbf{b} = \begin{vmatrix} \hat{\mathbf{i}} & 1 & 3 \\ \hat{\mathbf{j}} & 2 & 2 \\ \hat{\mathbf{k}} & 3 & 1 \end{vmatrix} = \begin{pmatrix} -4 \\ 8 \\ -4 \end{pmatrix}$$

Therefore $|\mathbf{a} \wedge \mathbf{b}| = \sqrt{4^2 + 8^2 + 4^2} = 4\sqrt{6}$. Hence the required unit vector is

$$\frac{1}{4\sqrt{6}}\begin{pmatrix} -4 \\ 8 \\ -4 \end{pmatrix} = \frac{1}{\sqrt{6}}\begin{pmatrix} -1 \\ 2 \\ -1 \end{pmatrix}$$

**Exercise 12*b***

For questions 1 and 2, the following column vectors are given:

$$\mathbf{a} = \begin{pmatrix} 2 \\ 1 \\ 3 \end{pmatrix}, \mathbf{b} = \begin{pmatrix} 3 \\ 5 \\ -2 \end{pmatrix}, \mathbf{c} = \begin{pmatrix} 6 \\ 2 \\ 1 \end{pmatrix}, \mathbf{d} = \begin{pmatrix} 3 \\ 0 \\ 2 \end{pmatrix}, \mathbf{e} = \begin{pmatrix} -1 \\ -2 \\ 8 \end{pmatrix}$$

1. Evaluate the vector products (a) $\mathbf{b} \wedge \mathbf{c}$, (b) $\mathbf{b} \wedge \mathbf{d}$, (c) $\mathbf{b} \wedge \mathbf{e}$.
2. Find unit vectors perpendicular to each of the pairs: (a) $\mathbf{c}$ and $\mathbf{d}$, (b) $\mathbf{c} - \mathbf{d}$ and $\mathbf{c} + \mathbf{e}$, (c) $(3\mathbf{a} - \mathbf{b})$ and $(3\mathbf{a} + \mathbf{b})$.

In questions 3 to 6, the following vectors in the *xy*-plane are given:

$$\mathbf{f} = \begin{pmatrix} 2 \\ 3 \\ 0 \end{pmatrix}, \mathbf{g} = \begin{pmatrix} 1 \\ -2 \\ 0 \end{pmatrix}, \mathbf{h} = \begin{pmatrix} -4 \\ 3 \\ 0 \end{pmatrix}, \mathbf{m} = \begin{pmatrix} -2 \\ -5 \\ 0 \end{pmatrix}$$

3. Evaluate the vector products: (a) $\mathbf{f} \wedge \mathbf{g}$, (b) $\mathbf{f} \wedge \mathbf{h}$, (c) $\mathbf{f} \wedge \mathbf{m}$. Comment on your results.
4. Evaluate the vector products: (a) $\mathbf{g} \wedge \mathbf{h}$, (b) $\mathbf{g} \wedge \mathbf{m}$, (c) $\mathbf{h} \wedge \mathbf{m}$. Is your comment from question 6 still valid? It should be.
5. (Trick questions.) Find vectors perpendicular to each of the pairs: (a) $2\mathbf{f} + 3\mathbf{g}$ and $2\mathbf{h} + 3\mathbf{m}$, (b) $\mathbf{f} + \mathbf{g} + \mathbf{h}$ and $2\mathbf{f} + 3\mathbf{g} + 4\mathbf{h}$, (c) $\mathbf{g} - \mathbf{m}$ and $\mathbf{h} - \mathbf{f}$.
6. Evaluate $(\mathbf{f} \wedge \mathbf{g}) \wedge \mathbf{h}$ and $\mathbf{f} \wedge (\mathbf{g} \wedge \mathbf{h})$.
   (a) Are these products equal?
   (b) Can these products be expressed as linear combinations of any pair of the original three vectors?

Questions 7 onwards are intended to demonstrate further points and possibilities in the study of vector products; we shall not dwell on them further at this stage.

7. Show that $\mathbf{b} = \mathbf{c} + \alpha\mathbf{a}$ implies that $\mathbf{a} \wedge \mathbf{b} = \mathbf{a} \wedge \mathbf{c}$. Is the converse true?
8. $$\mathbf{a} = \begin{pmatrix} 2 \\ -1 \\ 0 \end{pmatrix}, \mathbf{b} = \begin{pmatrix} 3 \\ 4 \\ 0 \end{pmatrix} \text{ and } \mathbf{c} = \begin{pmatrix} 4 \\ -3 \\ 0 \end{pmatrix}$$
   (a) Find the unit vector $\hat{\mathbf{b}}$ in the direction and sense of $\mathbf{b}$.
   (b) Evaluate the vector product $(\mathbf{c} - \mathbf{a}) \wedge \hat{\mathbf{b}}$.
   (c) Find $|(\mathbf{c} - \mathbf{a}) \wedge \hat{\mathbf{b}}|$. What does this quantity represent? Check your answer and assertion by using elementary methods of plane coordinate geometry.
9. A is the point (3, 4, 5), B is (2, 1, 3) and C is (4, 4, 4).
Find the perpendicular distance from the point C to the line $\overleftrightarrow{AB}$.

10. $$\mathbf{a} = \begin{pmatrix} a_1 \\ a_2 \\ a_3 \end{pmatrix} \text{ and } \mathbf{b} = \begin{pmatrix} b_1 \\ b_2 \\ b_3 \end{pmatrix}$$

Show that $\sin\theta = |\mathbf{a} \wedge \mathbf{b}|/k$, where $\theta$ is the angle between $\mathbf{a}$ and $\mathbf{b}$, and give algebraic expressions for $k$ and for $|\mathbf{a} \wedge \mathbf{b}|$.

If $\mathbf{a}$ and $\mathbf{b}$ are unit vectors, show that

$$\sin^2\theta = (a_2b_3 - a_3b_2)^2 + (a_3b_1 - a_1b_3)^2 + (a_1b_2 - a_2b_1)^2.$$

## 12.5 Miscellaneous exercises 12

1. Define the vector product of two column vectors as a determinant. Express the following vector product laws in determinant form, i.e. as determinant laws:

(a) $\mathbf{a}\wedge\mathbf{b} = -\mathbf{b}\wedge\mathbf{a}$ (b) $\mathbf{a}\wedge\mathbf{a} = \mathbf{0}$

(c) $\mathbf{a}\wedge(\mathbf{b}+\mathbf{c}) = \mathbf{a}\wedge\mathbf{b} + \mathbf{a}\wedge\mathbf{c}$ (d) $(\beta\mathbf{a})\wedge\mathbf{b} = \beta(\mathbf{a}\wedge\mathbf{b})$

2. $$\mathbf{p} = \begin{pmatrix} 3 \\ 1 \\ 4 \end{pmatrix} \text{ and } \mathbf{q} = \begin{pmatrix} -2 \\ 1 \\ -4 \end{pmatrix}$$

Evaluate the vector products (a) $\mathbf{p}\wedge\mathbf{p}$, (b) $\mathbf{q}\wedge\mathbf{q}$, (c) $\mathbf{p}\wedge\mathbf{q}$ and $\mathbf{q}\wedge\mathbf{p}$, (d) $(\mathbf{p}-\mathbf{q})\wedge(\mathbf{p}+\mathbf{q})$, (e) $(2\mathbf{p}-3\mathbf{q})\wedge(4\mathbf{p}+5\mathbf{q})$, (f) $(\alpha\mathbf{p}+\beta\mathbf{q})\wedge(\gamma\mathbf{p}+\delta\mathbf{q})$.

3. (a) (i) Define the scalar and vector products of two vectors **a**, **b** in terms of $a$, $b$ and the angle $\theta$ between the vectors, explaining carefully any sign conventions used.

Deduce the formula $|\mathbf{a}\wedge\mathbf{b}|^2 = a^2b^2 = (\mathbf{a}\cdot\mathbf{b})^2$.

(ii) Find the most general form for the vector **u** when $\mathbf{u}\wedge(\mathbf{i}+\mathbf{j}+2\mathbf{k}) = \mathbf{i}-\mathbf{j}$.

(b) A particle of mass $m$ moves so that its position vector **r** at time $t$ with respect to an origin O is given by $\mathbf{r} = (t^2-1)\mathbf{i} + 2t\mathbf{j}$.

Calculate the angular momentum, **h**, of the particle about O at time $t$, and its derivative $d\mathbf{h}/dt$. Find also the force **F** acting on the particle and its moment about O. (The moment of the force about O is defined as $\mathbf{r}\wedge\mathbf{F}$ and the angular momentum about O as $\mathbf{r}\wedge m\mathbf{v}$, where **v** is the velocity of the particle.) (JMB)

4. (a) Given that $\mathbf{x} + 1/a^2(\mathbf{a}\cdot\mathbf{x})\,\mathbf{a} = \mathbf{b}$, show that $\mathbf{a}\cdot\mathbf{x} = \frac{1}{2}\mathbf{a}\cdot\mathbf{b}$, and hence find **x** in terms of **a** and **b**.

(b) Find all the sets of vectors **p**, **q** and **r** that satisfy the following conditions: **p** is parallel to $\mathbf{i}+\mathbf{j}$ and $\mathrm{p} = 3$; **q** is parallel to $\mathbf{i}-\mathbf{j}$ and $\mathrm{q} = 1$; **r** satisfies $\mathbf{p} = \mathbf{q}\wedge\mathbf{r}$ and $\mathrm{r} = 9$.

('Parallel' includes the case of opposite directions). (JMB)

5. (a) In the plane of the triangle ABC squares ACXY, BCWZ are described, in the order given, externally to the triangle, on AC and BC respectively. Taking $\overrightarrow{CX} = \mathbf{b}$, $\overrightarrow{CA} = \mathbf{a}$, $\overrightarrow{CW} = \mathbf{q}$, $\overrightarrow{CB} = \mathbf{p}$, prove that $\mathbf{a}\cdot\mathbf{p} + \mathbf{q}\cdot\mathbf{b} = 0$. Deduce that $\overrightarrow{AW}\cdot\overrightarrow{BX} = 0$, and state the geometrical meaning of this equation.

(b) If **p** and **q** are non-null vectors such that the vector product $\mathbf{p}\wedge\mathbf{q} = \mathbf{0}$, show that $\mathbf{p} = \lambda\mathbf{q}$, where $\lambda$ is a scalar.

Three vectors **a**, **b**, **c** are such that

(i) $\mathbf{b}\wedge\mathbf{c} = \mathbf{c}\wedge\mathbf{a} \neq \mathbf{0}$.

Prove that (ii) $\mathbf{a}+\mathbf{b} = k\mathbf{c}$, where $k$ is a scalar.

If also (iii) $\mathbf{a}\wedge\mathbf{b} = \mathbf{b}\wedge\mathbf{c} = \mathbf{c}\wedge\mathbf{a} \neq \mathbf{0}$, prove that (iv) $\mathbf{a}+\mathbf{b}+\mathbf{c} = \mathbf{0}$.

Give geometrical interpretations of equations (iii) and (iv). (JMB)

6. Let **a** and **b** be non-zero vectors and $d$ a scalar.

(i) The equation $\mathbf{a}\cdot\mathbf{x} = d$ is to be solved for **x**. Writing $\mathbf{x} = \lambda\mathbf{a} + \mathbf{e}$, where **e** is an arbitrary vector perpendicular to **a**, show that the equation is satisfied if and only if $\lambda$ has a particular value (to be determined in terms of **a** and $d$). Interpret the equation $\mathbf{a}\cdot\mathbf{x} = d$ geometrically.

(ii) What condition must be satisfied by the vectors **a** and **b** if the equation $\mathbf{a}\wedge\mathbf{x} = \mathbf{b}$ has a solution? Given that this condition is satisfied, and writing $\mathbf{x} = \lambda\mathbf{a} + \mu\mathbf{b} + \gamma\mathbf{c}$, where $\lambda$, $\mu$, $\gamma$ are scalars and **c** is a unit vector perpendicular to **a** and **b** with **a**, **b**, **c** right-handed, show that the equation is satisfied if and only if $\mu$ and $\gamma$ have particular values (to be determined). Interpret the equation $\mathbf{a} \wedge \mathbf{x} = \mathbf{b}$ geometrically. (JMB)

7. (a) Four unit vectors **n**, **a**, **b**, **c** are used in the vector statements of the laws of reflection and refraction of light. They are the normal to the surface of separation of the two media and the direction of the incident, reflected and refracted rays respectively.

Interpret carefully the vector statements

$$\mathbf{a} \wedge \mathbf{n} = \mathbf{b} \wedge \mathbf{n}, \quad \mu\mathbf{a} \wedge \mathbf{n} = \mu'\mathbf{c} \wedge \mathbf{n}$$

where $\mu$ and $\mu'$ are the indices of refraction. Show $\mathbf{a} = \mathbf{b} + 2(\mathbf{a}\,.\,\mathbf{n})\mathbf{n}$. (MEI part)

# 13
# Vector Geometry (ii)

## Introduction

This chapter extends our geometrical experience to include situations that involve products of vectors; and also applies these experiences to obtain some of the basic results of three-dimensional coordinate geometry.

We often do not repeat relevant results from earlier chapters, but page references are given where they are helpful.

**Exercise 13*a***

This exercise is intended to ensure a satisfactory knowledge of the topics already covered in vector geometry, particularly in Chapters 2, 4, 11 and 12.

1. Find the modulus of each of the following vectors:

(a) $2\hat{\mathbf{i}} - 3\hat{\mathbf{j}}$, (b) $\begin{pmatrix} 4 \\ -3 \end{pmatrix}$, (c) $\begin{pmatrix} 5 \\ -3 \\ 2 \end{pmatrix}$, (d) $-10\hat{\mathbf{i}} + 6\hat{\mathbf{j}} - 4\hat{\mathbf{k}}$

2. Find the value of $a$ if the set of vectors

$$\left\{\begin{pmatrix} 5 \\ -3 \\ 2 \end{pmatrix}, \begin{pmatrix} a \\ 2 \\ 3 \end{pmatrix}, \begin{pmatrix} -1 \\ -2 \\ 4 \end{pmatrix}\right\}$$

is linearly dependent.

3. You are given the position vectors $\mathbf{p} = 3\mathbf{a} - 4\mathbf{b}$, $\mathbf{q} = 5\mathbf{a} + 3\mathbf{b}$ and $\mathbf{r} = \mathbf{a} - 6\mathbf{b}$ of the points P, Q and R respectively.

Find, in terms of **a** and **b**, position vectors for
(a) the midpoint of PQ
(b) the point dividing QR in the ration 1:3
(c) the point dividing RP *externally* in the ratio 1:3
(d) the centroid of the triangle PQR.

4. **a**, **b**, **c**, **d** are the position vectors of the vertices A, B, C, D, respectively, of the parallelogram ABCD. $G_1$ and $G_2$ are the respective centroids of the triangles ABD and BCD. Find position vectors for $G_1$ and $G_2$ in terms of **a**, **b**, **c**, **d**. $H_1$ and $H_2$ are the respective centroids of the triangles $ABG_1$ and $BCG_2$. Prove that $H_1H_2$, $G_1G_2$ and AC are all parallel, and find the ratio of their lengths.

5. Points A and B have position vectors $\mathbf{a} = 2\hat{\mathbf{i}} - 3\hat{\mathbf{j}} + 7\hat{\mathbf{k}}$ and $\mathbf{b} = 3\hat{\mathbf{i}} + 3\hat{\mathbf{j}} - \hat{\mathbf{k}}$. (a) Find the equation of the line AB. (b) Find a vector perpendicular to both **a** and **b** .

(c) Find the equation of the line perpendicular to both **a** and **b** and passing through the mid-point of AB.

6. Find the direction cosines of the following vectors:

$$\text{(a)} \begin{pmatrix} 1 \\ 2 \\ 9 \end{pmatrix} \quad \text{(b)} \begin{pmatrix} 3 \\ -12 \\ 13 \end{pmatrix} \quad \text{(c)} \begin{pmatrix} -40 \\ 9 \end{pmatrix}$$

7. Evaluate the scalar products and the vector products of the following pairs of vectors:

$$\text{(a)} \begin{pmatrix} 1 \\ 2 \\ 9 \end{pmatrix} \text{ and } \begin{pmatrix} 5 \\ -12 \\ 13 \end{pmatrix} \quad \text{(b)} \begin{pmatrix} 1 \\ 1 \\ 0 \end{pmatrix} \text{ and } \begin{pmatrix} -40 \\ 7 \\ 0 \end{pmatrix}$$

$$\text{(c)} \begin{pmatrix} 2 \\ 3 \\ 0 \end{pmatrix} \text{ and } \begin{pmatrix} -2 \\ 5 \\ 0 \end{pmatrix} \quad \text{(d)} \begin{pmatrix} 2 \\ 4 \\ 6 \end{pmatrix} \text{ and } \begin{pmatrix} -4 \\ -8 \\ -12 \end{pmatrix}$$

## 13.1 The section formula

Suppose the points A and B have Cartesian coordinates $(a_1, a_2, a_3)$ and $(b_1, b_2, b_3)$ respectively. Then they may be represented by column vectors

$$\mathbf{a} = \begin{pmatrix} a_1 \\ a_2 \\ a_3 \end{pmatrix} \quad \text{and} \quad \mathbf{b} = \begin{pmatrix} b_1 \\ b_2 \\ b_3 \end{pmatrix}$$

or by the corresponding position vectors **a** and **b**.

Suppose that P $(p_1, p_2, p_3)$ divides AB in the ratio $\alpha:\beta$. Then, by the section formula (page 64),

$$\mathbf{p} = \frac{\beta\mathbf{a} + \alpha\mathbf{b}}{\alpha + \beta}$$

Therefore

$$\begin{pmatrix} p_1 \\ p_2 \\ p_3 \end{pmatrix} = \frac{\beta\begin{pmatrix} a_1 \\ a_2 \\ a_3 \end{pmatrix} + \alpha\begin{pmatrix} b_1 \\ b_2 \\ b_3 \end{pmatrix}}{\alpha + \beta}$$

Therefore

$$p_i = \frac{\beta a_i + \alpha b_i}{\alpha + \beta} \text{ for } i = 1, 2, 3.$$

Thus each coordinate of P can be worked out separately, using the section formula. This is also true in two dimensions.

**Worked example 13.1**

Find the coordinates of the point dividing the line joining A (2, 3) and B(6, 15) in the ratio 2:3.

*Solution*

$$\mathbf{p} = \frac{3\begin{pmatrix}2\\3\end{pmatrix} + 2\begin{pmatrix}6\\15\end{pmatrix}}{3+2} = \frac{1}{5}\begin{pmatrix}18\\39\end{pmatrix}$$

hence the required point has coordinates (18/5, 39/5).

**Worked example 13.2**

Find the mid-point of the line joining (2, 3, 5) and (6, 7, 9).

*Solution*

The mid-point of AB has position vector $\mathbf{p} = \frac{1}{2}(\mathbf{a} + \mathbf{b})$. Therefore the required mid-point has coordinates

$$\left(\frac{2+6}{2}, \frac{3+7}{2}, \frac{5+9}{2}\right) = (4, 5, 6)$$

**Worked example 13.3**

Find the ratio $\alpha:\beta$ in which the point $(\frac{3}{2}, \frac{5}{4}, \frac{1}{4})$ divides the line joining (1, 2, −2) and (3, −1, 7).

*Solution*

Using the section formula for the $x$-coordinate,

$$\frac{3}{2} = \frac{\beta \times 1 + \alpha \times 3}{\alpha + \beta}$$

thus

$$3(\alpha + \beta) = 2(\beta + 3\alpha)$$

and so

$$\beta = 3\alpha$$

Therefore $\alpha:\beta = 1:3$. We may check this ratio with the other components.

**Worked example 13.4**

Find the coordinates of the centroid G of the triangle with vertices A (1, 3, −2), B (4, 6, 2) and C (3, 0, −1).

*Solution*

The centroid G of triangle ABC has position vector $\mathbf{g} = \frac{1}{3}(\mathbf{a} + \mathbf{b} + \mathbf{c})$ and column vector

$$\mathbf{g} = \frac{1}{3}\left[\begin{pmatrix}1\\3\\-2\end{pmatrix} + \begin{pmatrix}4\\6\\2\end{pmatrix} + \begin{pmatrix}3\\0\\-1\end{pmatrix}\right]$$

$$= \frac{1}{3}\begin{pmatrix}8\\9\\-1\end{pmatrix}$$

Therefore G has coordinates $(\frac{8}{3}, 3, -\frac{1}{3})$.

**Exercise 13*b***

For these questions, the points A, B, C, D, E and F have the respective coordinates A (2, 1, 3), B (3, 5, −2), C (6, 2, 1), D (3, 0, 2), E (−1, −2, 8) and F (2, 3, 1).

1. (i) Find the coordinates of the points dividing AB in the following ratios: (a) 2:3, (b) 1:4.
   (ii) Find the coordinates of the points dividing BC in the ratio: 5: −2.
   (iii) Find the coordinates of the points dividing CD in the ratio: −1:4.
2. Find the coordinates of the mid-points of the line segments AB, AC, AD, AE and AF.
3. (i) Find the coordinates of the centroid $G_1$ of the triangle BCD, the centroid $G_2$ of triangle CDE, the centroid $G_3$ of triangle DEB and the centroid $G_4$ of triangle BCE.
   (ii) Find the coordinates of the point dividing $G_1E$ in the ratio 1:3.
   (iii) Repeat (ii) for the medians $G_2B$, $G_3C$ and $G_4D$.
   (iv) State and prove a general result about the medians of a tetrahedron JKLM.
4. (i) Show that any point on AB may be regarded as having position vector

$$\begin{pmatrix} 2 \\ 1 \\ 3 \end{pmatrix} + t\begin{pmatrix} 1 \\ 4 \\ -5 \end{pmatrix}$$

where $t$ is a (variable) parameter.
   (ii) Which points correspond to the following parameters (values of $t$)? (a) 0, (b) 1, (c) $\frac{1}{2}$, (d) 0·4, (e) 0·6, (f) $-\frac{1}{2}$, (g) − 1.
5. Find the ratios in which the following points divide CD: (a) $(5\frac{1}{4}, 1\frac{1}{2}, 1\frac{1}{4})$, (b) (0, 2, −3), (c) (−3, −4, 4), (d) (1, −4/3, 8/3), (e) $(7\frac{1}{2}, 3, \frac{1}{2})$, (f) (36/5, 14/5, 3/5).
6. Find the lengths of the line segments AC, BC, DC, EC and FC.
7. Use the results of questions 10 and 11, and the cosine rule, to find the cosines of the angles AOC, BOC, DOC, EOC, and FOC.

## 13.2 The Cartesian equations of a straight line in three dimensions

Suppose the fixed point A has coordinates $(a_1, a_2, a_3)$, and the fixed position vector **c** has column vector

$$\mathbf{c} = \begin{pmatrix} c_1 \\ c_2 \\ c_3 \end{pmatrix}$$

Then we may regard $\{c_1, c_2, c_3\}$ as a set of direction ratios for the straight line through A parallel to **c**.

The equation of the line is given in position vector form by $\mathbf{r} = \mathbf{a} + t\mathbf{c}$, where $t$ is a variable parameter. (page 75) Suppose

$$\mathbf{r} = \begin{pmatrix} x \\ y \\ z \end{pmatrix}$$

Then

$$\begin{pmatrix} x \\ y \\ z \end{pmatrix} = \begin{pmatrix} a_1 \\ a_2 \\ a_3 \end{pmatrix} + t \begin{pmatrix} c_1 \\ c_2 \\ c_3 \end{pmatrix} \tag{1}$$

Therefore

$$x = a_1 + tc_1$$
$$y = a_2 + tc_2$$
$$z = a_3 + tc_3$$

Therefore

$$t = \frac{x - a_1}{c_1} = \frac{y - a_2}{c_2} = \frac{z - a_3}{c_3} \tag{2}$$

with $c_1$, $c_2$ and $c_3$ non-zero. This gives the coordinate form of the equations of the straight line through A in the direction given by **c**. If any of the components of **c** is zero, then Equ. 2 must be amended. For example, if $c_2 = 0$, then it becomes:

$$\frac{x - a_1}{c_1} = \frac{z - a_3}{c_3} \quad \text{and} \quad y = a_2, \text{ or } \frac{x - a_1}{c_1} = \frac{y - a_2}{0} = \frac{z - a_3}{c_3}$$

Note that, if the equations are written in the form of Equ. 2, then the denominators of the fractions are direction ratios for the line.

Alternatively, we may give the equation of the line through A and B. In that case, we may take $\mathbf{c} = \mathbf{AB} = \mathbf{b} - \mathbf{a}$, and re-write Equ. 2 as

$$\frac{x - a_1}{b_1 - a_1} = \frac{y - a_2}{b_2 - a_2} = \frac{z - a_3}{b_3 - a_3} \tag{3}$$

or in one of the modified forms if $b_i = a_i$ for any value of $i$.

**Worked example 13.5**

Find the equation(s) of the line joining A (1, 3, −2) and B (4, 1, 6), and find direction ratios for the line.

*Solution*

The equation(s) may be obtained by using Equations 1 or 3. Using Equ. 1, we have

$$\begin{pmatrix} x \\ y \\ z \end{pmatrix} = \begin{pmatrix} 1 \\ 3 \\ -2 \end{pmatrix} + t \begin{pmatrix} 4 - 1 \\ 1 - 3 \\ 6 + 2 \end{pmatrix}$$

that is

$$\begin{pmatrix} x \\ y \\ z \end{pmatrix} = \begin{pmatrix} 1 \\ 3 \\ -2 \end{pmatrix} + t \begin{pmatrix} 3 \\ -2 \\ 8 \end{pmatrix}$$

Using Equ. 3, or re-writing the above line, we have

$$t = \frac{x - 1}{3} = \frac{y - 3}{-2} = \frac{z + 2}{8}$$

A set of possible direction ratios for the line is $\{3, -2, 8\}$.

**Worked example 13.6**

Find the equations of the following straight lines:

(a) through A $(4, -5, -1)$ parallel to $\dfrac{x-2}{3} = \dfrac{y+3}{4} = \dfrac{z-1}{1}$;
(b) joining A $(2, 3, -1)$ and B $(-1, 3, 3)$,
(c) the median AD of the triangle ABC, where C is $(4, 4, 4)$.

*Solution*

(a) The given line has direction ratios 3, 4, 1. Therefore the required line has direction ratios 3, 4, 1. Therefore its equations are

$$\frac{x-4}{3} = \frac{y+5}{4} = \frac{z+1}{1}$$

Note that such expressions are not unique; we may, for example, subtract 1 from each fraction to obtain the alternative form:

$$\frac{x-7}{3} = \frac{y-1}{4} = \frac{z}{1},$$

where the important thing to note is that the direction is the same.

(b) $$\mathbf{AB} = \mathbf{b} - \mathbf{a} = \begin{pmatrix} -1 \\ 3 \\ 3 \end{pmatrix} - \begin{pmatrix} 2 \\ 3 \\ -1 \end{pmatrix} = \begin{pmatrix} -3 \\ 0 \\ 4 \end{pmatrix}$$

Therefore the equation of AB is

$$\begin{pmatrix} x \\ y \\ z \end{pmatrix} = \begin{pmatrix} 3 \\ 3 \\ -1 \end{pmatrix} + t \begin{pmatrix} -3 \\ 0 \\ 4 \end{pmatrix}$$

which may be given alternatively as

$$\frac{x-3}{-3} = \frac{z+1}{4} (= t),\ y = 3$$

(c) The median AD joins A to the mid-point D of BC. Its direction is given by

$$\mathbf{AD} = \mathbf{d} - \mathbf{a} = \tfrac{1}{2}\mathbf{b} + \tfrac{1}{2}\mathbf{c} - \mathbf{a} = \begin{pmatrix} -\frac{1}{2} \\ \frac{1}{2} \\ 4\frac{1}{2} \end{pmatrix}$$

Therefore its equation is

$$\begin{pmatrix} x \\ y \\ z \end{pmatrix} = \begin{pmatrix} 2 \\ 3 \\ -1 \end{pmatrix} + t \begin{pmatrix} -\frac{1}{2} \\ \frac{1}{2} \\ 4\frac{1}{2} \end{pmatrix}$$

and we see that the centroid G corresponds to $t = 2/3$.

**Worked Example 13.7**

One straight line passes through the points (1, 2, −2) and 2, −1, 1), and another passes through (−1, 2, 3) and is parallel to

$$\begin{pmatrix} 1 \\ 3 \\ -8 \end{pmatrix}$$

Find if they meet, and, if so, where.

*Solution*

Direction ratios for the first line are 2 − 1, −1 − 2, 1 + 2, i.e. 1, −3, 3. Therefore its equation is

$$\begin{pmatrix} x \\ y \\ z \end{pmatrix} = \begin{pmatrix} 1 \\ 2 \\ -2 \end{pmatrix} + t \begin{pmatrix} 1 \\ -3 \\ +3 \end{pmatrix} = \begin{pmatrix} 1 + t \\ 2 - 3t \\ -2 + 3t \end{pmatrix}$$

i.e. any point P on the line has coordinates $(1 + t, 2 - 3t, -2 + 3t)$ for some particular value of $t$. The equation of the second line is

$$\begin{pmatrix} x \\ y \\ z \end{pmatrix} = \begin{pmatrix} -1 \\ 2 \\ 3 \end{pmatrix} + u \begin{pmatrix} 1 \\ 3 \\ -8 \end{pmatrix} = \begin{pmatrix} -1 + u \\ 2 + 3u \\ 3 - 8u \end{pmatrix}$$

i.e. any point Q on the line has coordinates $(-1 + u, 2 + 3u, 3 - 8u)$ for some particular value of $u$. The two lines meet if they have a point in common, i.e. if we can find values of $t$ and $u$ so that P and Q coincide. This we can do if

$$1 + t = -1 + u, \quad 2 - 3t = 2 + 3u \quad \text{and} \quad -2 + 3t = 3 - 8u$$

That is, if

$$u = t + 2, \quad u = -t \quad \text{and} \quad u = \tfrac{5}{8} - \tfrac{3}{8}t$$

That is, if

$$u = 1 \quad \text{and} \quad t = -1$$

(If we had not been able to find such values of $t$ and $u$, then the lines would not have met.) Hence the coordinates of the common point are obtained by putting $u = 1$ or $t = -1$ in one of the equations above. Therefore the lines meet at (0, 5, −5).

**Exercise 13*c***

1. Find direction ratios, and the direction cosines of the lines joining the following pairs of points:
   (i) A (−1, 3, −2) and B (9, 0, 2);
   (ii) C (4, −3, 7) and D (6, −5, 8);
   (iii) E (2, 4, 6) and F (3, 6, 9).

For questions 2 to 5, give your answers in the form $\dfrac{x - \alpha}{\beta} = \dfrac{y - \gamma}{\delta} = \dfrac{z - \epsilon}{\varphi}$.

2. Find the equations of the straight lines joining each of the pairs of points in question 1.

3. Find the equations of the following straight lines, where the coordinates of the points are as given in question 1:

(i) through C parallel to AB;
(ii) through E parallel to CD.

4. Find the equations of the following straight lines:

(i) in the direction and sense of

$$\begin{pmatrix} 2 \\ 3 \\ 4 \end{pmatrix}$$

passing through (2, 3, 4);
(ii) passing through (2, 3, 4) and (3, 4, 5).

5. Find if the line through (2, 3, 4) and (3, 4, 5), from question 4 (ii), meets the line with equations

$$\frac{x-3}{3} = \frac{y+2}{-1} = \frac{z}{4}$$

6. Find the direction cosines of the following straight lines:

(i) $$\frac{x-3}{-1} = \frac{y+5}{3} = \frac{z-1}{-2}$$

(ii) $$\begin{pmatrix} x \\ y \\ z \end{pmatrix} = \begin{pmatrix} 4 \\ 21 \\ 28 \end{pmatrix} + t\begin{pmatrix} 6 \\ 7 \\ 8 \end{pmatrix}$$

## 13.3 The angle between two column vectors

We may combine a number of earlier results to give us the concept of the angle between two column vectors, where we regard the column vectors either as members of $R^3$ or as shorthand for linear combinations of the standard basis $\{\hat{\mathbf{i}}, \hat{\mathbf{j}}, \hat{\mathbf{k}}\}$.

If **a** and **b** are position vectors, then $\mathbf{a}.\mathbf{b} = ab\cos\theta$, using the usual notation.

If **a** and **b** are column vectors, then $\mathbf{a}.\mathbf{b} = a_1b_1 + a_2b_2 + a_3b_3$, using the usual notation. Also

$$a = |\mathbf{a}| = \sqrt{a_1^2 + a_2^2 + a_3^2} \quad \text{and} \quad b = |\mathbf{b}| = \sqrt{b_1^2 + b_2^2 + b_3^2}$$

Thus, if **a** and **b** are column vectors representing the respective position vectors,

$$a_1b_1 + a_2b_2 + a_3b_3 = \sqrt{(a_1^2 + a_2^2 + a_3^2)(b_1^2 + b_2^2 + b_3^2)}\cos\theta$$

and thus

$$\cos\theta = \frac{a_1b_1 + a_2b_2 + a_3b_3}{\sqrt{(a_1^2 + a_2^2 + a_3^2)(b_1^2 + b_2^2 + b_3^2)}}$$

This expression for $\cos\theta$ serves two purposes:

(i) By its derivation, it gives the cosine of the angle $\theta$ between the two position vectors $\mathbf{a}$ and $\mathbf{b}$ represented by the respective column vectors.

(ii) by *definition*, it gives the *cosine of the angle between the column vectors*

$$\mathbf{a} = \begin{pmatrix} a_1 \\ a_2 \\ a_3 \end{pmatrix} \quad \text{and} \quad \mathbf{b} = \begin{pmatrix} b_1 \\ b_2 \\ b_3 \end{pmatrix}$$

of the abstract vector space $R^3$. This definition may be extended to define the cosine of the angle between two members of the vector space $R^n$ of column vectors with $n$ entries, even though these vectors have no geometrical equivalents.

Now, two vectors $\mathbf{a}$ and $\mathbf{b}$ are orthogonal if and only if $\mathbf{a}.\mathbf{b} = 0$. We shall use the word orthogonal in the context of abstract scalar products as well as with scalar products where orthogonal and perpendicular are synonymous.

Thus the column vectors $\mathbf{a}$ and $\mathbf{b}$ are *orthogonal* $\Longleftrightarrow a_1b_1 + a_2b_2 + a_3b_3 = 0$. They are *orthonormal* if they are also both unit vectors.

**Worked Example 13.8**

Find the angles between the following pair of vectors:

(i) $\begin{pmatrix} 2 \\ 3 \end{pmatrix}$ and $\begin{pmatrix} -1 \\ 2 \end{pmatrix}$

(ii) $\begin{pmatrix} -2 \\ -1 \\ 3 \end{pmatrix}$ and $\begin{pmatrix} 3 \\ 2 \\ 1 \end{pmatrix}$

*Solution*

(i) If $\theta$ is the required angle, then

$$\cos\theta = \frac{2 \times -1 + 3 \times 2}{\sqrt{(2^2 + 3^2)[(-1)^2 + 2^2]}} = \frac{4}{\sqrt{65}} = \cos 30{\cdot}2^\circ$$

hence $\theta = 30{\cdot}2^\circ$.

(ii) If $\phi$ is the required angle, then

$$\cos\phi = \frac{-6 - 2 + 3}{\sqrt{(4 + 1 + 9)(9 + 4 + 1)}} = \frac{-5}{14} = -\cos 69{\cdot}1^\circ$$

hence $\phi = 180^\circ - 69{\cdot}1^\circ = 110{\cdot}9^\circ$.

**Worked Example 13.9**

Establish whether the angles between the following pairs of vectors are acute, obtuse, zero, or right angles:

(a) $\begin{pmatrix} 1 \\ 2 \\ 3 \end{pmatrix}$ and $\begin{pmatrix} 2 \\ -1 \\ 4 \end{pmatrix}$, (b) $\begin{pmatrix} 1 \\ 2 \\ 3 \end{pmatrix}$ and $\begin{pmatrix} 3 \\ -2 \\ -1 \end{pmatrix}$,

(c) $\begin{pmatrix} 1 \\ 2 \\ 3 \end{pmatrix}$ and $\begin{pmatrix} 3 \\ 0 \\ -1 \end{pmatrix}$, (d) $\begin{pmatrix} 1 \\ 2 \\ 3 \end{pmatrix}$ and $\begin{pmatrix} 3 \\ 6 \\ 9 \end{pmatrix}$

*Solution*

We have no need to actually find the angles, for, if $0 \leqq \theta \leqq \pi$,

the angle is acute $\iff \cos\theta > 0 \iff \mathbf{a}.\mathbf{b} > 0$,

the angle is obtuse $\iff \cos\theta < 0 \iff \mathbf{a}.\mathbf{b} < 0$, and so on,

and we thus inspect the scalar product.

(a) $\begin{pmatrix}1\\2\\3\end{pmatrix}.\begin{pmatrix}2\\-1\\4\end{pmatrix} = 2 - 2 + 12 = 12 > 0 \implies$ acute angle

(b) $\begin{pmatrix}1\\2\\3\end{pmatrix}.\begin{pmatrix}3\\-2\\-1\end{pmatrix} = 3 - 4 - 3 = -4 < 0 \implies$ obtuse angle

(c) $\begin{pmatrix}1\\2\\3\end{pmatrix}.\begin{pmatrix}3\\0\\-1\end{pmatrix} = 3 + 0 - 3 = 0 \implies$ right angle

(d) $\begin{pmatrix}3\\6\\9\end{pmatrix} = 3\begin{pmatrix}1\\2\\3\end{pmatrix} \implies$ zero angle

## 13.4 Orthogonal matrices

Let $\mathbf{a} = \begin{pmatrix}a_1\\a_2\\a_3\end{pmatrix}$, $\mathbf{b} = \begin{pmatrix}b_1\\b_2\\b_3\end{pmatrix}$ and $\mathbf{c} = \begin{pmatrix}c_1\\c_2\\c_3\end{pmatrix}$

Then we write $(\mathbf{a}|\mathbf{b}|\mathbf{c})$ to mean the matrix with columns **a**, **b** and **c**, namely

$$A = \begin{pmatrix}a_1 & b_1 & c_1\\a_2 & b_2 & c_2\\a_3 & b_3 & c_3\end{pmatrix}$$

Let A′ be the transpose of **A**. Then

$$A'A = \begin{pmatrix}a^2 & \mathbf{a}.\mathbf{b} & \mathbf{a}.\mathbf{c}\\ \mathbf{a}.\mathbf{b} & b^2 & \mathbf{b}.\mathbf{c}\\ \mathbf{a}.\mathbf{c} & \mathbf{b}.\mathbf{c} & c^2\end{pmatrix}$$

(The reader is advised to check the details, if necessary.)

Now suppose that $\{\mathbf{a}, \mathbf{b}, \mathbf{c}\}$ is an orthogonal set of vectors, i.e. the scalar products of all possible pairs of different vectors are zero. Then A′A is the diagonal matrix

$$\begin{pmatrix}a^2 & 0 & 0\\0 & b^2 & 0\\0 & 0 & c^2\end{pmatrix}$$

If, further, **a**, **b** and **c** are all unit vectors, i.e. $\{\mathbf{a}, \mathbf{b}, \mathbf{c}\}$ is an orthonormal set, then AA′ = A′A = I, the identity matrix. We then call the matrix A *orthogonal* (beware the difference in usage). Thus the following statements are equivalent to each other:

(i) $\{\mathbf{a}, \mathbf{b}, \mathbf{c}\}$ is an *orthonormal set*;
(ii) The matrix A = $(\mathbf{a}|\mathbf{b}|\mathbf{c})$ is *orthogonal*;
(iii) if A = $(\mathbf{a}|\mathbf{b}|\mathbf{c})$, then AA′ = A′A = I.

Further treatment of matrix properties is more relevant to a text on matrices, such as Brand and Sherlock, *Matrices; Pure and Applied* (Edward Arnold).

**Exercise 13*d***

For questions 1 to 4, you are given the vectors

$$\mathbf{p} = \begin{pmatrix} 2 \\ 2 \end{pmatrix}, \mathbf{q} = \begin{pmatrix} 3 \\ 1 \end{pmatrix}, \mathbf{r} = \begin{pmatrix} 1 \\ 3 \end{pmatrix}, \mathbf{s} = \begin{pmatrix} 4 \\ -2 \end{pmatrix}, \mathbf{t} = \begin{pmatrix} -1 \\ 3 \end{pmatrix} \text{ and } \mathbf{u} = \begin{pmatrix} -2 \\ -3 \end{pmatrix}$$

1. Find the lengths of each of the vectors **p**, **q**, **r**, **s**, **t**, **u**.
2. Find the cosines of the angles between **p** and each of **q**, **r**, **s**, **t**, **u**.
3. Find an orthonormal set of vectors, one of which is determined by **p**. Express **q**, **r**, **s**, **t** and **u** as linear combinations of this orthonormal set.
4. Prove that

$$\frac{1}{x(x+1)+1}\begin{pmatrix} -x & x(x+1) & x+1 \\ x+1 & -x & x(x+1) \\ x(x+1) & x+1 & -x \end{pmatrix}$$

is always orthogonal. (Note that $x = -1$ gives the identity matrix.)

5. Prove that

$$\left\{\begin{pmatrix} 1 \\ 5 \\ 4 \end{pmatrix}, \begin{pmatrix} 2 \\ -2 \\ 2 \end{pmatrix}, \begin{pmatrix} 3 \\ 1 \\ -2 \end{pmatrix}\right\}$$

is orthogonal.

6. Are the following sets of vectors orthogonal?

(a) $\left\{\begin{pmatrix} 2 \\ 5 \end{pmatrix}, \begin{pmatrix} 5 \\ 2 \end{pmatrix}\right\}$ (b) $\left\{\begin{pmatrix} 2 \\ 5 \end{pmatrix}, \begin{pmatrix} 5 \\ -2 \end{pmatrix}\right\}$ (c) $\left\{\begin{pmatrix} 1 \\ -2 \\ 1 \end{pmatrix}, \begin{pmatrix} 3 \\ -4 \\ 2 \end{pmatrix}, \begin{pmatrix} -7 \\ 2 \\ 5 \end{pmatrix}\right\}$

## 13.5 The equation of a plane

On page 76, we have vector forms for the equations of the planes (a) through a fixed point parallel to two given fixed vectors, and (b) through three fixed points. When we established these equations, we started by considering how we could give a unique description of the plane whose equation was required, and, at the time, found just the two possibilities (a) and (b). We now find a third possibility, which gives a simpler and more convenient equation, involving scalar products.

Suppose we are given a plane, and an origin of position vectors which may or may not lie in the plane. Suppose, first of all, that O is *not* in the plane. Take the point N such that N is in the plane, and **ON** is perpendicular to the plane (that is, **ON** is perpendicular to any line in the plane). The position vector $\mathbf{n} = \mathbf{ON}$ is called the *normal* from O to the plane, and the unit position vector $\hat{\mathbf{n}}$ in the direction and sense of **n** is called the *unit normal* from O to the plane. We claim that the location of the plane is uniquely specified by **n**, or by $\hat{\mathbf{n}}$ and the length of **n**.

Suppose $|\mathbf{n}| = p$. Then $\mathbf{n} = p\hat{\mathbf{n}}$. Suppose R is a point in the plane, with position vector **r**. Then ON is perpendicular to NR, that is $\mathbf{ON}.\mathbf{NR} = 0$.

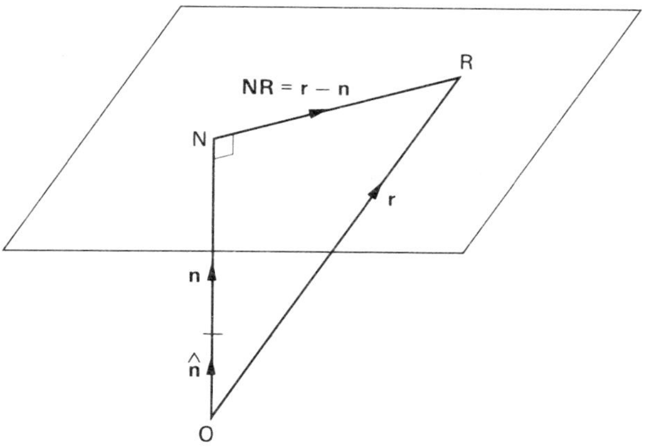


**Fig. 13.1.** The plane with normal **n**.

But

$$\mathbf{ON} = \mathbf{n} = p\hat{\mathbf{n}} \quad \text{and} \quad \mathbf{NR} = \mathbf{r} - \mathbf{n} = \mathbf{r} - p\hat{\mathbf{n}}$$

Therefore

$$p\hat{\mathbf{n}} \cdot (\mathbf{r} - p\hat{\mathbf{n}}) = 0$$

Therefore

$$\hat{\mathbf{n}} \cdot \mathbf{r} - p(\hat{\mathbf{n}} \cdot \hat{\mathbf{n}}) = 0 \quad (p \neq 0 \text{ since O is not in the plane})$$

Therefore

$$\hat{\mathbf{n}} \cdot \mathbf{r} = p(\hat{\mathbf{n}} \cdot \hat{\mathbf{n}}) = p \quad \text{since } \hat{\mathbf{n}} \text{ is a unit vector}$$

Therefore

$$\mathbf{r} \cdot \hat{\mathbf{n}} = p.$$

is the equation of the plane with unit normal $\hat{\mathbf{n}}$, at perpendicular distance $p \neq 0$ from the origin.

If, on the other hand, the plane passes through O, then we may take a unit normal $\hat{\mathbf{n}}$ to the plane, and the position vector $\mathbf{r}$ of any point R in the plane. Then $\hat{\mathbf{n}}$ and $\mathbf{r}$ are orthogonal, and so $\mathbf{r} \cdot \hat{\mathbf{n}} = 0$. Thus the equation $\mathbf{r} \cdot \hat{\mathbf{n}} = p$ also holds for $p = 0$.

The conclusion, therefore, is that the equation of a plane with unit normal $\hat{\mathbf{n}}$, at perpendicular distance $p$ from the origin, is $\mathbf{r} \cdot \hat{\mathbf{n}} = p$.

In coordinate form, take

$$\mathbf{r} = \begin{pmatrix} x \\ y \\ z \end{pmatrix} \quad \text{and} \quad \hat{\mathbf{n}} = \begin{pmatrix} n_1 \\ n_2 \\ n_3 \end{pmatrix}$$

Then $\mathbf{r} \cdot \hat{\mathbf{n}} = p$ implies that $n_1x + n_2y + n_3z = p$, and this is the equation of a plane in three-dimensional Cartesian coordinates.

**Worked example 13.10**

Find the equations of the following planes:
(a) through A (2, −1, 3) with normal

$$\mathbf{n} = \begin{pmatrix} 3 \\ 5 \\ 2 \end{pmatrix}$$

(b) through A (1, 2, −3), B (2, −1, 3) and C (3, 0, 4).

*Solution*

(a) We are given the normal

$$\mathbf{n} = \begin{pmatrix} 3 \\ 5 \\ 2 \end{pmatrix}$$

with $|\mathbf{n}|^2 = 3^2 + 5^2 + 2^2 = 38$. Therefore the unit normal is

$$\mathbf{n} = \frac{1}{\sqrt{38}} \begin{pmatrix} 3 \\ 5 \\ 2 \end{pmatrix}$$

and so the equation of the plane is

$$\frac{1}{\sqrt{38}}(3x + 5y + 2z) = p.$$

Now the plane passes through the point (2, −1, 3). Therefore

$$\frac{1}{\sqrt{38}}[3 \times 2 + 5 \times (-1) + 2 \times 3] = p \text{ and so } p = \frac{7}{\sqrt{38}}$$

Thus the equation of the plane is $3x + 5y + 2z = 7$.

Alternatively, we may say that the position vector **a** of A must satisfy the equation $\mathbf{r}.\hat{\mathbf{n}} = p$, in other words $\mathbf{a}.\hat{\mathbf{n}} = p$ gives the value of $p$. Therefore the required equation is $\mathbf{r}.\mathbf{n} = \mathbf{a}.\hat{\mathbf{n}}$, which is the general form of the equation of the plane through A with unit normal $\hat{\mathbf{n}}$. Even more simply, multiplying both sides by $p = |\mathbf{n}|$ gives $\mathbf{r}.(p\hat{\mathbf{u}}) = \mathbf{a}.(p\hat{\mathbf{n}})$, thus $\mathbf{r}.\mathbf{n} = \mathbf{a}.\mathbf{n}$, and we have no need to find $\hat{\mathbf{n}}$ explicitly. We will use this in (b).

(b) The unit normal $\hat{\mathbf{n}}$ is perpendicular to **AB** and to **CB**. Therefore we may take a normal

$$\begin{aligned} \mathbf{n} &= \mathbf{AB} \wedge \mathbf{CB} \\ &= (\mathbf{b} - \mathbf{a}) \wedge (\mathbf{b} - \mathbf{c}) \\ &= \begin{pmatrix} 1 \\ -3 \\ 6 \end{pmatrix} \wedge \begin{pmatrix} -1 \\ -1 \\ -1 \end{pmatrix} \\ &= \begin{pmatrix} 9 \\ -5 \\ -4 \end{pmatrix} \end{aligned}$$

The equation of the plane is $\mathbf{r} \cdot \mathbf{n} = \mathbf{a} \cdot \mathbf{n}$. That is

$$9x - 5y - 4z = 9 \times 1 + (-5) \times 2 + (-4) \times (-3) = 11$$

That is $9x - 5y - 4z = 11$.

**Worked example 13.11**

Find the direction cosines of the normal to the plane $3x - 6y + 7z = 22$, and the perpendicular distance from the origin to the plane.

*Solution*

$$\mathbf{n} = \begin{pmatrix} 3 \\ -6 \\ 7 \end{pmatrix}$$

is normal to the plane, and $|\mathbf{n}|^2 = 3^2 + (-6)^2 + 7^2 = 94$. Therefore the direction cosines of $\mathbf{n}$ are $3/\sqrt{94}$, $-6/\sqrt{94}$, $7/\sqrt{94}$, the components of $\hat{\mathbf{n}}$. The required perpendicular distance is $22/\sqrt{94}$.

**Worked example 13.12**

Planes $\pi_1$, $\pi_2$ and $\pi_3$ have respective equations

$$x - y + z = 3, \quad x - y + z = k \quad \text{and} \quad 2x - 3y + z = 5$$

(a) Find the angle between the planes $\pi_1$ and $\pi_3$.
(b) Find the distance between the planes $\pi_1$ and $\pi_2$.
(c) Find the equation of the line of intersection of $\pi_1$ and $\pi_3$.
(d) Find the equation of the plane $\pi_4$ through $(5, 1, -1)$ parallel to $\pi_2$. What is special about this plane?

*Solution*

(a) Fig. 13.2 shows a cross section perpendicular to the line of intersection of the planes, with $\hat{\mathbf{n}}_1$ normal to $\pi_1$ and $\hat{\mathbf{n}}_3$ normal to $\pi_3$. It demonstrates that the angle $\theta$ between the normals is one of the two angles between the planes, and that these two angles are supplementary. To avoid ambiguity, we say that the angle between the planes *is* the angle between the normals. Now $\hat{\mathbf{n}}_1 \cdot \hat{\mathbf{n}}_3 = \cos\theta$, since we have unit normals. Also

$$\hat{\mathbf{n}}_1 = \frac{1}{\sqrt{3}} \begin{pmatrix} 1 \\ -1 \\ 1 \end{pmatrix} \quad \text{and} \quad \hat{\mathbf{n}}_3 = \frac{1}{\sqrt{14}} \begin{pmatrix} 2 \\ -3 \\ 1 \end{pmatrix}$$

Therefore

$$\cos\theta = \frac{2 + 3 + 1}{\sqrt{3}\sqrt{14}} \text{ and so } \theta = \arccos(6/\sqrt{42})$$

(b) The planes $\pi_1$ and $\pi_2$ are parallel, with respective distances from the origin of $3/\sqrt{3}$ and $k/\sqrt{3}$. The distance between the planes is $|(3 - k)/\sqrt{3}|$. (See Fig. 13.3 for illustrations of the different cases.)

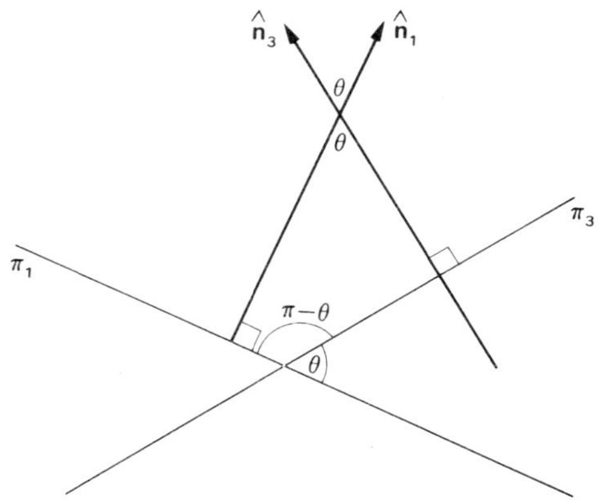


**Fig. 13.2.** The angle between two planes.

(c) We have

$$x - y + z = 3 \quad (\pi_1)$$

and

$$2x - 3y + z = 5 \quad (\pi_3)$$

Subtracting these equations we have

$$-x + 2y = -2$$

We will find each of $x$, $y$, $z$ in terms of a single parameter $t$, since we are unable to solve two equations in three unknowns uniquely. Let $y = t$. Then $x = 2t + 2$. Therefore

$$(2t + 2) - t + z = 3 \text{ and so } z = 1 - t$$

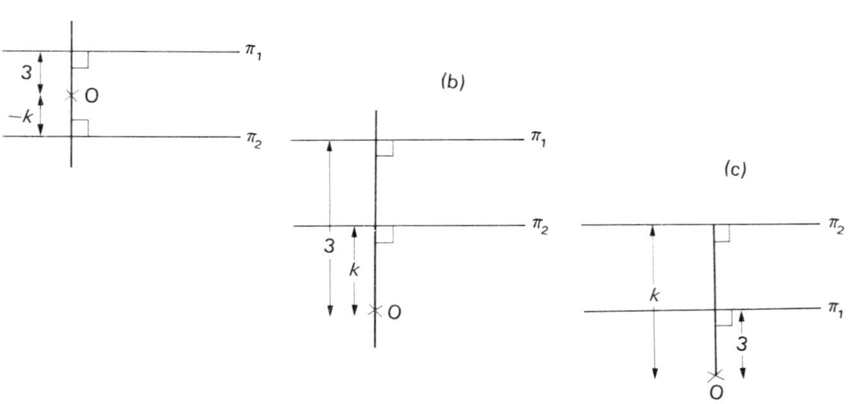


**Fig. 13.3.** The distance between two planes: (a) $k < 0$; (b) $3 > k > 0$; (c) $k > 3$.

Therefore

$$\begin{pmatrix} x \\ y \\ z \end{pmatrix} = \begin{pmatrix} 2+2t \\ t \\ 1-t \end{pmatrix} = \begin{pmatrix} 2 \\ 0 \\ 1 \end{pmatrix} + t\begin{pmatrix} 2 \\ 1 \\ -1 \end{pmatrix}$$

which is the equation of the line of intersection of the planes.

(d) A plane parallel to $\pi_2$ has equation $x - y + z = c$. If this plane passes through $(5, 1, -1)$, then $c = 5 - 1 - 1 = 3$. Therefore $\pi_4$ has equation $x - y + z = 3$, and is the plane $\pi_1$.

## 13.6 Further properties of straight lines

Suppose a given straight line has equation $\mathbf{r} = \mathbf{a} + t\hat{\mathbf{b}}$, that is, it passes through the point A and is parallel to the unit vector $\hat{\mathbf{b}}$. Take a point C not on the line, and such that CD is perpendicular to the line with D on the line. Then $\mathbf{d} = \mathbf{a} + t_1\hat{\mathbf{b}}$, where $t_1 = |\mathbf{AD}|$. But

$$\begin{aligned} |\mathbf{AD}| &= |\mathbf{AC}| \cos\theta, \text{ where } \theta \text{ is the angle between } \mathbf{AC} \text{ and } \mathbf{AD} \\ &= \mathbf{AC}\cdot\hat{\mathbf{b}} \text{ since } \theta \text{ is also the angle between } \mathbf{AC} \text{ and } \hat{\mathbf{b}}, \text{ and } |\hat{\mathbf{b}}| = 1 \\ &= (\mathbf{c} - \mathbf{a})\cdot\hat{\mathbf{b}} \end{aligned}$$

Therefore the foot of the perpendicular from C to the line has position vector $\mathbf{d} = \mathbf{a} + [(\mathbf{c} - \mathbf{a})\cdot\hat{\mathbf{b}}]\hat{\mathbf{b}}$. The length of this perpendicular is $|(\mathbf{c} - \mathbf{a}) \wedge \hat{\mathbf{b}}|$, from page 187.

Now take a second straight line, with equation $\mathbf{r} = \mathbf{e} + u\hat{\mathbf{f}}$ and suppose the two straight lines are not coincident, not parallel (i.e. $\hat{\mathbf{b}} \neq \pm\, \hat{\mathbf{f}}$), and do not meet. Such lines are called *skew*. The fact that they do not meet means that there are *no* values of the parameters $t$ and $u$ such that $\mathbf{a} + t\hat{\mathbf{b}} = \mathbf{e} + u\hat{\mathbf{f}}$.

Take points M and N on the respective lines, with $\mathbf{m} = \mathbf{a} + t_2\hat{\mathbf{b}}$ and $\mathbf{n} = \mathbf{e} + u_1\hat{\mathbf{f}}$. Then $\mathbf{MN} = \mathbf{e} - \mathbf{a} + u_1\hat{\mathbf{f}} - t_2\hat{\mathbf{b}}$. Now suppose that $\mathbf{MN}$ is perpendicular to *both* straight lines, that is, $\mathbf{MN}$ is a common perpendicular to the two lines. Then $\mathbf{MN}\cdot\hat{\mathbf{b}} = 0 = \mathbf{MN}\cdot\hat{\mathbf{f}}$.

Therefore

$$\mathbf{e}\cdot\hat{\mathbf{b}} - \mathbf{a}\cdot\hat{\mathbf{b}} + u_1\hat{\mathbf{f}}\cdot\hat{\mathbf{b}} - t_2 = 0 \text{ since } \hat{\mathbf{b}}\cdot\hat{\mathbf{b}} = 1$$

and $\quad \mathbf{e}\cdot\hat{\mathbf{f}} - \mathbf{a}\cdot\hat{\mathbf{f}} + u_1 - t_2\hat{\mathbf{b}}\cdot\hat{\mathbf{f}} = 0.$

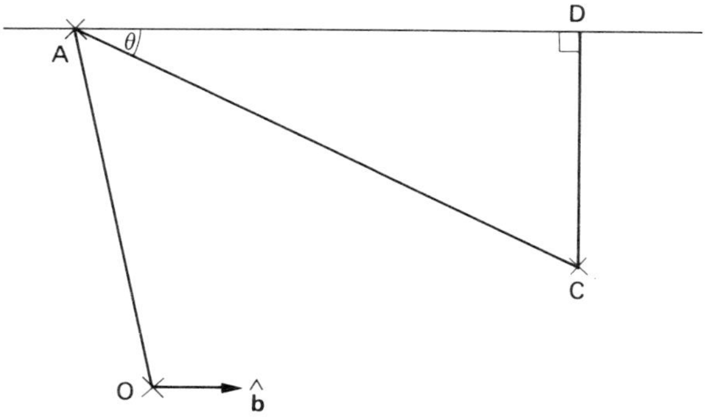


**Fig. 13.4.** The perpendicular from C to a line.

These are two equations in the two unknowns $t_2$ and $u_1$, since all the vectors are fixed. We may, in general, solve these equations to give just one pair of values of $t_2$ and $u_1$. We may solve these equations uniquely if

$$\begin{vmatrix} \hat{\mathbf{f}}.\hat{\mathbf{b}} & -1 \\ 1 & -\hat{\mathbf{b}}.\hat{\mathbf{f}} \end{vmatrix} \neq 0$$

i.e. if $\hat{\mathbf{f}}.\hat{\mathbf{b}} \neq \pm 1$, i.e. if $\hat{\mathbf{f}}$ and $\hat{\mathbf{b}}$ are not parallel, which was part of our original assumption.

Thus two skew lines have a unique common perpendicular. The length of this perpendicular is then the shortest distance between the two lines.

**Exercise 13*e***

1. Find the distance from the origin to the plane $2x + 3y - 4z = 5$
2. Find the plane through (1, 1, 1) normal to

$$\begin{pmatrix} 2 \\ -1 \\ 5 \end{pmatrix}$$

3. Find the plane through (1, 1, 1), (4, −3, 2) and (2, −1, 5)
4. Find the plane through (2, 5, 6) containing vectors parallel to

$$\begin{pmatrix} 1 \\ 1 \\ 1 \end{pmatrix} \text{ and } \begin{pmatrix} 3 \\ 0 \\ -2 \end{pmatrix}$$

5. Find the plane through the origin parallel to $3x - 17y + 2z = 21$.
6. Find the plane through (4, −2, −4) parallel to $x + y + z = 6$.
7. Find the angle between the planes $x + y + z = 6$ and $3x - 17y + 2z = 0$.
8. Find the distance between the planes:
$2x - 6y + z = 12$ and $2x - 6y + z = 12$.
9. Find the equations of the following planes:
(a), the $(x - y)$-plane;
(b) the plane through the points (1, 0, 0), (0, 1, 0) and (0, 0, 1).
10. Find the equations of the following planes:
(a) with normal

$$\begin{pmatrix} 3 \\ 4 \\ 5 \end{pmatrix}$$

distant 5 from the origin,

(b) with normal

$$\begin{pmatrix} 2 \\ 3 \\ 4 \end{pmatrix}$$

through (2, 3, 4).

11. Find the point of intersection of the plane $5x - 3y + 7z = 9$ and the line

$$\begin{pmatrix} x \\ y \\ z \end{pmatrix} = \begin{pmatrix} 1 \\ -2 \\ 3 \end{pmatrix} + t\begin{pmatrix} -1 \\ -5 \\ 3 \end{pmatrix}$$

## 13.7 Geometry with products of vectors

**Worked Example 13.13**

ABCD is a tetrahedron, with the opposite sides AB and CD perpendicular, and with AC and BD perpendicular. Prove that the third pair of opposite sides, namely AD and BC, are also perpendicular.

*Solution*

We use position vectors, referred to some origin O.
AB is perpendicular to CD, thus

$$\mathbf{AB} \cdot \mathbf{CD} = 0$$

therefore

$$(\mathbf{b} - \mathbf{a}) \cdot (\mathbf{d} - \mathbf{c}) = 0$$

and so

$$\mathbf{b} \cdot \mathbf{d} - \mathbf{b} \cdot \mathbf{c} - \mathbf{a} \cdot \mathbf{d} + \mathbf{a} \cdot \mathbf{c} = 0$$

Similarly, $\mathbf{AC} \cdot \mathbf{BD} = 0$, thus

$$\mathbf{c} \cdot \mathbf{d} - \mathbf{c} \cdot \mathbf{b} - \mathbf{a} \cdot \mathbf{d} + \mathbf{a} \cdot \mathbf{b} = 0$$

Subtracting the last two lines:

$$\mathbf{b} \cdot \mathbf{d} - \mathbf{c} \cdot \mathbf{d} + \mathbf{a} \cdot \mathbf{c} - \mathbf{a} \cdot \mathbf{b} = 0$$

hence

$$(\mathbf{b} - \mathbf{c}) \cdot (\mathbf{d} - \mathbf{a}) = 0$$

therefore

$$\mathbf{CB} \cdot \mathbf{AD} = 0$$

and so AD and BC are perpendicular, as required.

**Work Example 13.14**

OABC is a tetrahedron, where O is the origin of position vectors. G is the centroid of the triangle ABC. Prove that

$$GA^2 + GB^2 + GC^2 = a^2 + b^2 + c^2 - 3g^2$$

using the usual notation.

*Solution*

$$\mathbf{g} = \tfrac{1}{3}(\mathbf{a} + \mathbf{b} + \mathbf{c}) \text{ thus } \mathbf{AG} = \mathbf{g} - \mathbf{a} = \tfrac{1}{3}(\mathbf{b} + \mathbf{c} - 2\mathbf{a})$$

$$\begin{aligned} \mathrm{GA}^2 = \mathrm{AG}^2 = \mathbf{AG}\,.\,\mathbf{AG} &= \tfrac{1}{9}(\mathbf{b} + \mathbf{c} - 2\mathbf{a})\,.\,(\mathbf{b} + \mathbf{c} - 2\mathbf{a}) \\ &= \tfrac{1}{9}(b^2 + \mathbf{b}\,.\,\mathbf{c} - 2\mathbf{a}\,.\,\mathbf{b} + \mathbf{c}\,.\,\mathbf{b} + c^2 - 2\mathbf{a}\,.\,\mathbf{c} - \\ &\quad - 2\mathbf{a}\,.\,\mathbf{b} - 2\mathbf{a}\,.\,\mathbf{c} + 4a^2) \end{aligned}$$

Therefore

$$\mathrm{GA}^2 = \tfrac{1}{9}(4a^2 + b^2 + c^2 + 2\mathbf{b}\,.\,\mathbf{c} - 4\mathbf{a}\,.\,\mathbf{b} - 4\mathbf{a}\,.\,\mathbf{c})$$

By cyclic symmetry,

$$\mathrm{GB}^2 = \tfrac{1}{9}(a^2 + 4b^2 + c^2 + 2\mathbf{c}\,.\,\mathbf{a} - 4\mathbf{b}\,.\,\mathbf{c} - 4\mathbf{b}\,.\,\mathbf{a})$$

and

$$\mathrm{GC}^2 = \tfrac{1}{9}(a^2 + b^2 + 4c^2 + 2\mathbf{a}\,.\,\mathbf{b} - 4\mathbf{c}\,.\,\mathbf{a} - 4\mathbf{c}\,.\,\mathbf{b})$$

Add:

$$\mathrm{GA}^2 + \mathrm{GB}^2 + \mathrm{GC}^2 = \tfrac{1}{9}[6(a^2 + b^2 + c^2) - 6(\mathbf{b}\,.\,\mathbf{c} + \mathbf{c}\,.\,\mathbf{a} + \mathbf{a}\,.\,\mathbf{b})]$$

Also

$$\begin{aligned} g^2 = \mathbf{g}\,.\,\mathbf{g} &= \tfrac{1}{9}(\mathbf{a} + \mathbf{b} + \mathbf{c})\,.\,(\mathbf{a} + \mathbf{b} + \mathbf{c}) \\ &= \tfrac{1}{9}(a^2 + b^2 + c^2 + 2\mathbf{b}\,.\,\mathbf{c} + 2\mathbf{c}\,.\,\mathbf{a} + 2\mathbf{a}\,.\,\mathbf{b}) \end{aligned}$$

Therefore

$$\tfrac{6}{9}(\mathbf{b}\,.\,\mathbf{c} + \mathbf{c}\,.\,\mathbf{a} + \mathbf{a}\,.\,\mathbf{b}) = 3g^2 - \tfrac{3}{9}(a^2 + b^2 + c^2)$$

Therefore

$$\begin{aligned} \mathrm{GA}^2 + \mathrm{GB}^2 + \mathrm{GC}^2 &= \tfrac{6}{9}(a^2 + b^2 + c^2) - 3g^2 + \tfrac{3}{9}(a^2 + b^2 + c^2) \\ &= a^2 + b^2 + c^2 - 3g^2 \end{aligned}$$

as required.

**Worked example 13.15**

We define the *vector area* of a triangle PQR to be $\tfrac{1}{2}\mathbf{PQ} \wedge \mathbf{PR}$, since we showed in Chapter 12 that a vector product may be represented by the area of a triangle. The

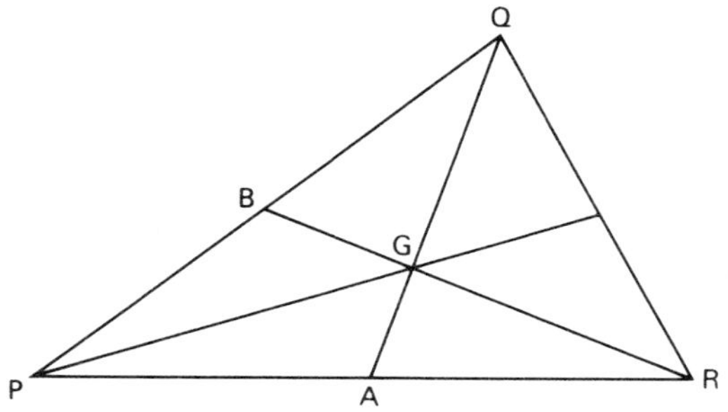


**Fig. 13.5.**

mid-points of RP and PQ are A and B, respectively, and the centroid of triangle PQR is G. Prove that the triangle GQR is equal in area to the quadrilaterial PBGA.

*Solution*

Referred to an origin O,

$$\mathbf{a} = \tfrac{1}{2}\mathbf{p} + \tfrac{1}{2}\mathbf{r}, \quad \mathbf{b} = \tfrac{1}{2}\mathbf{p} + \tfrac{1}{2}\mathbf{q}, \quad \mathbf{g} = \tfrac{1}{3}(\mathbf{p} + \mathbf{q} + \mathbf{r})$$

$$\begin{aligned}
\text{Area of triangle GQR} &= |\mathbf{GQ} \wedge \mathbf{GR}| \\
&= |(\mathbf{q} - \mathbf{g}) \wedge (\mathbf{r} - \mathbf{g})| \\
&= |(\tfrac{2}{3}\mathbf{q} - \tfrac{1}{3}\mathbf{p} - \tfrac{1}{3}\mathbf{r}) \wedge (\tfrac{2}{3}\mathbf{r} - \tfrac{1}{3}\mathbf{p} - \tfrac{1}{3}\mathbf{q})| \\
&= \tfrac{1}{9}|3\mathbf{q} \wedge \mathbf{r} + 3\mathbf{p} \wedge \mathbf{q} - 3\mathbf{p} \wedge \mathbf{r}| \\
&= \tfrac{1}{3}|-\mathbf{p} \wedge \mathbf{q} + \mathbf{p} \wedge \mathbf{r} + \mathbf{r} \wedge \mathbf{q}|
\end{aligned}$$

$$\begin{aligned}
\text{Area of PBGA} &= \text{area of } \triangle\,\text{PBG} + \text{area of } \triangle\,\text{PGA} \\
&= |\mathbf{PB} \wedge \mathbf{PG}| + |\mathbf{PG} \wedge \mathbf{PA}| \\
&= |\mathbf{PG} \wedge (\mathbf{PA} - \mathbf{PB})| = |\mathbf{PG} \wedge \mathbf{BA}| \\
&= |(\mathbf{g} - \mathbf{p}) \wedge (\mathbf{a} - \mathbf{b})| \\
&= |(\tfrac{1}{3}\mathbf{q} + \tfrac{1}{3}\mathbf{r} - \tfrac{2}{3}\mathbf{p}) \wedge (\tfrac{1}{2}\mathbf{r} - \tfrac{1}{2}\mathbf{q})| \\
&= \tfrac{1}{6}|2\mathbf{q} \wedge \mathbf{r} - 2\mathbf{p} \wedge \mathbf{r} + 2\mathbf{p} \wedge \mathbf{q}| \\
&= \text{area of } \triangle\,\text{GQR}
\end{aligned}$$

as required.

**Exercise 13*f***

1. Use vector methods to prove Pythagoras' theorem.
2. In a tetrahedron, prove that each pair of opposite edges is equal in length if and only if the line joining the mid-points of any two opposite edges is perpendicular to each of those edges.
3. ABCD is a tetrahedron, with E and F the mid-points of AC and BD respectively. Prove that $AB^2 + BC^2 + CD^2 + DA^2 = AC^2 + BD^2 + 4EF^2$.
4. ABC is a triangle, and H is the point of intersection of the perpendiculars from B and C to the opposite sides. Express this in two scalar product equations. Hence show that AH is perpendicular to BC, and deduce that the *altitudes* AH, etc, of a triangle are concurrent. The point H is the *orthocentre* of the triangle.
5. Show that the perpendicular bisectors of the sides of a triangle are concurrent. The method is suggested in question 4.

## 13.8 Conics

We state some facts which will prove useful later; we make no attempt at a full analytical treatment of the subject, for which the reader is referred to any standard coordinate geometry text.

We define a *conic* as the locus of the point P in a plane, where SP = $e$PM, with S a fixed point in the plane, M the foot of the perpendicular from P to a fixed line $d$ in the plane, and $e$ a positive constant. The fixed line d is called a *directix* of the conic, S is called a *focus*, and the chord of the conic through S parallel to $d$ is called the *latus rectum*.

Further,

if $e = 0$, the conic is called a *circle*;

if $0 < e < 1$, the conic is called an *ellipse*;

if $e = 1$, the conic is called a *parabola*;

if $e > 1$, the conic is called a *hyperbola*.

Fig. 13.6 shows a parabola. If we take axes as shown, then it can be proved that the point with position vector

$$\begin{pmatrix} x \\ y \end{pmatrix} = \begin{pmatrix} at^2 \\ 2at \end{pmatrix}$$

lies on the parabola, and that the parabola has equation $y^2 = 4ax$, where $2a$ is the perpendicular distance from the focus S to the directix $d$. In the diagram, SP = PM. S has coordinates $(a, 0)$ and $d$ has equation $x = -a$. Further properties of the parabola are indicated in Exercise 13*g*.

Fig. 13.7 shows an ellipse, AA′ and BB′ are called its *major* and *minor* axes respectively, and have lengths $2a$ and $2b$. If we choose axes as shown, then the point with position vector

$$\begin{pmatrix} x \\ y \end{pmatrix} = \begin{pmatrix} a\cos\theta \\ b\sin\theta \end{pmatrix}$$

lies on the ellipse, where $\theta$ is the angle shown. The circle is called the *auxiliary circle*. In the diagram, SP = $e$PM, and since we define $b^2 = a^2(1 - e^2)$, the equation of the

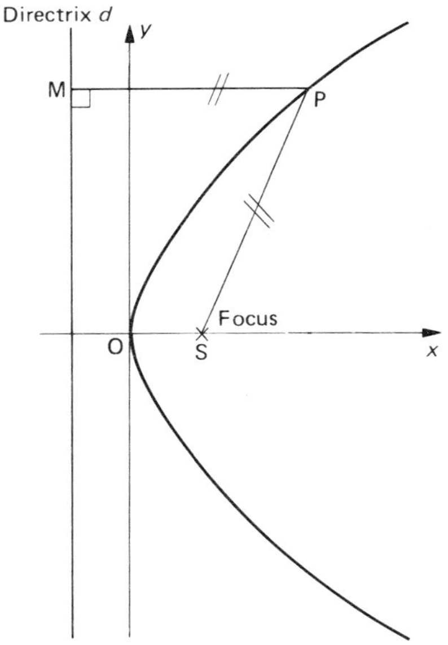


**Fig. 13.6.** A parabola.

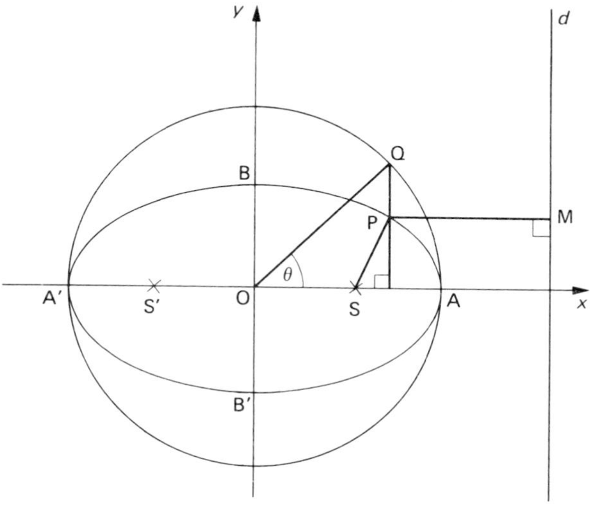


**Fig. 13.7.** An ellipse.

ellipse becomes

$$\frac{x^2}{a^2} + \frac{y^2}{b^2} = 1$$

It has focuses S $(ae, 0)$ and S' $(-ae, 0)$, and directrices $x = \pm\, a/e$. Further properties are indicated in Exercise 13*g*.

Fig. 13.8 shows a hyperbola. The lines $l$ and $l'$ are its *asymptotes*, and have equations $x/a = \pm\, y/b$. If we choose axes as shown, then the point with position vector

$$\begin{pmatrix} x \\ y \end{pmatrix} = \begin{pmatrix} a\sec t \\ b\tan t \end{pmatrix}$$

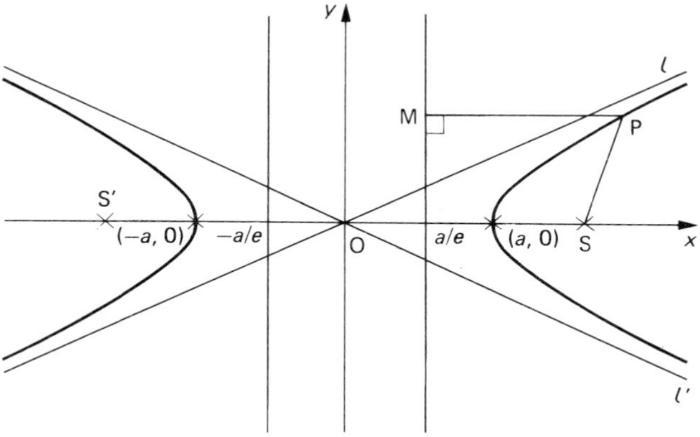


**Fig. 13.8.** A hyperbola.

lies on the hyperbola. The equation of the hyperbola shown is

$$\frac{x^2}{a^2} - \frac{y^2}{b^2} = 1$$

where $b^2 = a^2(e^2 - 1)$, $e$ being the eccentricity. It has focuses S $(ae, 0)$ and S′ $(-ae, 0)$ and directrices $x = \pm a/e$. Further properties are indicated in Exercise 13*g*.

If the asymptotes of a hyperbola are orthogonal, then $a = b$ and the hyperbola is called a *rectangular hyperbola*. For example, $x^2 - y^2 = a^2$ is the equation of a rectangular hyperbola. If we are dealing with a rectangular hyperbola, though, it is more usual to draw it with the axes as asymptotes (as in Fig. 13.9). The rectangular hyperbola shown has equation $xy = c^2$, and the point P with position vector

$$\begin{pmatrix} x \\ y \end{pmatrix} = \begin{pmatrix} ct \\ c/t \end{pmatrix}$$

lies on it. Further properties are indicated in Exercise 13*g*.

The equations of these conics may also be expressed in polar coordinates.

Fig. 13.10 shows part of a conic, with focus S and directrix *d*. Take S as the origin of polar coordinates, and **SN** to determine the direction and sense of the initial line, where N is the foot of the perpendicular from S to *d*.

L′L is the latus rectum, of length $2l$. Therefore SL has length $l$. Consider any point P$(r, \theta)$ on the conic. Then SP = $e$PM
and so

$$r = e(\text{SN} - \text{SQ})$$
$$r = e(\text{SN} - r\cos\theta)$$

In particular, when P is at L, $r = 1$, $\theta = \frac{1}{2}\pi$ and so $l = e(\text{SN} - 0)$ i.e. SN $= l/e$.

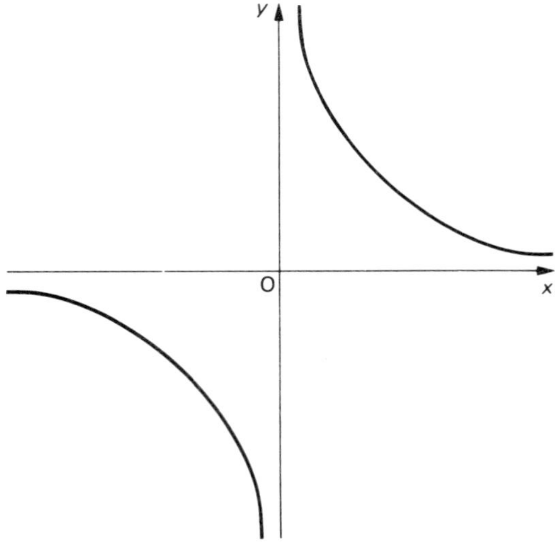


**Fig. 13.9.** A rectangular hyperbola.

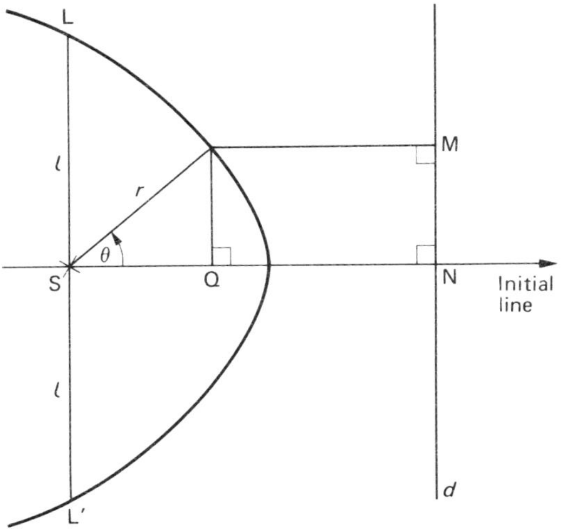


**Fig. 13.10.** A conic in polar coordinates.

Therefore

$$r = e\left(\frac{l}{e} - r\cos\theta\right) = l - er\cos\theta$$

Therefore

$$l = r(1 + e\cos\theta)$$

is the equation of the conic.

This equation is valid for circles, ellipses and parabolas. For hyperbolas, it gives the equation only of the near branch—that part nearest to the focus used as origin. If we use the same focus as origin, then the equation of the other branch is $l = r(e\cos\theta - 1)$. (see Exercise 13*g*).

**Exercise 13*g***

This exercise indicates some of the standard properties of conics, and some possible extensions of the results of Section 13.8. It may be omitted by those readers only interested in knowing the basic results for later application.

1. Find the equation of the tangent to the parabola $y^2 = 4ax$ at the point $(at^2, 2at)$, and hence find the equation of the normal to the parabola at this point.
2. The parabola $y^2 = 4ax$ has focus S$(a,0)$; P is the point $(at^2, 2at)$ on the parabola, and O is the origin. Find unit vectors in the direction and sense of each of: (a) **OS**, vector $\hat{\mathbf{s}}$; (b) **SP**, vector $\hat{\mathbf{c}}$; (c) the tangent at **P**, vector $\hat{\mathbf{u}}$. Evaluate the scalar products $\hat{\mathbf{s}} \cdot \hat{\mathbf{u}}$ and $\hat{\mathbf{c}} \cdot \hat{\mathbf{u}}$. What geometrical conclusion can you draw about the parabola?
3. Find the equations of the tangent and normal to the ellipse $(x^2/a^2) + (y^2/b^2) = 1$ at the point $(a\cos\theta, b\sin\theta)$.
4. An ellipse has equation $(x^2/a^2) + (y^2/b^2) = 1$, and focuses S $(ae, 0)$ and S′ $(-ae, 0)$. P is the point $(a\cos\theta, b\sin\theta)$ on the ellipse. Prove that $|\mathbf{SP}| + |\mathbf{PS'}| = 2a$.

5. Find the equations of the tangent and normal to the rectangular hyperbola $xy = c^2$ at the point $(ct, c/t)$.

6. Prove that $y = mx + c$ meets $x^2 + y^2 = a^2$ at the points whose $x$-coordinates are given by the quadratic equation

$$(1 + m^2)x^2 + 2mcx + (c^2 - a^2) = 0.$$

Find $c$ in terms of $a$ and $m$ if this equation has equal roots. What geometrical significance does this case of equal roots have?

7. Prove that the polar equation of that branch of a hyperbola which is the farther from the focus S used as origin O is $l = r(e \cos \theta - 1)$. (See page 215)

8. On page 215, we give the polar equation of a circle as $l = r(1 + e \cos \theta)$. Reconcile this with the appropriate polar equation of a circle as used in Chapter 5.

## 13.9 Surfaces

### (i) The sphere

A sphere is the locus of points R at a fixed distance $c$ from a fixed point A. Therefore it has vector equation $|\mathbf{r} - \mathbf{a}| = e$.

If we take

$$\mathbf{r} = \begin{pmatrix} x \\ y \\ z \end{pmatrix} \text{ and } \mathbf{a} = \begin{pmatrix} a_1 \\ a_2, \\ a_3 \end{pmatrix},$$

then this gives us the Cartesian equation of a sphere as

$$(x - a_1)^2 + (y - a_2)^2 + (z - a_3)^2 = c^2$$

### (ii) The cone

The surface of a cone consists of all points whose position vectors are inclined at the same fixed angle $\alpha$ to the axis of the cone, which we will suppose has direction $\hat{\mathbf{a}}$. Thus, if $\mathbf{r}$ is the position vector of any point R on the surface of a cone, then

$$\cos \alpha = \frac{\mathbf{r} \cdot \hat{\mathbf{a}}}{|\mathbf{r}||\hat{\mathbf{a}}|} \quad \text{and so } \mathbf{r} \cdot \hat{\mathbf{a}} = |\mathbf{r}| \cos \alpha$$

is the equation of the surface of the cone, since $\hat{\mathbf{a}}$ is a unit vector. Or, if $\mathbf{a} = a\hat{\mathbf{a}}$, then $\mathbf{r} \cdot \mathbf{a} = a(\mathbf{r} \cdot \hat{\mathbf{a}}) = a|\mathbf{r}| \cos \alpha = c|\mathbf{r}|$, where $c$ is a constant.

In coordinate form, take

$$\mathbf{r} = \begin{pmatrix} x \\ y \\ z \end{pmatrix} \quad \text{and} \quad \hat{\mathbf{a}} = \hat{\mathbf{k}} = \begin{pmatrix} 0 \\ 0 \\ 1 \end{pmatrix}, \text{ say}$$

Then

$$(\mathbf{r} \cdot \mathbf{a})^2 = |\mathbf{r}|^2 \cos^2 \alpha$$

thus

$$z^2 = (x^2 + y^2 + z^2) \cos^2 \alpha$$

hence

$$z^2 \sin^2 \alpha = (x^2 + y^2) \cos^2 \alpha$$

and so

$$\frac{x^2 + y^2}{z^2} = \tan^2 \alpha$$

### (iii) The cylinder

Fig. 13.11 shows a cylinder with axis in the direction $\hat{\mathbf{a}}$. $\pi$ is a plane through the origin perpendicular to $\hat{\mathbf{a}}$, and S is a point on the cylinder and on $\pi$, and having position vector $\mathbf{s}$. Suppose R is any point on the cylinder, with position vector $\mathbf{r}$. Then the projection $\mathbf{ON} = \mathbf{n}$ of $\mathbf{r}$ onto $\hat{\mathbf{a}}$ is $(\mathbf{r} \cdot \hat{\mathbf{a}})\hat{\mathbf{a}}$. Therefore

$$\mathbf{r} = \mathbf{s} + (\mathbf{r} \cdot \hat{\mathbf{a}})\hat{\mathbf{a}} \quad \text{and so} \quad \mathbf{s} = \mathbf{r} - (\mathbf{r} \cdot \hat{\mathbf{a}})\hat{\mathbf{a}}.$$

The cylinder is defined by $|\mathbf{s}| =$ constant, $c$ say. Therefore its vector equation is $|\mathbf{r} - (\mathbf{r} \cdot \hat{\mathbf{a}})\mathbf{a}| = c$. Now take

$$\mathbf{r} = \begin{pmatrix} x \\ y \\ z \end{pmatrix} \quad \text{and} \quad \hat{\mathbf{a}} = \hat{\mathbf{k}} = \begin{pmatrix} 0 \\ 0 \\ 1 \end{pmatrix}, \quad \text{say}$$

Therefore

$$|\mathbf{r} - (\mathbf{r} \cdot \hat{\mathbf{a}})\mathbf{a}|^2 = c^2$$

thus

$$x^2 + y^2 + (z - z)^2 = c^2$$

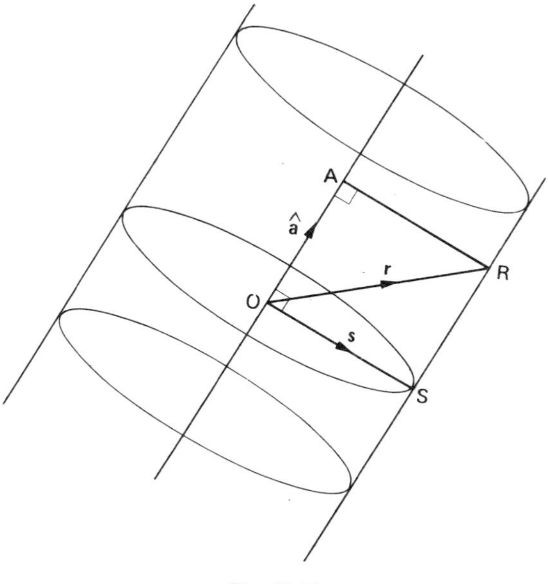


**Fig. 13.11.**

and so

$$x^2 + y^2 = c^2$$

is the Cartesian equation of a cylinder. This is not to be confused with the equation of a circle, since we are now working in three dimensions and $z$, being unspecified, can take on *any* value. The equation is, however, the equation of the circle of cross section of the cylinder for a *fixed* value of $z$.

**Exercise 13*h***

1. S is the point $(a, 0, 0)$, and $\pi$ is the plane $x = -a$. Find the Cartesian equation of the locus of points $P(x, y, z)$ such that $SP = PM$, where M is the foot of the perpendicular from P to $\pi$.
2. In the $x - y$-plane, an ellipse has equation $(x^2/a^2) + (y^2/b^2) = 1$. The usual $z$-axis is now added, and the given ellipse is rotated through 4 right angles about $Ox$. Find the Cartesian equation of the resulting surface.
3. Find the equation of the plane which touches the sphere

$$(x - 1)^2 + (y + 1)^2 + (z - 5)^2 = 13^2$$

at the point $(4, 3, 17)$.

4. Find the equation of a cone with vertical angle $60°$ and axis $\begin{pmatrix} 1 \\ 1 \\ 1 \end{pmatrix}$.

## 13.10 Miscellaneous exercises 13

1. The points A, B, C have position vectors **a**, **b**, **c** given by

$$\mathbf{a} = \begin{pmatrix} 2 \\ 0 \\ 0 \end{pmatrix} \quad \mathbf{b} = \begin{pmatrix} 0 \\ 5 \\ 0 \end{pmatrix} \quad \mathbf{c} = \begin{pmatrix} 3 \\ 2 \\ 9 \end{pmatrix}$$

and O is the origin.

(i) Find the perpendicular distance of C from the plane OAB and, hence or otherwise, the volume of the tetrahedron OABC.

(ii) Show that the Cartesian equation of the plane through A, B, C is $5x + 2y - z = 10$.

(iii) Find the direction cosines of the line drawn from O perpendicular to and towards the plane ABC, and the coordinates of the foot of this perpendicular. (MEI).

2. Two adjacent portions of the roof of a building are parts of the planes whose equations are $z = \frac{1}{2}x + 12$, $z = \frac{2}{3}y + 12$; the $z$-axis is vertical, the origin is a point on the horizontal ground and distances are measured in metres. The line $l$ of intersection of the planes meets the ground at P.

(i) Find the coordinates of P.

(ii) Express the equation of $l$ in the form

$$\frac{x - a}{p} = \frac{y - b}{q} = \frac{z - c}{r}$$

(iii) Write down the direction cosines $\cos\theta_1$, $\cos\theta_2$, $\cos\theta_3$ of the line $l$ and interpret the angles $\theta_1$, $\theta_2$, $\theta_3$ in relation to the building.

(iv) Calculate, to the nearest half degree, the angles between each of the given planes and the ground. Show that the angle inside the roof space between the two given planes is an obtuse angle (you are not required to calculate the value of the angle.) (MEI)

3. O is a fixed origin in a vector space of two dimensions. A given line passes through a fixed point A and is parallel to a fixed unit vector $\hat{\mathbf{u}}$. P is a variable point on the given line. $\mathbf{OA} = \mathbf{a}$, $\mathbf{OP} = \mathbf{r}$ and the length of AP is $t$. Interpret the equation $\mathbf{r} = \mathbf{a} + t\hat{\mathbf{u}}$.

B is another fixed point, not on the given line, and $\mathbf{OB} = \mathbf{b}$. Show that the position vector of the foot of the perpendicular from B to the given line is $\mathbf{a} + [\hat{\mathbf{u}}.(\mathbf{b} - \mathbf{a})]\hat{\mathbf{u}}$. Does this result hold also in three dimensions?

Find the perpendicular distance of the point (3, 0, 1) from the line whose Cartesian equation is

$$\frac{x-1}{3} = \frac{y+2}{4} = \frac{z}{12}$$ (MEI)

4. (a) Find the values of the scalar $\alpha$ if the two vectors $\mathbf{p} = (2, -3, 5)$, $\mathbf{q} = (3, \alpha, -3)$ are inclined to each other at an angle of: (i) $\frac{1}{2}\pi$; (ii) $\frac{2}{3}\pi$.

(b) The points A, B, C and D have position vectors **a**, **b**, **c** and **d** respectively with respect to a fixed origin and

$$(\mathbf{d} - \mathbf{a}).(\mathbf{b} - \mathbf{c}) = 0 = (\mathbf{d} - \mathbf{b}).(\mathbf{c} - \mathbf{a})$$

Show that $(\mathbf{d} - \mathbf{c}).(\mathbf{a} - \mathbf{b}) = 0$.

Interpret this result geometrically when the points A, B, C, and D are coplanar. (MEI)

5. Find in Cartesian coordinates the equation of the plane through the three points (1, 1, 1), (4, 1, 0), (3, 0, 1).

Find also the coordinates of the foot of the perpendicular from the origin to this plane. (SMP)

6. Find the coordinates of the mirror image of the origin in the plane whose equation in Cartesian coordinates is $2x - y + 2z = 3$. (SMP)

7. Show that the line l given by

$$\frac{x+1}{5} = \frac{y-1}{3} = \frac{z+1}{2}$$

is the intersection of the planes $3x - 5y + 8 = 0$ and $2y - 3z - 5 = 0$. Show that every plane containing the line $l$ can be expressed in the form $\lambda(3x - 5y + 8) + \mu(2y - 3z - 5) = 0$. How should $\lambda$, $\mu$ be chosen in order to ensure that the plane is perpendicular to the plane $5x - y + 2z = -2$? Hence or otherwise obtain the equation of the orthogonal projection of the line $l$ on the plane $5x - y + 2z = -2$, expressing your answer in vector form $\mathbf{x} = t\mathbf{a} + \mathbf{b}$. (MEI)

8. The fixed point C and a variable point P have position vectors **c**, **r** respectively in three-dimensional Euclidean space. Describe in geometrical terms the locus $\Gamma$ defined by $\mathbf{r}.\mathbf{c} = |\mathbf{r}||\mathbf{c}| \cos \alpha$ where $\alpha$ is a given acute angle. If $\mathbf{c} = (a, b, c)$ and $\mathbf{r} = (x, y, z)$, express the equation of $\Gamma$ in Cartesian form and show that, for all real numbers $\lambda$,

$$(x, y, z) \in \Gamma \text{ implies that } (\lambda x, \lambda y, \lambda z) \in \Gamma$$

Taking the special case $\mathbf{c} = (4, 0, 3)$, $\cos\alpha = \frac{4}{5}$, show that $\Gamma$ meets the plane $z = 6$ in a parabola and that the sphere $|\mathbf{r} - \mathbf{c}| = 3$ touches the plane at the focus of this parabola. (MEI)

9. A cube with base OABC is placed with the edges OA, OC along the axes O$x$, O$y$ and the edges AA′, BB′, CC′ parallel to O$z$. The length of each edge is $2a$ and P, Q. R are mid-points of OA, A′B′, B′C′ respectively. Express the vectors **PQ**, **PR**, **QR** in terms of the base vectors **i**, **j**, **k** and use these expressions to find the angle of the triangle PQR.

Find also the unit vector normal to the plane PQR, and write the equation of the plane in terms of vectors and also in terms of Cartesian coordinates $x$, $y$, $z$. (MEI)

10. Find the equation of the cone with vertex at the origin which passes through the curve of intersection of the plane $x + y + z + 1 = 0$ and the sphere $x^2 + y^2 + z^2 - 1 = 0$.

Show that if the line $x/l = y/m = z/n$ lies entirely on the cone (such a line is called a generator), then $lm + mn + nl = 0$. Hence, or otherwise, show that the plane $2x - y + 2z = 0$ cuts this cone in two perpendicular generators. (MEI)

11. Find the distance of the point **P**(2, 4, 7) from the plane determined by the points (3, 4, 4), (4, 5, 7), and (6, 8, 9). (JMB)

12. A point P on the line joining the points A, B, whose position vectors are **a**, **b** has position vector $\mathbf{a} + t(\mathbf{b} - \mathbf{a})$. What is the geometrical significance of $t$?

A point Q is taken on CD with position vector $\mathbf{c} + s(\mathbf{d} - \mathbf{c})$. Find equations to give $s$ and $t$ in terms of **a**, **b**, **c** and **d** so that PQ may be perpendicular in both to AB and to CD and show that in general there is just one pair of values.

Find the vectors **p** and **q** if **a**, **b**, **c**, **d** are, respectively,

$$\begin{pmatrix}2\\0\\-1\end{pmatrix}, \begin{pmatrix}5\\6\\5\end{pmatrix}, \begin{pmatrix}-1\\2\\3\end{pmatrix}, \begin{pmatrix}7\\0\\1\end{pmatrix}. \qquad \text{(SMP)}$$

13. The line $L_1$ is the line of intersection of the planes $2x - y - 3 = 0$, $x + z - 3 = 0$. The equations of the line $L_2$ are $x - 2 = y + 2 = z + 3$.

Find the equation of the plane P which passes through $L_1$ and is parallel to $L_2$.

Hence, or otherwise, find the shortest distance between $L_1$ and $L_2$.

Show that the point Q(1, 1, −2) lies in the plane P and determine the equations of the straight line in this plane which is perpendicular to the line $L_2$, and which passes through Q. (AEB)

14. The six faces of a rectangular solid have vector equations:

$$\mathbf{r}.\mathbf{k} = 0,\ \mathbf{r}.(\mathbf{i} + \mathbf{j}) = 2,\ \mathbf{r}.(\mathbf{j} - \mathbf{i}) = 2$$
$$\mathbf{r}.\mathbf{k} = 2,\ \mathbf{r}.(\mathbf{i} + \mathbf{j}) = 4,\ \mathbf{r}.(\mathbf{j} - \mathbf{i}) = -2$$

where **i**, **j**, **k** represent unit vectors along perpendicular axes O$x$, O$y$, O$z$. Prove that the acute angle between the diagonals through the points 2**i** and 2**j** is $\arccos\left(\frac{1}{7}\right)$.

Find the vector equations of the planes parallel to O$z$ through these diagonals. (L)

15. Find equations for the transversal of the lines

$$\frac{x-2}{1} = \frac{y+1}{-2} = \frac{z}{-1} \quad \text{and} \quad \frac{x+6}{-2} = \frac{y-2}{8} = \frac{z+2}{1}$$

which is perpendicular to both. Prove that the shortest distance between the given two lines is $\sqrt{53}$.

Show that by taking the mid-point of the common perpendicular to any two skew lines as origin, the equations of the two lines can be taken in the form $y = mx$, $z = c$ and $y = -mx$, $z = -c$.

Hence show that, if P and Q are points one on each line such that PQ subtends a right angle at the new origin, the locus of the mid-point of PQ is a hyperbola in the plane $z = 0$. (L)

# 14
# Work, Energy and Power

## 14.1 Work and energy

In Chapter 11, on scalar products, we defined the work done on a particle by a constant force $\mathbf{F}$ in causing a displacement $\mathbf{x}$ as $\mathbf{F}.\mathbf{x}$; or as $Fx$ if a force of magnitude $F$ causes a displacement $x$ in the same direction and sense. We may extend these definitions to cover the case of a variable force $\mathbf{F}$ which is a vector function $\mathbf{F}(\mathbf{x})$ of the vector variable $\mathbf{x}$, where $\mathbf{x}$ is the position vector of the particle at time $t$. We define the *work* done by the force $\mathbf{F}$ in moving the particle from the position given by $\mathbf{x} = \mathbf{a}$ to the position given by $\mathbf{x} = \mathbf{b}$ to be $W$, where

$$W = \lim_{\Delta\mathbf{x}\to 0} \sum_{\mathbf{x}=\mathbf{a}}^{\mathbf{x}=\mathbf{b}} \mathbf{F}(\mathbf{x}).\Delta\mathbf{x} = \int_{\mathbf{x}=\mathbf{a}}^{\mathbf{x}=\mathbf{b}} \mathbf{F}.\mathrm{d}\mathbf{x}$$

That is, the total work done by $\mathbf{F}$ is the limit of the sum of the amounts of work done during the successive infinitesimal displacements $\Delta\mathbf{x}$.

We may see at once that if $\mathbf{F}$ is constant, then $W = \mathbf{F}.(\mathbf{b} - \mathbf{a})$, which agrees with our earlier definition.

We note, too, that work in this context is associated with movement and displacement, and is really a shorthand way of saying *mechanical work*. We will also distinguish between the amounts of work done by different types of force.

Our intuition tells us that, when work is done, changes may occur in position and/or velocity. For example, if a particle of mass $m$ is being hauled at a constant speed through a vertical distance $h$ by means of a rope slung over a smooth pulley, we use a force and mechanical work is clearly done. Also, there is no overall momentum change. However, something *has* changed, due to the change in position of this mass. This quantity is called *energy*, and the particular type of energy in this example is called the *potential energy* of the mass.

During the lifting of the particle, the only forces acting are the tension $T$ in the rope, and the weight $mg$ of the particle. Since the velocity is constant, there is no acceleration, and so $T = mg$. Thus the tension in the rope does work $Th = mgh$ in opposing the weight of the particle. This quantity $mgh$ represents energy possessed by the particle by virtue of its changed position, and is its *potential energy* (PE). It must be stressed that potential energy is relative—strictly speaking, we should say that the particle has gained an amount $mgh$ of potential energy. The gain in potential energy of a particle of mass $m$ from gaining height $h$ is $mgh$. The unit of potential energy is the same as that of work, namely the joule, where $1\,\mathrm{J} = 1\,\mathrm{Nm}$.

In vector form, the work done by the force $\mathbf{F}$ in moving a particle of mass $m$ from its position $\mathbf{x}$ at time $t$ to some fixed position $\mathbf{c}$ is given by the scalar function $V(\mathbf{x})$ of the vector variable $\mathbf{x}$, where

$$V(\mathbf{x}) = \int_{\mathbf{x}=\mathbf{x}}^{\mathbf{x}=\mathbf{c}} \mathbf{F} \cdot \mathrm{d}\mathbf{x}$$

This function $V(\mathbf{x})$ is defined to be the potential energy of the particle at $\mathbf{x}$, relative to the fixed position $\mathbf{c}$, subject to certain conditions regarding the nature of the force $\mathbf{F}$, which we are about to describe.

The integral in the definition may be ambiguous—who is to say whether the work done in moving a particle from $\mathbf{x}$ to $\mathbf{c}$ can be described by a single function? May we not have to do more work if we move the particle by one route, rather than another? A system of forces in which the work done is independent of the path taken is called a *conservative system*.

Consider two examples:

(1) A particle of mass $m$ is dragged from A to B on a rough horizontal surface by a constant force $P$, the coefficient of friction between the particle and the surface being $\mu$. The distance from A to B is 5 metre.

Travelling directly, the work done is $(P - \mu mg)5$. Travelling via C (see Fig. 14.1), where ACB is a right-angled triangle, the work done is
$(P - \mu mg)(4 + 3) \neq [(P - \mu mg)5$.

Thus the work done in this case depends on the route chosen—the system of forces is *not* a conservative system.

(2) A stone of mass $m$ is thrown vertically upwards from a beach to land on top of a cliff of height $h$. The only force on the stone is its weight $mg$. In one instance, the stone just reaches the top of the cliff. In another, the stone rises above the top of the cliff, and falls back onto it. But, in both cases, the gain in potential energy is $mgh$; that is, the work done is the same. This system of forces *is* a conservative system.

The condition for a conservative system may be expressed as:

$$\int_{\mathbf{x}=\mathbf{a}}^{\mathbf{x}=\mathbf{b}} \mathbf{F} \cdot \mathrm{d}\mathbf{x} = \int_{\mathbf{x}=\mathbf{a}}^{\mathbf{x}=\mathbf{c}} \mathbf{F} \cdot \mathrm{d}\mathbf{x} + \int_{\mathbf{x}=\mathbf{c}}^{\mathbf{x}=\mathbf{b}} \mathbf{F} \cdot \mathrm{d}\mathbf{x}$$

which says that the work done in moving the particle direct from $\mathbf{a}$ to $\mathbf{b}$ is the same as the work done in moving the particle direct from $\mathbf{a}$ to $\mathbf{b}$ by way of $\mathbf{c}$. This may also be stated as

$$\oint \mathbf{F} \cdot \mathrm{d}\mathbf{x} = 0,$$

where the sign $\oint$ indicates that the integral is to be evaluated for values of $\mathbf{x}$ around

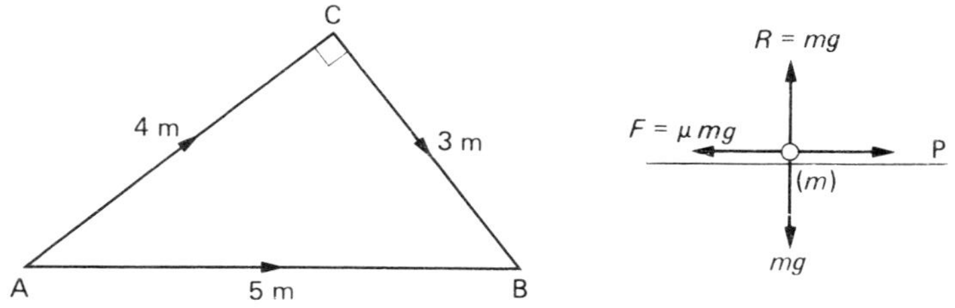


Fig. 14.1.

a closed path. This says that, in a conservative system, there is no work done in moving a body if it returns to its initial position.

Our full definition of potential energy now becomes: if a particle is acted upon by forces, of which **F** is the resultant of all the conservative forces, then its *potential energy* $V(\mathbf{x})$, at **x**, relative to **c**, is defined to be

$$V(\mathbf{x}) = \int_{\mathbf{x}=\mathbf{x}}^{\mathbf{x}=\mathbf{c}} \mathbf{F} \cdot \mathrm{d}\mathbf{x}$$

In the example of the particle of mass $m$ being hauled up by a rope through a vertical distance $h$, the potential energy of the particle at the top, relative to the bottom, is

$$V(h) = \int_h^0 (-mg)\,\mathrm{d}x = [-mgx]_h^0 = mgh,$$

since the weight $mg$ is the only conservative force acting. In most of our examples, the weight of a particle is likely to be the only conservative force.

Finally, work may also cause a change in a body's energy due to a change in its velocity; this type of energy is called *kinetic energy* (KE). Energy can also appear in other forms, such as heat, light, and so on, where the amounts of energy concerned are negligible in our systems. Sometimes—as in the case of nuclear energy—our methods are not always applicable, and the amounts of potential and kinetic energy involved may be negligible in those cases.

## 14.2 The energy integral

The quantitative results of work and energy arise from our second method of integrating Newton's second law. (The first method gave us the impulse–momentum integral in Chapter ten.)

Newton's second law tells us that $\mathrm{d}(m\mathbf{v})/\mathrm{d}t = \mathbf{F}$, and we shall assume that the mass $m$ of the particle is constant. Now, if we take the scalar product of **F** with $\mathrm{d}\mathbf{x}/\mathrm{d}t$ and integrate with respect to $t$, we obtain the work done by **F**. This we will do. Therefore

$$\frac{\mathrm{d}\mathbf{x}}{\mathrm{d}t} \cdot \frac{\mathrm{d}(m\mathbf{v})}{\mathrm{d}t} = \mathbf{F} \cdot \frac{\mathrm{d}\mathbf{x}}{\mathrm{d}t}$$

Therefore

$$\frac{\mathrm{d}}{\mathrm{d}t}(\tfrac{1}{2}m\mathbf{v} \cdot \mathbf{v}) = \mathbf{F} \cdot \frac{\mathrm{d}\mathbf{x}}{\mathrm{d}t} \tag{1}$$

since

$$\frac{\mathrm{d}}{\mathrm{d}t}(\tfrac{1}{2}m\mathbf{v} \cdot \mathbf{v}) = \tfrac{1}{2}m\mathbf{v} \cdot \frac{\mathrm{d}\mathbf{v}}{\mathrm{d}t} + \tfrac{1}{2}m\frac{\mathrm{d}\mathbf{v}}{\mathrm{d}t} \cdot \mathbf{v} = m\frac{\mathrm{d}\mathbf{x}}{\mathrm{d}t} \cdot \frac{\mathrm{d}\mathbf{v}}{\mathrm{d}t} \tag{2}$$

We state the result of Equ. 2 without proof. Now integrate Equ. (1) with respect to $t$, assuming that $\mathbf{x} = \mathbf{a}$ and $\mathbf{v} = \mathbf{u}$ when $t = t_1$, and $\mathbf{x} = \mathbf{x}$ and $\mathbf{v} = \mathbf{v}$ when $t = t$. We get

$$[\tfrac{1}{2}m\mathbf{v} \cdot \mathbf{v}]_{\mathbf{v}=\mathbf{u}}^{\mathbf{v}} = \int_{t=t_1}^{t} \mathbf{F} \cdot \frac{\mathrm{d}\mathbf{x}}{\mathrm{d}t}\,\mathrm{d}t$$

Therefore

$$\tfrac{1}{2}m\mathbf{v}^2 - \tfrac{1}{2}m\mathbf{u}^2 = \int_{\mathbf{x}=\mathbf{a}}^{\mathbf{x}} \mathbf{F}.\mathrm{d}\mathbf{x}$$

Thus the work done in moving the particle from **a** to **x** by the resultant force F—*including* conservative and non-conservative components—is $\tfrac{1}{2}m\mathbf{v}^2 - \tfrac{1}{2}m\mathbf{u}^2$. This defines the change in kinetic energy between times $t_1$ and $t$; where $\tfrac{1}{2}m\mathbf{v}^2$ is the *kinetic energy* of the particle at time $t$.

Thus the equation

$$\left[\tfrac{1}{2}m\mathbf{v}^2\right]_{\mathbf{v}=\mathbf{u}}^{\mathbf{v}=\mathbf{v}} = \int_{\mathbf{x}=\mathbf{a}}^{\mathbf{x}=\mathbf{x}} \mathbf{F}.\mathrm{d}\mathbf{x} \qquad \text{(WE1)}$$

may be described by

change in KE = work done by resultant force

Now suppose we have a conservative system of forces, with resultant **F**, and that potential energy is defined relative to **c**. That is,

$$V(\mathbf{a}) = \int_{\mathbf{x}=\mathbf{a}}^{\mathbf{x}=\mathbf{c}} \mathbf{F}.\mathrm{d}\mathbf{x} \quad \text{and} \quad V(\mathbf{x}) = \int_{\mathbf{x}=\mathbf{x}}^{\mathbf{x}=\mathbf{c}} \mathbf{F}.\mathrm{d}\mathbf{x}$$

Therefore

$$\int_{\mathbf{x}=\mathbf{a}}^{\mathbf{x}=\mathbf{x}} \mathbf{F}.\mathrm{d}\mathbf{x} = V(\mathbf{a}) - V(\mathbf{x}) = -(V(\mathbf{x}) - V(\mathbf{a}))$$

Thus Equ. WE1 gives

$$\left[\tfrac{1}{2}m\mathbf{v}^2\right]_{\mathbf{v}=\mathbf{u}}^{\mathbf{v}=\mathbf{v}} = -(V(\mathbf{x}) - V(\mathbf{a}))$$

That is

$$(\tfrac{1}{2}m\mathbf{v}^2 - \tfrac{1}{2}m\mathbf{u}^2) = -(V(\mathbf{x}) - V(\mathbf{a}))$$

That is

gain in kinetic energy = loss in potential energy

Or, potential energy + kinetic energy is constant for a conservative system. This is the *principle of conservation of energy* (PCE) *for a conservative system.*

In a non-conservative system, this result is not valid only because of the work done by the non-conservative forces—those conservative forces in the system do not serve to change the *total* energy, Equ. WE1 may be stated as: the work done by the resultant force on a particle is equal to the change in kinetic energy. Now this work may be given in two parts: the work done by the conservative forces, which, by definition, is minus the change in potential energy; and the work done by the non-conservative forces. Therefore we may say:

Work done by non-conservative forces − change in PE = change in KE

or:

work done by non-conservative forces = change in (PE + KE) (WE2)

This states that the change in total energy is due to the action of non-conservative forces, and equal to the work done by them.

## 14.3 Worked examples

Before working examples, we will re-state the results of the previous paragraph, in the forms in which we most often apply them.

Work done by resultant force = change in kinetic energy (WE1)

where work is defined as $\int \mathbf{F}\cdot d\mathbf{x}$ between suitable limits, and the kinetic energy of a particle of mass $m$ and velocity $\mathbf{v}$ is $\frac{1}{2}m\mathbf{v}^2$. If $\mathbf{F}$ is constant, then the work done is $\mathbf{F}\cdot\mathbf{x}$ in a change of displacement $\mathbf{x}$.

In a conservative system the PCE is: PE + KE = constant, where the gain in potential energy of a particle of mass $m$ is $mgh$ for a gain $h$ in height.

Any change in (PE + KE) of a particle is due to the action of non-conservative forces, and equal to the work done by them. (WE2)

**Worked example 14.1**

Find the distance travelled by a particle of mass 4 kg which is accelerated from 2 m s$^{-1}$ to 5 m s$^{-1}$ by a constant resultant force of 3 N.

*Solution*

If the distance is $x$, then the work done is $3x$. The change in kinetic energy is $(\frac{1}{2}\times 4\times 5^2 - \frac{1}{2}\times 4\times 2^2)$ J = 42 J. Therefore $3x = 42$, and so $x = 14m$.

**Worked example 14.2**

A body of mass $m$ is dropped from a height $h$. Use the work-energy equation to find its velocity when it reaches the ground.

*Solution*

The body experiences a constant force $mg$, its weight. Therefore the work done by the force is $mgh$. If its velocity at ground level is $v$, then the change in KE is $\frac{1}{2}mv^2$. Therefore $\frac{1}{2}mv^2 = mgh$, thus $v^2 = 2gh$ and so $v = \sqrt{(2gh)}$.

**Worked example 14.3**

(a) A car of mass 950 kg pulls a caravan of mass 375 kg up a slope of angle 30°. The car exerts a tractive force of 9 550 N, and the road offers a resistance of 2 N kg$^{-1}$ to each. Find the speed attained from rest after the car and caravan have travelled 200 m.

(b) The towbar now snaps, and the caravan first rolls up the slope, then down again. Find the speed it would achieve if it reached the starting point.

*Solution*

(a) Select $\hat{\mathbf{i}}$ parallel to the slope, and $\hat{\mathbf{j}}$ perpendicular to the slope, as in Fig. 14.2. We have shown the details of the forces in the $\hat{\mathbf{i}}$ direction only, as there is no change of motion in the $\hat{\mathbf{j}}$ direction. The net force in the $\hat{\mathbf{i}}$ direction is

$$F = (9\,550 - 950\,g\sin 30^\circ - 2\times 950 - 375\,g\sin 30^\circ - 2\times 375)\text{ N}$$
$$= (9\,550 - 4\,660 - 1\,900 - 1\,840 - 750)\text{ N}$$

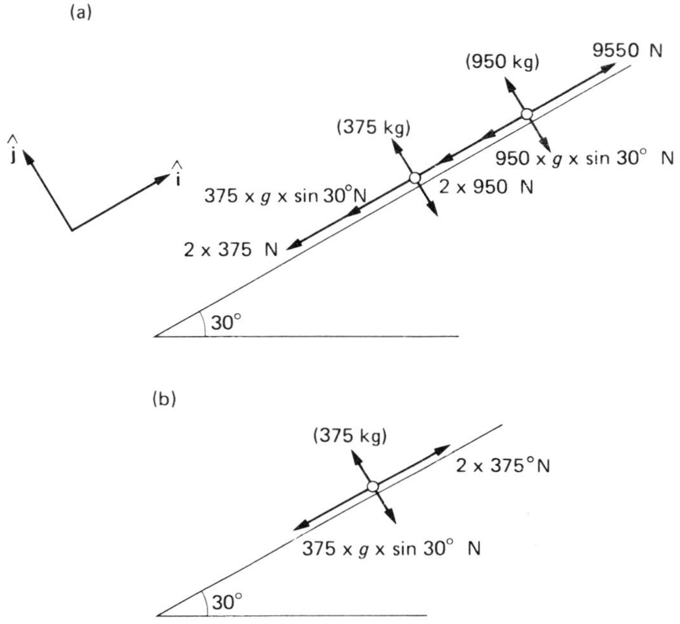


**Fig. 14.2.** Worked example 14.3. (a) A car towing a caravan up a hill. (b) The caravan running down the hill.

thus

$$F = 400 \text{ N}$$

Therefore the work done by $F$ is $400 \text{ N} \times 200 \text{ m} = 80\,000$ J. If the speed attained is $v$, then the change in KE is $\frac{1}{2} \times (950 + 375) \times v^2$.
Therefore

$$\tfrac{1}{2} \times 1325 \times v^2 = 80\,000$$

Therefore

$$v^2 = \frac{160\,000}{1\,325} \quad \text{and so} \quad v = 10{\cdot}99 \text{ m s}^{-1} \approx 11{\cdot}0 \text{ m s}^{-1},$$

or $v = 39{\cdot}55 \text{ km h}^{-1} \approx 39{\cdot}6 \text{ km h}^{-1}$.

(b) The motion of the caravan is in two parts. When it is moving up the slope, it experiences a net force of $(2 \times 375 + 375 \times g \times \sin 30°)$ N down the slope, which destroys its kinetic energy of $\frac{1}{2} \times 375 \times (10{\cdot}99)^2$ J, as it travels a further distance $a$ up the slope. Therefore

$$(2 \times 375 + 375 \times g \times \sin 30°)\, a = \tfrac{1}{2} \times 375 \times (10{\cdot}99)^2$$

Therefore

$$a = \frac{\frac{1}{2} \times (10{\cdot}99)^2}{2 + \frac{1}{2}g} = \frac{(10{\cdot}99)^2}{4 + g} = 8{\cdot}738 \text{ m}$$

The second part of the motion is for the caravan to run 208·7 m downhill, under a net downhill force of $(375 \times g \times \sin 30° - 2 \times 375)$ N, as shown in Fig. 14.2b. Suppose its speed at the end is $V$. Then, by the work–energy equation,

$$(375 \times g \times \sin 30° - 2 \times 375) \times 208{\cdot}7 = \tfrac{1}{2} \times 375 \times V^2$$

Therefore

$$V^2 = 2(\tfrac{1}{2}g - 2) \times 208{\cdot}7 = 5{\cdot}81 \times 208{\cdot}7$$

Therefore

$$V = 34{\cdot}82 \text{ m s}^{-1} \approx 34{\cdot}8 \text{ m s}^{-1},$$

or $V = 125{\cdot}4$ km h$^{-1}$ $\approx 125$ km h$^{-1}$—a good reason for avoiding steep hills with caravans.

**Worked example 14.4**

A sledge of mass 20 kg slides down a smooth mountain from a hut 3000 m above sea level to a town 2950 m above sea level. Find the speed with which it arrives, if it started from rest at the top.

*Solution*

Change in height = 50 m, thus loss of PE = $20 \times g \times 50 = 9810$ J. If its speed at the bottom is $v$, then the gain in KE $= \frac{1}{2} \times 20 \times v^2 = 10v^2$.
Therefore $10v^2 = 9810$, by PCE. Therefore $v^2 = 981$ and $v = 31{\cdot}3$ m s$^{-1}$. Note that we had no need to consider the route taken by the sledge.

**Worked example 14.5**

A stone of mass 3 kg is thrown vertically upwards from the top of a cliff of height 50 m with speed 10 m s$^{-1}$. Find: (a) the greatest height of the stone above the beach below the cliff; (b) the speed with which the stone strikes the beach.

*Solution*

We will measure potential energy relative to the beach. We often refer to our reference level as the *zero* PE *level*, and write that the PE at this level is zero, without mentioning explicitly the relative nature. Thus, in this example, we say that the PE of the stone at the top of the cliff is $3 \times g \times 50 = 1471{\cdot}5$ J.

(a) The greatest height $h$ of the stone occurs when its speed $v$ is zero. Therefore, using PCE, $3 \times g \times 50 + \frac{1}{2} \times 3 \times 10^2 = 3 \times g \times h + 0$. Therefore

$$h = \frac{1471{\cdot}5 + 150}{29{\cdot}43} = \frac{1621{\cdot}5}{29{\cdot}43} = 55{\cdot}11 \text{ m} \approx 55{\cdot}1 \text{ m}.$$

(b) Suppose the stone strikes the beach with speed $V$. Then, using PCE, $1621{\cdot}5 = \frac{1}{2} \times 3 \times V^2 + 0$. Therefore

$$V^2 = \tfrac{2}{3} \times 1621{\cdot}5 \quad \text{thus} \quad V = 32{\cdot}88 \text{ m s}^{-1} \approx 32{\cdot}9 \text{ m s}^{-1}$$

**Worked example 14.6**

A particle of mass 2 kg is dragged up a line of greatest slope of a plane inclined at 30° to the horizontal. The coefficient of friction between the plane and the particle is $\frac{1}{4}$, and the force dragging the particle is 20 N parallel to the plane. Find the distance the particle travels when its speed increases from 2 m $s^{-1}$ to 8 m $s^{-1}$.

*Solution*

Select $\hat{\mathbf{i}}$ in the direction and sense of the motion, as shown in Fig. 14.3. Suppose the required distance is $d$. Then the gain in height is $h = d \sin 30°$, that is, $h = \frac{1}{2}d$. The normal reaction $R$ is given by $R = 2 \times g \times \frac{1}{2}\sqrt{3} = g\sqrt{3}$. Friction $F$ is limiting, and so $F = \frac{1}{4}R = \frac{1}{4}g\sqrt{3}$. The resultant non-conservative force in the $\hat{\mathbf{i}}$ direction is $20 - \frac{1}{4}g\sqrt{3}$. Using the work-energy Equ. 2,

$$(20 - \tfrac{1}{4}g\sqrt{3})d = (\tfrac{1}{2} \times 2 \times 8^2 - \tfrac{1}{2} \times 2 \times 2^2) + 2 \times g \times \tfrac{1}{2}d$$

Therefore

$$(20 - \tfrac{1}{4}g\sqrt{3} - g)d = 60$$

Therefore

$$d = \frac{60}{20 - 4{\cdot}247 - 9{\cdot}81} = \frac{60}{5{\cdot}943} = 10{\cdot}09 \text{ m} \approx 10{\cdot}1 \text{ m}$$

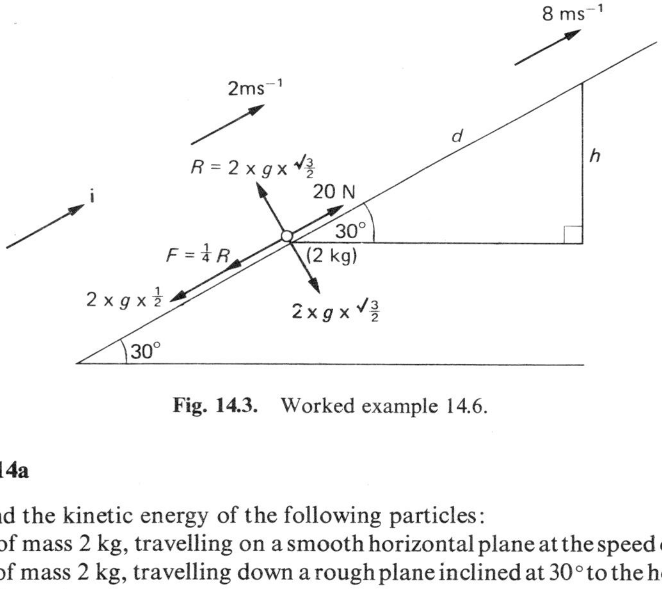


**Fig. 14.3.** Worked example 14.6.

**Exercise 14a**

1. Find the kinetic energy of the following particles:
(a) A, of mass 2 kg, travelling on a smooth horizontal plane at the speed of 7 m $s^{-1}$.
(b) B, of mass 2 kg, travelling down a rough plane inclined at 30° to the horizontal, at 7 m $s^{-1}$.
(c) C, of mass 4 kg, travelling with velocity

$$\begin{pmatrix} 1 \\ 2 \\ -3 \end{pmatrix} \text{ m s}^{-1}$$

2. A body of mass $m$ slides down a rough slope inclined at 30° to the horizontal, the coefficient of friction between the body and the slope being $\frac{1}{4}$. Find the kinetic energy of the body after it has travelled 5 m from rest. Find the work done by the frictional force in opposing the motion of the body, and hence find the kinetic energy of the body if it slides 5 m down a smooth slope of the same inclination.

3. A particle is accelerated from 3 m $s^{-1}$ to 7 m $s^{-1}$ over a distance of 5 m by a force of 12 N. Find the mass of the particle.

4. A car of mass 900 kg can accelerate from rest to 50 km $h^{-1}$ when travelling 48 m over rough horizontal ground when opposed by a resistance of 2 N $kg^{-1}$. Find the tractive force of the car, and the braking force required to stop the car in half the distance.

5. A boy of mass 55 kg climbs eighty 120 mm steps to reach the top of a smooth helter-skelter, stands in the queue at the top, and then slides down. Find: (a) the work done in climbing the stairs; (b) his speed when he returns to ground level; (c) his speed half-way down.

6. A particle of mass $m$ is dragged up a line of greatest slope of a plane inclined at 20° to the horizontal, by a constant force of $3{\cdot}5\,mg$ parallel to the plane. The particle's speed increases from $6\sqrt{g}$ to $12\sqrt{g}$ over a distance of 20 m. Find the coefficient of friction between the particle and the plane.

7. A stone is thrown upwards at an angle of 30° to the horizontal with a speed of 12 m $s^{-1}$ by a man standing on the edge of a cliff 30 m high. With what speed will it strike the water at the foot of the cliff?

8. A particle of mass $m$ is on one end of a light rod of length $a$, which is smoothly hinged to a point A at its other end. If the rod starts in a horizontal position, and the particle then has a speed $u$, find the speed of the particle when the rod is pointing vertically downwards, and hence find the magnitude and direction of the impulse of the tension in the rod as it swings from the horizontal to the vertical.

9. A bullet of mass $m$ is fired into a fixed block of wood of mass $M$, and penetrates to a distance $d$. Find the force of resistance if the bullet enters the wood with speed $u_1$.

If this resistance force remains the same and constant, find to what distance the bullet will penetrate if the block is free to move on a smooth horizontal surface.

10. A smooth circular loop of radius 2 m is fixed in a vertical plane, with A its highest point, and B its lowest point. Two beads C and D can slide freely round the hoop, C, of mass 3 kg, is released from rest at A and strikes D, of mass 6 kg, and initially at rest, at B. Find the coefficient of restitution between the beads if C comes to rest. Find the vertical height to which C rises after the second impact.

## 14.4 Energy in strings and springs

Elastic strings and springs have potential energy when they are stretched, by virtue of being stretched; and, similarly, springs have potential energy when compressed.

For, suppose an elastic string of stiffness $k$ is stretched from its natural length $a$ to a length $a + X$. When the extension of the string is $x$, for $0 \leqq x \leqq X$, then the tension is $kx$, by Hooke's law. Therefore the work done by the tension in stretching the string is

$$\int_0^X kx\,\mathrm{d}x = \left[\tfrac{1}{2}kx^2\right]_0^X = \tfrac{1}{2}kX^2$$

which is the potential energy of the string.

Thus the potential energy of a string or spring which has extension $X$ is $\tfrac{1}{2}kX^2$. Similarly, it may be shown that the PE of a spring compressed by an amount $X$ is also $\tfrac{1}{2}kX^2$.

**Worked example 14.7**

A mass $M$ is attached to a light elastic spring of natural length $a$. An extension $e$ is produced when the spring is suspended from a fixed point with the mass attached to the lower end. In this position, a small mass $m$ is added to the mass $M$, and the combined mass is allowed to fall from rest. Find the greatest extension in the spring, and investigate the motion of the combined mass.

*Solution*

Using Fig. 14.4a, in the equilibrium position, and where $\hat{\mathbf{i}}$ is chosen vertically downwards. Using Newton's second law, in the $\hat{\mathbf{i}}$ direction, $Mg = T$. Using Hooke's law, $T = ke$. Therefore $Mg = ke$ and so $k = Mg/e$. Now take the equilibrium position to determine the zero PE level. Then the energy of the system in this position is $\frac{1}{2}ke^2 = \frac{1}{2}Mge$. In the lowest position, shown in Fig. 14.4b, the energy of the system is

$$\tfrac{1}{2}k(d + e)^2 - (M + m)gd = \frac{Mg}{2e}(d + e)^2 - (M + m)gd$$

Therefore, using PCE,

$$\frac{Mg}{2e}(d + e)^2 - (M + m)gd = \tfrac{1}{2}Mge$$

Therefore

$$Md^2 + 2Mde + Me^2 - 2Med - 2med = Me^2$$

Therefore

$$Md^2 = 2med \quad \text{thus} \quad d = 2me/M$$

and the greatest extension is $d + e = (2m + M)e/M$.

In the general case, shown in Fig. 14.4c, suppose that the velocity of the combined mass is $\dot{x}\hat{\mathbf{i}}$ when the extension is $x\hat{\mathbf{i}}$.
Then, using PCE,

$$\tfrac{1}{2}Mge = \tfrac{1}{2}(m + M)\dot{x}^2 + \frac{Mg}{2e}(x + e)^2 - (m + M)gx \qquad (1)$$

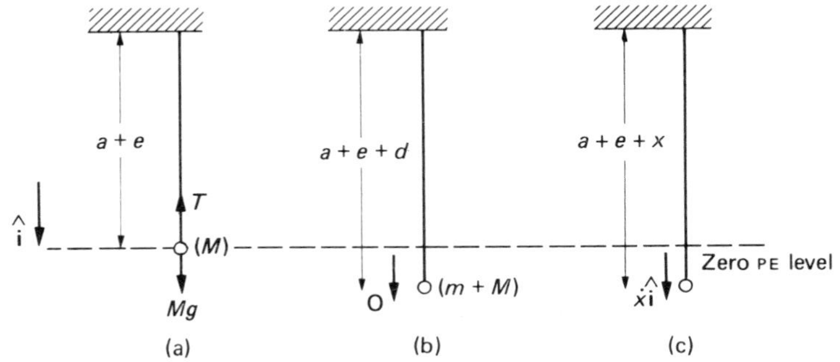


**Fig. 14.4.** Worked example 14.7. (a) Equilibrium position; (b) lowest position; (c) general position.

This is the *energy equation* of the motion, which may be integrated to give $x$ in terms of $t$, and thus describe the motion completely. Alternatively, it may be differentiated to give the *equation of motion*, which is what would have been obtained by our previous methods, namely direct application of Newton's second law. We will present the second method.

Differentiate Equ. 1 with respect to $t$:

$$0 = (m + M)\,\dot{x}\ddot{x} + \frac{Mg}{e}(x + e)\dot{x} - (m + M)g\dot{x}$$

Therefore

$$\ddot{x} = -\frac{Mg}{e(m + M)}\left(x + e - \frac{(m + M)e}{M}\right) = -\frac{Mg}{e(m + M)}\left(x - \frac{m}{M}e\right)$$

Let $y = x - (m/M)e$, so that $\ddot{y} = \ddot{x}$. Then

$$\ddot{y} = -\frac{Mg}{e(m + M)}y$$

which represents simple harmonic motion (SHM) of period $2\pi\sqrt{[e(m + M)/Mg]}$, about the centre given by $y = 0$, that is $x = (m/M)e = \frac{1}{2}d$.

This SHM equation has general solution $y = A\cos(\omega t + \epsilon)$, where $A$ and $\epsilon$ are constants and $\omega = \sqrt{[Mg/e(m + M)]}$. We may determine the constants from initial conditions. When $t = 0$, $x = 0$ and $y = -(m/M)e = A\cos\epsilon$. Also, when $t = 0$, $\dot{x} = 0$ and $\dot{y} = 0 = -A\omega\sin\epsilon$ and so $\epsilon = 0$, as we may take the principal value of arcsin 0. Therefore

$$A = -\frac{m}{M}e \quad \text{and} \quad x = -\frac{m}{M}e\cos\omega t + \frac{m}{M}e$$

That is,

$$x = \frac{m}{M}e(1 - \cos\omega t) \quad \text{where} \quad \omega = \sqrt{\frac{Mg}{e(m + M)}}$$

This example demonstrates an important method of solving problems: instead of using Newton's second law directly, we may write down the energy equation, and differentiate it to obtain the equation of motion. Since the two methods are equivalent, and produce the same result eventually, it is generally not helpful to use both within the same problem.

**Exercise 14*b***

1. A mass of 4 kg is attached to a light elastic spring of natural length 0·5 m. An extension of 0·2 m is produced when the spring is suspended from a fixed point with the mass attached to the lower end. In this position, the mass is struck by another particle of mass 2 kg, falling vertically with a speed of 3 m s$^{-1}$. The two masses coalesce, and the system starts to oscillate. Investigate the motion, assuming that momentum is conserved when the two particle collide.

2. Two identical light elastic strings, each of natural length $a$ and stiffness $mg/a$, are attached at one end of each to a particle of mass $m$. The other ends are attached to two points in the same horizontal plane at a distance $2a\sqrt{3}$ from each other. Show that the particle hangs in equilibrium at a depth $a$ below these points,

and find the corresponding extension in each string. When the particle is displaced a further $x$ vertically show that $2a\sqrt{[1 + x(2a + x)/4a^2]} - a \approx a + \frac{1}{2}x$ is the extension in each string. Using this approximation investigate the motion of the particle when displaced slightly from equilibrium and released.

## 14.5 Loss of energy on impact

We now reconsider a problem involving the collision of two smooth spheres, particularly in respect of any energy changes that may take place.

**Worked example 14.8**

Two smooth spheres, of masses $m$ and $3m$, and the same radius, are travelling at right angles to each other with respective speed $5u$ and $2u$. They collide with their line of centres inclined at 30° to the direction of motion of the sphere of mass $m$ as shown in Fig. 14.5. If the coefficient of restitution between the spheres is $\frac{1}{2}$, investigate their motion after collision, including a consideration of the energy changes involved.

*Solution*

Select $\hat{\mathbf{i}}$ and $\hat{\mathbf{j}}$ in the directions of motion of the two spheres, as shown in Fig. 14.5, so that the line of centres is given by

$$\mathbf{a} = \begin{pmatrix} \sqrt{3} \\ 1 \end{pmatrix}$$

and the velocities before impact by

$$\begin{pmatrix} 5u \\ 0 \end{pmatrix} \text{ and } \begin{pmatrix} 0 \\ 2u \end{pmatrix}.$$

Suppose the respective velocities afterwards are

$$\mathbf{v} = \begin{pmatrix} v_1 \\ v_2 \end{pmatrix} \text{ and } \mathbf{w} = \begin{pmatrix} w_1 \\ w_2 \end{pmatrix}$$

Using PCLM

$$m\begin{pmatrix} 5u \\ 0 \end{pmatrix} + 3m\begin{pmatrix} 0 \\ 2u \end{pmatrix} = m\begin{pmatrix} v_1 \\ v_2 \end{pmatrix} + 3m\begin{pmatrix} w_1 \\ w_2 \end{pmatrix} \quad (1)$$

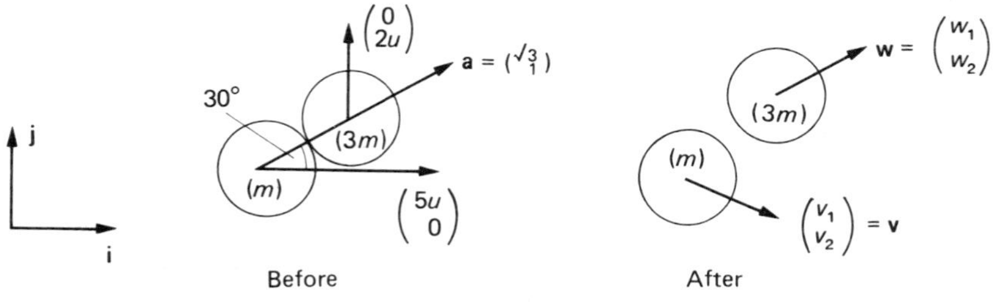


**Fig. 14.5.** Worked example 14.8.

Using NEL

$$-\tfrac{1}{2}\left[\begin{pmatrix}0\\2u\end{pmatrix} - \begin{pmatrix}5u\\0\end{pmatrix}\right]\cdot\begin{pmatrix}\sqrt{3}\\1\end{pmatrix} = \left[\begin{pmatrix}w_1\\w_2\end{pmatrix} - \begin{pmatrix}v_1\\v_2\end{pmatrix}\right]\cdot\begin{pmatrix}\sqrt{3}\\1\end{pmatrix}$$

Therefore

$$-5u\sqrt{3} + 2u = -2[(w_1 - v_1)\sqrt{3} + w_2 - v_2] \qquad (2)$$

Finally, the impulse on collision is in the **a** direction. Therefore

$$\begin{pmatrix}v_1\\v_2\end{pmatrix} - \begin{pmatrix}5u\\0\end{pmatrix} = k\begin{pmatrix}\sqrt{3}\\1\end{pmatrix}$$

Therefore $k = v_2$, and so

$$v_1 - 5u = v_2\sqrt{3} \qquad (3)$$

From Equ. 1,

$$v_2 = 2u - \tfrac{1}{3}v_2 \quad \text{and} \quad w_1 = \tfrac{5}{3}u - \tfrac{1}{3}v_1 = v_2\sqrt{3}/3$$

From Equ. 3,

$$v_1 = 5u + v_2\sqrt{3}$$

Substituting in Equ. 2 now gives:

$$\begin{aligned}-5u\sqrt{3} + 2u &= -2(-v_2 - 5u\sqrt{3} - 3v_2 + 2u - \tfrac{1}{3}v_2 - v_2)\\ &= -2[(2 - 5\sqrt{3})u - 16v_2/3]\end{aligned}$$

Therefore $32v_2/3 = -3(5\sqrt{3} - 2)$ and so $v_2 = -9(5\sqrt{3} - 2)u/32$. Therefore

$$\mathbf{v} = \frac{u}{32}\begin{pmatrix}25 + 18\sqrt{3}\\18 - 45\sqrt{3}\end{pmatrix} = \begin{pmatrix}1\cdot443\\-1\cdot529\end{pmatrix}u \approx \begin{pmatrix}1\cdot44\\-1\cdot53\end{pmatrix}u$$

and

$$\mathbf{w} = \frac{u}{32}\begin{pmatrix}45 - 6\sqrt{3}\\70 - 15\sqrt{3}\end{pmatrix} = \begin{pmatrix}1\cdot082\\1\cdot376\end{pmatrix}u \approx \begin{pmatrix}1\cdot08\\1\cdot38\end{pmatrix}u$$

The kinetic energy of the sphere of mass $m$ before the collision is $25mu^2/2$. After the collision, its KE is $\tfrac{1}{2}mu^2(1\cdot443^2 + 1\cdot529^2) = 2\cdot211\,mu^2 \approx 2\cdot21\,mu^2$. Thus the sphere of mass $m$ loses KE $(12\cdot5 - 2\cdot21)mu^2 = 10\cdot39\,mu^2 \approx 10\cdot4\,mu^2$. The kinetic energy of the sphere of mass $3m$ before the collision is $6\,mu^2$. After the collision, its KE is $\tfrac{1}{2} \times 3\,mu^2\,(1\cdot082^2 + 1\cdot376^2) = 4\cdot594\,mu^2 \approx 4\cdot59\,mu^2$. Thus the sphere of mass $m$ loses KE $(6 - 4\cdot59)\,mu^2 = 1\cdot41\,mu^2$. The total loss of KE is therefore $11\cdot8\,mu^2$, which is $(11\cdot8/18\cdot5) \times 100 \approx 64\%$ of the original kinetic energy.

**Exercise 14*c***

1. A smooth sphere of mass 2 kg is at rest when it is struck by a sphere of the same radius, but of mass 3 kg, moving with $\alpha$ speed of 3 m s$^{-1}$. The two spheres subsequently move in the same straight line. Find the total loss of kinetic energy: (a) if the spheres coalesce on collision; (b) if the coefficient of restitution between the spheres is $0\cdot7$.

2. Two spheres, of masses $m$ and $2m$, are moving in the same direction and

sense with speeds $3u$ and $2u$ when they collide. Find the coefficient of restitution between the spheres if 1/34 of the total kinetic energy is destroyed by the collision.

3. A particle of mass 3 kg and velocity

$$\begin{pmatrix} 2 \\ 3 \end{pmatrix} \text{ m s}^{-1}$$

collides with a particle of mass 2 kg and velocity

$$\begin{pmatrix} -1 \\ -2 \end{pmatrix} \text{ m s}^{-1}$$

giving it an impulse in the direction of

$$\begin{pmatrix} 0 \\ 1 \end{pmatrix}$$

If the coefficient of restitution between the particles is $\frac{3}{4}$, find the kinetic energy destroyed as a percentage of the initial kinetic energy.

## 14.6 Power

*Power* is defined as the rate at which work is being done. Thus, if the work done between times $t_1$ and $t$ is

$$W = W(t) = \int_{t=t_1}^{t} \mathbf{F}\,.\,\mathrm{d}\mathbf{x}$$

then the power at time $t$, or the rate of working at time $t$, is

$$P = P(t) = \frac{\mathrm{d}}{\mathrm{d}t}\int_{t=t_1}^{t} \mathbf{F}\,.\,\mathrm{d}\mathbf{x} = \frac{\mathrm{d}}{\mathrm{d}t}\int_{t=t_1}^{t} \mathbf{F}\,.\,\frac{\mathrm{d}\mathbf{x}}{\mathrm{d}t}\mathrm{d}t = \mathbf{F}\,.\,\frac{\mathrm{d}\mathbf{x}}{\mathrm{d}t} = \mathbf{F}\,.\,\mathbf{v}$$

where $\mathbf{v}$ is the velocity of the particle at time $t$. The unit of power is the *watt*, where 1 W = 1 J s$^{-1}$.

In the case of a particle moving in a straight line with velocity $v$, and being acted upon by a force $F$ in that line, then $P = Fv$.

## 14.7 Worked examples

**Worked example 14.9**

A cyclist and his machine have a combined mass of 90 kg. Without pedalling, the cyclist travels at a steady speed of 24 km h$^{-1}$ down a hill inclined at an angle of arcsin (1/30) to the horizontal. At what rate must the cyclist work in order to travel at the same constant speed: (a) on the level; (b) up a hill inclined at an angle of arcsin (1/40) to the horizontal, assuming that the resistances to motion, other than gravity, remain constant?

*Solution*

When the cyclist is travelling down the hill at a steady speed, the resultant force is $90g \times (1/30) - R$, where $R$ is the resistance to motion. There is no acceleration. Therefore, by Newton's second law, $3g - R = 0$, and so $R = 3g$.

(a) To travel at a steady speed against the resistance $R = 3\,g$, the cyclist must apply an effective force $F = 3g$. Therefore the power required is

$$3g \times 24 \times 10^3/3600 \text{ N m s}^{-1} = 20g \text{ W} \approx 196 \text{ W}$$

(b) When travelling up a slope of angle arcsin (1/40), the cyclist must apply an effective force $F' = 90g \times (1/40) + 3g = 21\,g/4$. Therefore his power in this case is

$$F' \times 24 \times \frac{1000}{3600} = \frac{21g}{4} \times \frac{24\,000}{3\,600} = 35g \text{ W} \approx 343 \text{ W}$$

**Worked Example 14.10**

A train of total mass 180 t has a maximum power output of 540 kW. The resistances to its motion total 7200 N, excluding gravity. If the train is ascending a slope of angle arcsin (1/250), and working at its maximum rate, find the time and distance taken to reach a speed of 9 m s$^{-1}$ from rest. Take $g = 10$ m s$^{-2}$.

*Solution*

The forces on the train are shown in Fig. 14.6. Suppose the speed at time $t$ is $v$, and the force at time $t$ is $F$. Then $Fv = 540\,000$, thus $F = 540\,000/v$. Apply Newton's second law in the direction of motion:

$$F - \frac{180\,000\,g}{250} - 7200 = 180\,000\,a.$$

Therefore

$$a = \frac{\mathrm{d}v}{\mathrm{d}t} = \frac{(540\,000/v) - (180\,000/25) - 7200}{180\,000} = \frac{3}{v} - \frac{1}{25} - \frac{1}{25} = \frac{75 - 2v}{25v}$$

Therefore

$$\int_0^9 \frac{25v\,\mathrm{d}v}{75 - 2v} = \int_0^T \mathrm{d}t,$$

where $T$ is the required time.

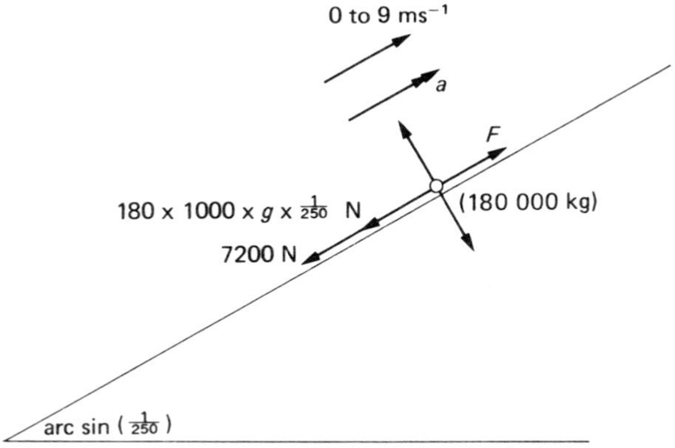


**Fig. 14.6.** Worked example 14.10.

Therefore

$$T = \int_0^9 \frac{-\frac{1}{2}(1875 - 50v - 1875)\,dv}{(1875 - 50v)/25} = \int_0^9 \left(-\frac{25}{2} + \frac{25}{2} \times \frac{1875}{1875 - 50v}\right) dv$$

$$= \left[-\frac{25}{2}v + \frac{25}{2} \times \frac{1875}{-50}\ln(1875 - 50v)\right]_0^9$$

$$= -(225/2) + (1875/4)\ln(1875/1425) = (-112{\cdot}5 + 128{\cdot}3)\text{s}$$

Therefore the time taken is 15·8 s ≈ 16 s. Also

$$a = v\frac{dv}{dx} = \frac{75 - 2v}{25v}$$

thus

$$\int_0^X dx = \int_0^9 \frac{25v^2\,dv}{75 - 2v}$$

where $X$ is the required distance. Therefore

$$X = \int_0^9 \frac{-\frac{1}{2}(1875v - 50v^2 - 1875v)\,dv}{(1875 - 50v)/25} = \int_0^9 \left(-\frac{25v}{2} + \frac{75}{2} \times \frac{25v}{75 - 2v}\right) dv$$

$$= \left[-25v^2/4\right]_0^9 + 75T/2 = (-506{\cdot}25 + 592{\cdot}6)\text{m}$$

Therefore the distance covered is 86·35 m ≈ 86 m.

**Exercise 14*d***

1. A car of mass 900 kg rolls at a steady speed of 30 km h$^{-1}$ down a slope inclined at an angle of arcsin (1/20) to the horizontal against a constant resistance. Assuming that the resistance does not change, find the rate at which the car's engine must work to travel at the same speed: (a) on the level; (b) *up* the same hill.

2. A train of mass 200 t has a maximum power output of 300 kW. The resistances to motion, excluding gravity, total 8000 N. If the train is travelling on horizontal ground, find the constant speed that can be maintained with half the maximum power output; and the acceleration at this speed if the maximum power output is applied.

3. Find the power output required for:
   (a) An engine working a conveyor belt to lift 500 kg of grain each minute to a height of 20 m if frictional and other resistances may be neglected.
   (b) The locomotive of a train of total mass 250 *t*, which has a constant cruising speed of 16 m s$^{-1}$ on a straight horizontal track against resistances of 150 N t$^{-1}$.

4. The engine of a car works at a constant rate. The car has a maximum speed of $u$ on the level, and $v$ up a slope of angle $\alpha$. Find the maximum speed of the car down the same slope, if the net resistance is the same in each case.

5. A car of mass 800 kg is travelling on a straight horizontal road against negligible resistances, and increases its speed from 18 km h$^{-1}$ to 36 km h$^{-1}$ in travelling 0·5 km. Find the time taken (a) if the car exerts a constant force. (b) if the car works at a constant rate.

6. A train of mass m travels between two adjacent stations by means of a straight horizontal track of length 2 km, and against negligible resistance. The train starts

from rest at station A, works at a constant rate P for the first $\frac{1}{2}$ km, travels at a constant speed for the next $1\frac{1}{4}$ km, and exerts a constant braking force for the final $\frac{1}{4}$ km, coming to rest at station B. Find the time taken for each section.

## 14.8 Further worked examples

**Worked Example 14.11**

An 18 W motor can operate a conveyor belt at a steady speed of $0{\cdot}6\ \mathrm{m\,s^{-1}}$ at full power, if the conveyor belt is unloaded. When grain is poured vertically onto the conveyor belt, a second identical motor works at full power and maintains the movement of the belt at the same speed as before.

(a) Find the rate at which the grain arrives.

(b) Find the horizontal component of velocity which must be given to the grain if the belt is to handle 50% more grain.

*Solution*

$18\ \mathrm{W} = 18\ \mathrm{N\,m\,s^{-1}} = 30\ \mathrm{N} \times 0{\cdot}6\ \mathrm{m\,s^{-1}}$. Therefore the motor overcomes an effective resistance force of 30 N in order to work the conveyor belt at the steady speed of $0{\cdot}6\ \mathrm{m\,s^{-1}}$.

(a) Suppose an amount $A$ of grain arrives each second. Then the momentum given to the grain is $A \times 0{\cdot}6$ (in N s), each second. The second motor effectively provides a force of 30 N to move the grain, giving it an impulse of 30 N s each second. Therefore

$$A \times 0{\cdot}6 = 30 \text{ and so } A = 30/0{\cdot}6 = 50\ \mathrm{kg}$$

Therefore the grain arrives at $50\ \mathrm{kg\,s^{-1}}$.

(b) The grain now arrives at $75\ \mathrm{kg\,s^{-1}}$.

$$\text{The momentum gained each second} = 75 \times 0{\cdot}6 - \text{initial momentum}$$

$$\text{The impulse each second} = 30\ \mathrm{N\,s}$$

as in (a). Therefore

$$75 \times 0{\cdot}6 - \text{initial momentum} = 30$$

thus

$$\text{initial momentum} = 15\ \mathrm{N\,s}.$$

Therefore

$$\text{initial horizontal speed} = 15/75 = 0{\cdot}2\ \mathrm{m\,s^{-1}}$$

Thus the belt will handle 50% more grain if the grain arrives with a horizontal velocity component of $0{\cdot}2\ \mathrm{m\,s^{-1}}$.

**Worked example 14.12**

A gun of mass $M$ on a smooth horizontal surface fires a shell of mass $m$ with a speed $u$ at an angle of 30° to the horizontal. The gun is brought to rest by a spring of comparitively negligible mass, and stiffness $3Mg/a$, where the spring is at its natural length $a$ before firing. Find:

(a) the speed $V$ of recoil of the gun at the instant of firing;

(b) the distance $d$ the gun travels before being brought to rest.

*Solution*

(a) The shell gains horizontal momentum $mu \cos 30° = \frac{1}{2}mu\sqrt{3}$. Therefore the horizontal momentum of the gun is $\frac{1}{2}mu\sqrt{3}$, in the opposite sense. Therefore $MV = \frac{1}{2}mu\sqrt{3}$, and so $V = mu\sqrt{3}/2M$.

(b) As the gun begins to move, it has kinetic energy $\frac{1}{2}MV^2 = 3m^2u^2/8M$. When the gun comes to rest, the spring has potential energy $\frac{1}{2}kd^2 = 3Mgd^2/2a$. Therefore

$$\frac{3m^2u^2}{8M} = \frac{3Mgd^2}{2a}$$

Therefore

$$d^2 = \frac{m^2u^2a}{4M^2g} \text{ and so } d = \frac{mu}{2M}\sqrt{\frac{a}{g}}$$

## 14.9 Miscellaneous exercises 14

1. A boat of mass 600 kg, initially at rest, slides a distance of 20 m down a slipway inclined at 13° to the horizontal. The frictional force opposing motion is equal to the weight of 60 kg. Find:

(i) the kinetic energy of the boat at the bottom of the slipway, using the kilogram as the unit of mass, and the metre per second as the unit of velocity;

(ii) the velocity of the boat at this moment expressed in metres per second. (MEI)

2. State Hooke's law and obtain an expression for the potential energy stored in a light elastic string of natural length $a$ and modulus $\lambda$ stretched to a length $(a + b)$.

The ends of this string are fixed to two points A and B on the same level at a distance $3a$ apart. A particle of mass $m$ is fixed to the mid-point of the string and is released from rest at the mid-point of AB. If the particle first comes to rest after falling through a distance $2a$, find its acceleration at this instant. (L)

3. Two spheres moving in opposite directions along the same path collide directly. Their masses are $2m$ and $3m$, and their speeds immediately before collision are $7u$ and $3u$ respectively. Show that after impact the speed of the heavier sphere lies between $u$ and $5u$. Find the ratio of their kinetic energies after impact if nine-tenths of the total kinetic energy is lost in the collision. (L)

4. A lorry of mass 2 400 kg is travelling along a level road at steady speed of 48 km $h^{-1}$. If there is a total resistance of 50 N per 100 kg mass, calculate the rate kilowatts at which the lorry's engine is working.

When the lorry's engine is working at the rate of 21 kW, the conditions remaining the same, calculate the acceleration of the lorry when its speed is 42 km $h^{-1}$. (L)

5. A particle A of mass $m$, moving with speed $2u$, collides directly with a particle B of mass $M$ moving in the same direction with speed $u$. After the collision A continues to move in the same direction but with speed $u$. From that the coefficient of restitution between the two particles is $m/M$ and deduce that after the collision the kinetic energy of A is less than that of B.

If the ratio of these kinetic energies is 1:6, show further that $m/M = 2 - \sqrt{3}$. (JMB)

6. A certain game involves projecting a circular brass disc along a horizontal slate surface so as to strike a similar disc at rest. In any such impact momentum is conserved but a fraction $k$ ($< \frac{1}{2}$) of energy is lost. One disc (A) is moving *directly* towards the centre of another (B) with speed $u$ just before impact, and the discs separate at a relative speed $2w$ after impact prove: (i) that A's motion after impact is in the same direction as before it; and (ii) that $w = \frac{1}{2}u\sqrt{(1 - 2k)}$.

If $k = 0{\cdot}095$ and the motion of each disc over the slate after impact is resisted by a constant horizontal frictional force, prove that the ratio of the distances moved after impact is about 1 to 360. (MEI)

7. Sand pours over the lip of a chute and falls vertically onto a conveyer belt which is moving horizontally at a steady speed of 0·5 metre per second. If the supply of sand is steady at the rate of 50 kg per second, what horizontal momentum is given to the sand each second? Find the force that is required to give the sand this momentum.

If 10 W is the power required to operate the conveyor belt without a load, find whether a motor of maximum power 25 W can deal with sand at the rate of supply of 50 kg per second.

If the chute were modified so that the sand was delivered with a horizontal component of velocity of 0·5 metre per second in the direction of motion of the belt, find the maximum speed at which the belt could move the load, assuming that the power required for the belt itself is unaltered and the sand is delivered at the same rate as before. (MEI)

8. In jumping vertically upwards, an animal exerts a thrust on the ground which we shall assume remains constant at $T$ newton until the moment of take-off. During this period of pressure on the ground the centre of mass of the animal is raised from a height of a metre to a height of $(a + d)$ metre and its velocity, which is vertical, is increased from zero to $V$ metre per second. If the animal has a mass of $M$ kg, write down the relation between $T$, $d$, $V$ and $M$. (Do not substitute a value for $g$.)

If the jump carries the centre of mass of the animal to a height of $(a + h)$ metre, write down the relation between $V$, $h$ and $d$, and deduce that $h = Td/Mg$. Assuming that $T$ varies only as the area of the cross section of the jumping limbs, show that all animals of similar shape and build should jump to the same height, irrespective of their size. (MEI)

9. The resistance to a car is proportional to the square of its speed. The car can cruise at 120 km per hour on the level, exerting a power of $P$ watt, and it can coast down a hill of 1 in 20 at the same speed (i.e. exerting no power).

What would be its acceleration, at a power of $P$ watt, on the level at 60 km per hour?

If it maintains this power while accelerating from 60 km per hour to 90 km per hour on the level, show that it would go about 400 m during this acceleration. (MEI)

10 A particle is moved in the $(x, y)$-plane, in a field of force with components $(2x, y)$. If the particle is moved from $(0, 0)$ to $(a, b)$ along a straight line, then from $(a, b)$ to $(0, b)$ along the line $y = b$, and finally from $(0, b)$ back to $(0,0)$ along the $y$-axis, find the work done.

Assuming that the work done during a movement from $(0, 0)$ to $(x, y)$ is a function $W(x, y)$ of $x$, $y$, independent of the particular path taken, find an expression for $W(x, y)$. Illustrate by sketching some curves on which $W$ takes a constant value. (SMP)

# Answers to the Exercises

## Chapter 1

### Exercise 1*a*, page 8

**1.** **E(2, 0), F(1, 2), G(3, 2), H(7, 6)** **2.** E(−8, −8), F(2, 2)

### Exercise 1*b*, page 12

1. $5\sqrt{74} \approx 43{\cdot}0$ mm 2. $|\mathbf{a} + \mathbf{b}| = 70$ mm or 10 mm $|\mathbf{a} - \mathbf{b}| = 10$ mm or 70 mm $|2\mathbf{a} + 3\mathbf{b}| = 170$ mm or 10 mm 3. $|\mathbf{u} + \mathbf{v}| = 1$, $|\mathbf{u} - \mathbf{v}| = \sqrt{65} \approx 8{\cdot}06$, $|2\mathbf{u} + 3\mathbf{v}| = \sqrt{5} \approx 2{\cdot}24$

### Exercise 1*c*, page 20

1. (a) 5 m on bearing 036·9°, (b) 5 m on bearing 143·1°,
   (c) $6\sqrt{5} \approx 13{\cdot}4$ m on bearing 026·6°, (d) $\sqrt{337} \approx 18{\cdot}4$ m on bearing 150·6°
2. (a) $\sqrt{2} \approx 1{\cdot}41$ m s$^{-1}$ on bearing 045°, (b) $\sqrt{13} \approx 3{\cdot}6$ m s$^{-1}$ on bearing 033·7°,
   (c) $\sqrt{34} \approx 5{\cdot}83$ m s$^{-1}$ on bearing 149·0°, (d) $\sqrt{13} \approx 3{\cdot}6$ m s$^{-1}$ on bearing 146·3°
3. (a) $1{\cdot}53\hat{\mathbf{i}} + 1{\cdot}29\hat{\mathbf{j}}$, (b) $-2\hat{\mathbf{i}} + 0\hat{\mathbf{j}}$, (c) $-2\hat{\mathbf{i}} + 3{\cdot}46\hat{\mathbf{j}}$
4. (a) $\sqrt{3} \approx 1{\cdot}73$, (b) $5\sqrt{2} \approx 7{\cdot}07$, (c) $\sqrt{29} \approx 5{\cdot}39$, (d) $\sqrt{6} \approx 2{\cdot}45$
5. (a) 2·12 kg m s$^{-1}$ on bearing 311·7°, (b) 12·2 kg m s$^{-1}$ on bearing 076·6°,
   (c) 4·80 kg m s$^{-1}$ on bearing 107·1°
6. From A to B: 76·5 km h$^{-1}$; returning 119 km h$^{-1}$
7. Bearing 337·4°, time $\frac{1}{2}$ h
8. (a) 180 s, (b) 225 s
9. (i) X is headed 36·9° from straight across, Y travels 31·0° from straight across;
   (ii) X takes 45 s longer

### Exercise 1*d*, page 28

1. (a) (i) $-2\hat{\mathbf{i}} - 6\hat{\mathbf{j}}$ along $y = 3x - 5\frac{1}{2}$, (ii) 6·32, 251·6°
   (b) (i) $2\hat{\mathbf{i}} + 4\hat{\mathbf{j}}$ along $y = 2x - 3\frac{1}{2}$, (ii) 4·47, 63·4°
   (c) (i) $\hat{\mathbf{i}} + \hat{\mathbf{j}}$ along $y = x - 1$, (ii) 1·41, 45°.
2. (a) equivalent to $5\hat{\mathbf{a}}$, acting through (7/5, 9/5)
   (b) equivalent to $7\hat{\mathbf{a}}$, acting through (17/7, 15/7)
   (c) equivalent to $6\hat{\mathbf{a}}$, acting through (5/3, 1)
3. (a) magnitude 8, distance $1\frac{1}{2}$ from each
   (b) magnitude 18, distance $5d/18$ from the longer original
4. (a) $3\hat{\mathbf{i}}$ through (1/3, 4/3), (b) $3\hat{\mathbf{i}} - \hat{\mathbf{j}}$ through (9/7, −10/7)

### 1.15 Miscellaneous Exercises 1, page 29

1. (i) D($-5$, 2), (ii) E ($-8$, 11), (iii) F ($-6$, 6) 2. (i) $\mathbf{x} + 3\mathbf{y}$,
(ii) $\sqrt{85} \approx 9{\cdot}22$, arctan (7/6) = 49·4° 3. (i) $\sqrt{13} \approx 3{\cdot}61$ N, bearing 326°,
(ii) $\sqrt{13} \approx 3{\cdot}61$ N, bearing 146° 5. S meets R at (3, $\frac{1}{2}$), $\sqrt{80} \approx 8{\cdot}94$ N, tan (angle) = $\frac{1}{2}$
6. $2\mathbf{b} - 3\mathbf{a} = \overrightarrow{OD}$, $\mathbf{b} - 2\mathbf{a} = \overrightarrow{OE}$ 7. (i) 1, (ii) $\sqrt{3} \approx 1{\cdot}73$
8. (i) $x/384$, greatest value of $x$ is 1536 km, (ii) 004·1°

## Chapter 2

### Exercise 2*a*, page 32

1 to 6. These questions are answered in the text, in Section 2.3.

### Exercise 2*b*, page 36

3. Many possible answers 5. $3\beta = 4\alpha$

### Exercise 2*c*, page 40

1. (a) $\begin{pmatrix} 9 \\ -8 \\ 5 \end{pmatrix}$ (b) $\begin{pmatrix} -5 \\ 5 \\ -4 \end{pmatrix}$ (c) $\begin{pmatrix} -16 \\ 7 \\ 8 \end{pmatrix}$
2. (a) $\sqrt{26} \approx 5{\cdot}10$, (b) $\sqrt{30} \approx 5{\cdot}48$, (c) $\sqrt{241} \approx 15{\cdot}5$
3. With **d**, $\alpha = -2$, $\beta = 1$, $\gamma = 1$, for example, is one of infinitely many possibilities.
With **e**, $\alpha = \beta = \gamma = 0$ is the only possibility.

### Exercise 2*d*, page 42

1. (iii) $\mathbf{c} = -2\mathbf{a} + 0\mathbf{b} + 0\mathbf{e}$ and $\mathbf{d} = 2\mathrm{a} - \mathbf{b} + 0\mathbf{e}$
2. $x_1\begin{pmatrix} 1 \\ 1 \\ 1 \end{pmatrix} + (x_2 - x_1)\begin{pmatrix} 0 \\ 1 \\ 1 \end{pmatrix} + (-x_3 + x_2)\begin{pmatrix} 0 \\ 0 \\ -1 \end{pmatrix}$

### Exercise 2*e*, page 45

1. (a) $\sqrt{13} \approx 3{\cdot}61$, (b) $\sqrt{97} \approx 9{\cdot}85$, (c) $\sqrt{13} \approx 3{\cdot}61$
2. $\alpha = \pm 1{\cdot}96$, $\beta = \pm 5{\cdot}20$ (both to 3S)
3. $\beta_0 = -4\frac{1}{2}$, $\hat{\mathbf{i}} = -4\mathbf{a} + 3\mathbf{b}$, $\hat{\mathbf{j}} = -3\mathbf{a} + 2\mathbf{b}$, $\mathbf{c} = -37{\cdot}2\mathbf{a} + 27{\cdot}8\mathbf{b}$

### 2.9 Miscellaneous Exercises 2, page 46

1. (a) and (b) plane of $\hat{\mathbf{i}}$ and $\hat{\mathbf{j}}$, i.e. plane of O$x$ and O$y$
(c) plane of $\hat{\mathbf{i}} + \hat{\mathbf{j}}$ and $\hat{\mathbf{i}} - \hat{\mathbf{j}} - \hat{\mathbf{k}}$ (d) the whole space
2. $\hat{\mathbf{i}} = \frac{1}{3}(\mathbf{a} + \mathbf{b} + \mathbf{c})$, $\hat{\mathbf{j}} = \frac{1}{3}(\mathbf{b} + \mathbf{c} - 2\mathbf{a})$, $\hat{\mathbf{k}} = \frac{1}{3}(\mathbf{a} + \mathbf{c} - 2\mathbf{b})$ 3. (a) $\sqrt{21} \approx 4{\cdot}58$, (b) 26·9
4. $\alpha = -8/17$ 5. (a) Yes, (b) no, (c) $\alpha = \pm 2/\sqrt{13} = -2\beta/3$
6. It is important *either* to establish clearly which space is spanned by each set *or* to show that each member of each set is a linear combination of the other set.
7. $k = 1$

## Chapter 3

### Exercise 3*a*, page 50

1. $x(3) = 126$ m and $a(3) = -6$ m s$^{-2}$, $x(4) = 125$ m and $a(4) = 6$ m s$^{-2}$
2. the motion is oscillatory, being simple harmonic motion. 3. 36 m

4. (a) 13/6 m, (b) 5 m
5. $a(2) = 0$ m s$^{-2}$, $a(3) = 2$ m s$^{-2}$
When $v = 0$ m s$^{-1}$, $a(3) = 2$ m s$^{-2}$ and $a(1) = -2$ m s$^{-2}$.
6. $2(1 + \sqrt{2})$ m $\approx 4{\cdot}83$ m 7. $x(t) = \frac{1}{2}\cos t - \frac{1}{14}\cos 7t - \frac{3}{7}$ and $a(t) = \frac{7}{2}\cos 7t - \frac{1}{2}\cos t$
8. $a(t) = -2t^{-3}$ and $x(t) = 2 - t^{-1}$ 9. $v(t) = u + \frac{1}{2}kt^2$ and $x(t) = b + ut + \frac{1}{6}kt^3$
11. 23/8 m 12. $a = 9x$ 13. $x(t) = (1 - t)^{-1}$ and $a(t) = 2(1 - t)^{-3}$

## Exercise 3*b*, page 56

1. $-\mathbf{a}/u^2, \mathbf{a}\cos u$ 2. $\ddot{\mathbf{r}} = -n^2\mathbf{r}$
3. (a) $-3u^{-4}\mathbf{a} - u^{-2}\mathbf{b}$, (b) $e^u\mathbf{a} + e^{-u}\mathbf{b}$, (c) $2u\cos(u^2)\mathbf{a} + \dfrac{1}{1 + u^2}\mathbf{b}$
4. (a) $|6t\hat{\mathbf{i}} - 2t\hat{\mathbf{j}}| = 2\sqrt{10}\, t$
(b) $|\cos t\, \hat{\mathbf{i}} - \sin t\, \hat{\mathbf{j}} + \sec^2 t\, \hat{\mathbf{k}}| = \sqrt{1 + \sec^4 t}$

## Exercise 3*c*, page 60

1. (a) $-\frac{1}{2}u^{-2}\mathbf{a} + \ln u\, \mathbf{b} + \mathbf{c}$, (b) $e^u\mathbf{a} + e^{-u}\mathbf{b} + \mathbf{c}$, (c) $\frac{1}{2}(u + \frac{1}{2}\sin 2u)\mathbf{a} + \ln(\sec u)\mathbf{b} + \mathbf{c}$
2. (a) $t^2\hat{\mathbf{i}} + \frac{1}{4}t^4\hat{\mathbf{j}} + \mathbf{c}$, (b) $-\frac{1}{2}\cos 2t\hat{\mathbf{i}} - \frac{1}{3}\sin 3t\hat{\mathbf{j}} + \mathbf{c}$,
(c) $\sin t(2 + \cos^2 t)\hat{\mathbf{i}} - \cos t(2 + \sin^2 t)\hat{\mathbf{j}} + \mathbf{c}$
3. (a) both give $\frac{1}{2}t^2\sqrt{13}$
(b) (i) $\dfrac{2}{11}t(9 + 4t^2)^{1/2} + \dfrac{9}{11}\ln\left|\dfrac{2t + (9 + 4t^2)^{1/2}}{3}\right|$
(ii) $t(9 + t^2)^{1/2}$
4. (a) $\frac{2}{3}\hat{\mathbf{i}} + 2\hat{\mathbf{k}}$, (b) $\frac{1}{2}\ln 2(\hat{\mathbf{i}} + \hat{\mathbf{j}}) + \frac{1}{2}\hat{\mathbf{k}}$
5. $\mathbf{x}(t) = (t^2 + t - 1)\hat{\mathbf{i}} + (t - \frac{1}{2}t^2 - 1\frac{1}{2})\hat{\mathbf{j}}$, $\mathbf{a}(t) = 2\hat{\mathbf{i}} - \hat{\mathbf{j}}$

## 3.8 Miscellaneous Exercises 3, page 58

1. (i) $v(t) = t^4/4 - 5t^3/3 - 7t + 101/12$
(ii) $x(t) = 1 + 101t/12 - 7t^2/2 - 5t^4/12 + t^5/20$
(iii) $a(10/3) = -689/27$ m s$^{-2}$
2. (a) $(3\cos 3u - 3\cos u)\mathbf{a} - 3\sin^3 u\mathbf{b}$
(b) $2u^2(\mathbf{a} - \mathbf{b})/(u^2 + 2u)^2$
3. (a) $|-\sec^2 t\hat{\mathbf{j}} + \sec t\tan t\hat{\mathbf{k}}| = \sec^2 t(2\sec^2 t - 1)^{1/2}$
(b) $|-\hat{\mathbf{i}} + \hat{\mathbf{j}} - 2t\hat{\mathbf{k}}| = (2 + 4t^2)^{1/2}$
4. (a) $\mathbf{r}'(t) = (2t - 5)\hat{\mathbf{i}} + \frac{1}{4}e^t\hat{\mathbf{j}}$
$\int_t^{2t}\mathbf{r}(t)\mathrm{d}t = (7t^3/3 - 15t^2/2 + 6t)\hat{\mathbf{i}} + \frac{1}{4}e^t(e^t - 1)\hat{\mathbf{j}}$
(b) $\mathbf{r}'(t) = 3\cos t\hat{\mathbf{i}} + (2\sin 2t - \sin t)\hat{\mathbf{j}}$
$\int_t^{2t}\mathbf{r}(t)\mathrm{d}t = 3(\cos t - \cos 2t)\hat{\mathbf{i}} + (\frac{3}{2}\sin 2t - \sin t - \frac{1}{2}\sin 4t)\hat{\mathbf{j}}$
5. (a) $\frac{3}{2}u^2\mathbf{a} - (5u^3/3 - u^2 + 3u)\mathbf{b} + \mathbf{c}$
(b) $(u - 2\ln|u + 2|)\mathbf{a} + 2\ln|u + 2|\,\mathbf{b} + \mathbf{c}$
6. (a) $|t\hat{\mathbf{i}} - \ln|\sec t|\hat{\mathbf{j}} + \ln|\sec t + \tan t|\hat{\mathbf{k}}| = \left[t^2 + (\ln|\sec t|)^2 + (\ln|\sec t + \tan t|)^2\right]^{\frac{1}{2}}$
(b) $|(t - \frac{1}{2}t^2)\hat{\mathbf{i}} + (t + \frac{1}{2}t^2)\hat{\mathbf{j}} + (t - t^3/3)\hat{\mathbf{k}}| = t(54 - 3t^2 + 2t^4)^{\frac{1}{2}}/3\sqrt{2}$
7. $\mathbf{x}(t) = (t - 3t^2/2 + 3/2)\hat{\mathbf{i}} + (t^3/3 - 4/3)\hat{\mathbf{j}}$, $\mathbf{a}(t) = -3\hat{\mathbf{i}} + 2t\hat{\mathbf{j}}$
8. (i) $v(t) = 5 + 4t - t^2$ and $x(t) = 5t + 2t^2 - t^3/3$
(ii) $x(5) = 100/3$ m
(iii) $v(6) = -7$ m s$^{-1}$ and $a(6) = -8$ m s$^{-2}$
9. (i) $v(0) = 9$ m s$^{-1}$
(ii) $v = 0$ m s$^{-1}$ for $t = 1$ s and $t = 3$ s
(iii) $a = 0$ m s$^{-1}$ for $t = 2$ s
10. 21·8 cm s$^{-1}$, 36·5° W of N; another 7 seconds

# Chapter 4

## Exercise 4*a*, page 66

1. (i) $\frac{3}{5}\mathbf{a} + \frac{2}{5}\mathbf{b}$, (ii) $\frac{19}{25}\mathbf{a} + \frac{6}{25}\mathbf{b}$, (iii) $\frac{6}{25}\mathbf{a} + \frac{19}{25}\mathbf{b}$, (iv) $\frac{1}{2}\mathbf{a} + \frac{1}{2}\mathbf{b}$ 2. (i) $\frac{3}{2}\mathbf{p} - \frac{1}{2}\mathbf{q}$, (ii) $-2\mathbf{p} + 3\mathbf{q}$, (iii) $-9\mathbf{p} + 10\mathbf{q}$ 3. (i) $\frac{1}{2}\mathbf{l} + \frac{1}{2}\mathbf{m}$, (ii) $\frac{1}{3}(\mathbf{l} + \mathbf{m} + \mathbf{n})$, (iii) $\frac{1}{2}\mathbf{m} + \frac{1}{2}\mathbf{n}$, (iv) $\frac{1}{3}(\mathbf{l} + \mathbf{m} + \mathbf{n})$ 4. (i) yes, (ii) no

## Exercise 4*b*, page 74

1. for OAC, $\frac{1}{3}\mathbf{b}$; for OAB, $\frac{1}{3}\mathbf{a} + \frac{1}{3}\mathbf{b}$; for ABC, $\frac{2}{3}\mathbf{b}$ 4. $\mathbf{e} = \frac{1}{3}\mathbf{q} + \frac{2}{3}\mathbf{p}$, $\mathbf{f} = \frac{1}{3}\mathbf{q} + \frac{2}{3}\mathbf{r}$, EF/PR = 2/3 5. $\mathbf{p} = 2\mathbf{b} - \mathbf{a}$, $\mathbf{q} = 2\mathbf{c} - \mathbf{a}$, $\mathbf{r} = \mathbf{b} + \mathbf{c} - \mathbf{a}$
6. P is the mid-point of XR, where R divides YZ in the ratio 1:4
   P divides YQ in the ratio 3:2, where Q divides XZ in the ratio 1:5
   P divides ZS in the ratio 9:1, where S divides XY in the ratio 4:5.

## Exercise 4*c*, page 79

1. (i) $\mathbf{r} = (2 - t)\hat{\mathbf{i}} + (2t - 1)\hat{\mathbf{j}} + (3 - 4t)\hat{\mathbf{k}}$, (ii) $\alpha = -3$, $\beta = 7$
2. (i) $\mathbf{r} = (2 - t + u)\hat{\mathbf{i}} + (-1 + 2t + 4u)\hat{\mathbf{j}} + (3 - 4t - 5u)\hat{\mathbf{k}}$, (ii) (a) no, (b) yes
4. $\mathbf{e} = 10\mathbf{u} - 29\mathbf{v} + 9\mathbf{w}$
5. Line through $P_0$ parallel to $\mathbf{d}$.
   $\mathbf{P_0P}$ is in the same sense as $\mathbf{d}$ for $\alpha > 0$, opposite sense for $\alpha < 0$. P is at $P_0$ for $\alpha = 0$.

## 4.9 Miscellaneous Exercises 4, page 79

1. (i) $\mathbf{c} = \frac{5}{8}\mathbf{a} + \frac{3}{8}\mathbf{b}$, (ii) 3:2, (iii) $\mathbf{c} = \frac{7}{2}\mathbf{b} - \frac{5}{2}\mathbf{a}$ 2. $\mathbf{f} = \frac{1}{2}\mathbf{a} + \frac{1}{2}\mathbf{c}$ 3. OY/YA = 2/7 and XC/CY = 3/1 7. $h = 4/3$, $k = 4/9$, AP/PQ = 3/1 and OQ/QB = 4/5
8. AF:FE = 3:1

# Chapter 5

## Exercise 5*a*, page 86

2. $r = 4\sin\theta$; (i) $r = 4$, (ii) $r = 8\sin\theta$ 3. $r^2 - 3\sqrt{3}\,r\cos(\theta - 60°) + 9/2 = 0$, centre $(3\sqrt{3}/2, 60°)$, radius 3/2 6. (i) $\theta = 0$, (ii) $r\cos(\theta - \pi/6) = 2\sqrt{3}$, (iii) $r\cos(\theta - 2\pi/3) = 2$ 7. (i) $(2\sqrt{2}, \frac{3}{4}\pi)$, (ii) $(4, \pi/6)$, (iii) $(3, 41{\cdot}8°)$, $(3, 138{\cdot}2°)$
8. (i) $(1, \pi/3)$, (ii) $(1, 5\pi/6)$, (iii) $(\sqrt{2}, \frac{1}{2}\pi)$, (iv) $(2\sqrt{2}, \pi/12)$, (v) $(2\sqrt{2}, 13\pi/12)$, (vi) $(\sqrt{29}, 128{\cdot}2°)$.

## Exercise 5*b*, page 92

1. (a) (5, 53.1°) or (5, 0·93 rad), (b) (13, 114·4°) or (13, 2·00 rad), (c) (17, 241·9°) or (17, 4·22 rad), (d) (41, 282·7°) or (41, 4·93 rad) 2. (a) (1·73, 1), (b) (−2·83, 2·83), (c) (−1·5, −2·60), (d) (2, −3·46) 3. (a) (1·63, 1·63), (b) (0, −2·2), (c) (−3·47, −2·41), (d) (2·46, −2.46) 4. (a) $5/\sqrt{41}, 4/\sqrt{41}$; (b) $1/\sqrt{5}, 2/\sqrt{5}$; (c) 0, 1; (d) $-2/\sqrt{29}, -5/\sqrt{29}$ 5. (i) $4/\sqrt{17}, -1/\sqrt{17}$, (ii) (1, −4), (iii) $(\sqrt{82}, 353{\cdot}7°) \approx (9{\cdot}06, 353{\cdot}7°)$ 6. (a) $0, -1/\sqrt{5}, -2/\sqrt{5}$; (b) $-2/3\sqrt{5}$, $4/3\sqrt{5}, 5/3\sqrt{5}$ (c) $5/\sqrt{74}, 7/\sqrt{74}, 0$; (d) $1/\sqrt{6}, 1/\sqrt{6}, -2/\sqrt{6}$.
7. (i) direction cosines $-4/\sqrt{26}, 1/\sqrt{26}, -3/\sqrt{26}$
   (ii) direction cosines for **OA** are $3/\sqrt{17}, -2/\sqrt{17}, 2/\sqrt{17}$
   direction cosines for **OB** are $-1/\sqrt{3}, -1/\sqrt{3}, -1/\sqrt{3}$
8. (i) $-\frac{1}{3}, -\frac{2}{3}, \frac{2}{3}$, (ii) $(-\frac{7}{3}, -\frac{11}{3}, \frac{14}{3})$ (iii) 111·5°

## 5.7 Miscellaneous Exercises 5, page 95

2. $r = -3\sin\theta$, (a) $r = 3$, (b) $r^2 + 6r\sin\theta = 0$
3. Circle $r^2 - 4r\cos(\theta - \pi/6) - 12 = 0$; tangent $r\cos(\theta - \pi/6) = 6$
4. (a) $\theta = 0$, (b) $r(4\cos\theta - 3\sin\theta) = 12$, (c) $r(5\sin\theta - 4\cos\theta) = 20$
5. (i) $(1, \pi/3)$, (ii) $(1, 5\pi/6)$, (iii) $(\sqrt{2}, 13\pi/12)$ (iv) $(\sqrt{13}, \pi/3 - \arctan(\frac{3}{2}))$
6. (a) $(\sqrt{13}, -56\cdot3°)$ or $(3\cdot61, 0\cdot983 \text{ rad})$, (b) $(\sqrt{90}, 18\cdot4°)$ or $(9\cdot49, 0\cdot322 \text{ rad})$
   (c) $(\sqrt{113}, 228\cdot8°)$ or $(10\cdot6, 3\cdot99 \text{ rad})$, (d) $(5, 216\cdot9°)$ or $(5, 3\cdot79 \text{ rad})$
7. (a) $(-3\cdot42, -1\cdot53)$, (b) $(-1\cdot72, -3\cdot94)$, (c) $(2\cdot75, 4\cdot76)$, (d) $(5\cdot76, -1\cdot67)$
8. (i) $-7/5\sqrt{2}, 1/5\sqrt{2}$, (ii) $(17, -7)$, (iii) $(32, \frac{1}{2}\pi)$
9. (i) $-3/7, 6/7, 2/7$ are the direction cosines, (ii) angle $115\cdot4°$
10. (i) $(3\cdot49, 1\cdot49, -1\cdot48)$, (ii) $114\cdot0°$
11. Cylindrical: (a) $(\sqrt{8}, \frac{1}{4}\pi, 1)$, (b) $(\sqrt{10}, 288\cdot4°, 2)$, (c) $(\sqrt{41}, 51\cdot3°, -2)$,
    (d) $(\sqrt{8}, 225°, 4)$
    Spherical: (a) $(3, 70\cdot5°, 45°)$, (b) $(\sqrt{14}, 57\cdot7°, 288\cdot4°)$, (c) $(3\sqrt{5}, 107\cdot3°, 51\cdot3°)$,
    (d) $(2\sqrt{6}, 35\cdot3°, 225°)$.
12. (a) Cartesian $(1\cdot5, 2\cdot60, 5)$, spherical $(5\cdot83, 31\cdot0°, 60°)$
    (b) Cartesian $(-1\cdot30, 2\cdot25, 1\cdot5)$, cylindrical $(2\cdot60, 120°, 1\cdot5)$

## Exercise 6*a*, page 97

1. $2\cdot28$ s 2. $11\frac{2}{3}$ m 3. $2v$ or $2v/3$ 4. $u = 46\frac{7}{8}$ m s$^{-1}$, $v = 15\frac{5}{8}$ m s$^{-1}$
5. $(a - b)\hat{\mathbf{v}}$, $(c - b)\hat{\mathbf{v}}$, $2a + b = 3c$
6. $t = 0$ s, 1 s

## Exercise 6*b*, page 103

1. $24\cdot4$ km h$^{-1}$, bearings 215°, 035°
2. 117 km h$^{-1}$ at an angle of 59° to the car's velocity. $14\cdot3$ m apart, $0\cdot44$ s after the train reaches the level crossing. 3. $10\cdot6$ km h$^{-1}$ 4. $29\cdot2$ km h$^{-1}$ from bearing 239°
5. $\alpha = 2$, $\beta = -2$, collide at $\frac{11}{3}\hat{\mathbf{i}} + \frac{2}{3}\hat{\mathbf{j}} - \frac{2}{3}\hat{\mathbf{k}}$ 6. $-6\mathbf{i} - 25\mathbf{j} - 16\mathbf{k}$, $13\mathbf{i} + 53\mathbf{j} + 34\mathbf{k}$
7. from 017°, from 343°, $8\cdot49$ knot at 090°, 8 knot

## 6.4 Miscellaneous Exercises 6, page 104

1. (a) 25 km h$^{-1}$, on bearing 030°; $1\cdot44$ s
   (b) $83\cdot1$ km h$^{-1}$, on bearing $090\cdot7°$
2. Collide at $14\hat{\mathbf{i}} + 12\hat{\mathbf{j}} + 18\hat{\mathbf{k}}$.
   $\mathbf{v}_{AB} = -\frac{14}{3}\hat{\mathbf{j}} - \frac{7}{3}\hat{\mathbf{k}}$, distance $21\cdot6$ m
3. $3\cdot5$ m s$^{-1}$, 81°48′, $3\cdot61$ m s$^{-1}$, 73°54′ 4. (i) $(1, -1\cdot8)$, (ii) $17\cdot8$ m s$^{-1}$, S $52\cdot5$°E
5. $4\cdot20$ to $4\cdot30$ km 6. $\sqrt{[100(11 + 6\sqrt{3})]}$ 7. $v_1 = \sqrt{3}\,u/3$, $v_2 = 2\sqrt{3}\,u/3$
8. $2\mathbf{i} - \mathbf{j} + 2\mathbf{k}$, $6\mathbf{i} + 2\mathbf{j} + 4\mathbf{k}$, $\mathbf{i} + \mathbf{j} + 3\mathbf{k}$, $\sqrt{11}$
9. Steer at $\arccos(0\cdot4)$ west or east of north; closest distance is then 8 nautical miles. Steer on bearing 120°; closest distance is then $14\cdot4$ nautical miles.
10. $5\cdot77$ m s$^{-1}$, $3\cdot33$ m s$^{-1}$. (i) $10\cdot9°$ to normal; (ii) $10\cdot9°$ to normal, 30° to one side.
11. Direction W $2\theta$°N. (i) $6\cdot72$ km; (ii) $2\cdot94$ min, N $27\cdot8$°E
12. $-\mathbf{i} - 2\mathbf{j}$, shortest distance 2; velocity $7\mathbf{i} - \mathbf{j}$; position vector of C is $8\mathbf{i} - 3\mathbf{j}$.

## Exercise 7*a*, page 111

1. $0\cdot85$ N, between the forces of 3 N and 4 N and inclined to the 4 N force at $78\cdot3°$.
2. zero
3. $\begin{pmatrix}1\\4\\2\end{pmatrix}$ N, magnitude $\sqrt{21} \approx 4\cdot58$, direction cosines $\dfrac{1}{\sqrt{21}}, \dfrac{4}{\sqrt{21}}, \dfrac{2}{\sqrt{21}}$

4. Zero   5. 7·81 N at 153·7° to 5 N force
6. The resultant acts along the fifth side of a regular pentagon

**Exercise 7*b*, page 120**

Space considerations prevent us from drawing the diagrams which are the solutions to these questions.

**Exercise 8*a*, page 130**

1. $\sqrt{26}/3$ m s$^{-2} \approx 1{\cdot}70$ m s$^{-2}$, with polar angle $-\arctan(0{\cdot}2) = -11{\cdot}3°$ relative to O$x$ as the initial line.   2. $\frac{1}{25}$ m s$^{-2}$; 2·9°
3. acceleration $\frac{1}{4}$ m s$^{-2}$; retardation 0·0455 m s$^{-2}$   4. (a) 7·5 N, (b) $56\frac{1}{4}$ N
5. 1·5 m s$^{-2}$, $208\frac{1}{3}$ m, $16\frac{2}{3}$ s   6. 1·54 s, 9·22 m   7. $mgk/M$   8. $g\sin\alpha\cos\beta$
10. 4·20 m s$^{-2}$, 28·0 N, 0·690 s   11. 1·75 s
12. 0·0467 m s$^{-2}$. Tensions (from the front) 2900 N, 1933 N, 967 N.
13. (i) 9·807 N. (ii) 5·97 × $10^{24}$ kg, (iii) 9·774 m s$^{-2}$, 0·34% error; (iv) 9·0°, 9·777 m s$^{-2}$, 0·31% error.   14. $g\cos 2\alpha(\tan 2\alpha - \tan\alpha)$

**Exercise 8*b*, page 133**

1. 1·6 m, 1·25 N   2. $\frac{1}{2}g$
3. equilibrium position is 0·8 m from A, motion is SHM with period $2\pi\sqrt{(2/5)}$
4. $5\sqrt{15}/8$ N $\approx 2{\cdot}42$ N

**Exercise 8*c*, page 136**

1. The 15 kg mass accelerates downwards always,
   the mass $M$ accelerates downwards for $M > 11\frac{1}{4}$ kg,
   the pulley accelerates upwards for $M > 7\frac{1}{2}$ kg.
2. Tension in string supporting fixed pulley $= 320g/11$,
   tension in string around fixed pulley $= 160g/11$,
   tension in string around movable pulley $= 32g/11$,
   accelerations of 2 kg, 4 kg and 8 kg masses are $5g\hat{\mathbf{j}}/11$, $-3g\hat{\mathbf{j}}/11$ and $-g\hat{\mathbf{j}}/11$ respectively, where $\hat{\mathbf{j}}$ is vertically upwards,
   acceleration of pulley is $(g/11)\hat{\mathbf{j}}$
3. wedge: $\dfrac{gm\sin\alpha\cos\alpha}{M + m\sin^2\alpha}$ horizontally,
   particle: components $g\sin\alpha$ down the wedge,
   $\dfrac{gm\sin\alpha\cos\alpha}{M + m\sin^2\alpha}$ perpendicular to the wedge, towards the ground,

**8.7 Miscellaneous Exercises 8, page 136**

1. 0·43 m s$^{-2}$, 5·25 m s$^{-2}$   2. $\frac{1}{2}$ m s$^{-2}$, 600 N   3. 0·19 m s$^{-2}$, 3·2 m s$^{-2}$
4. 796 N, 1·50 kg   5. 1/8, 7 kg   6. (a) 2·18 m s$^{-2}$; (b) 45·8 N, 24·0 N; (c) 2·45 m
7. $r = \dfrac{1}{2 + \cos\theta}$, $\dot{\mathbf{r}} = -\dfrac{2\sin\theta\,\dot\theta}{(2 + \cos\theta)^2}\hat{\mathbf{i}} + \dfrac{2\cos\theta + 1}{(2 + \cos\theta)^2}\hat{\mathbf{j}}$
8. $5mg/3$ in string around fixed pulley, $5mg/2$ in other string.
   Acceleration of 5 kg mass is $2g/3$ downwards

### Exercise 9*a*, page 140

1. $\mathbf{v}(t) = \begin{pmatrix} -\sin t \\ \cos t \\ 1 \end{pmatrix}, \mathbf{a}(t) = \begin{pmatrix} -\cos t \\ -\sin t \\ 0 \end{pmatrix}$

   $|\mathbf{v}(t)| = \sqrt{2}, |\mathbf{a}(t)| = 1$

   The particle moves on the surface of a vertical cylinder, steadily gaining height

2. (a) $\mathbf{x}(0) = \begin{pmatrix} 4 \\ 5 \\ 5 \end{pmatrix}$ m, $\mathbf{v}(0) = \begin{pmatrix} 0 \\ 0 \\ -10 \end{pmatrix}$ m s$^{-1}$, $\mathbf{a}(0) = \mathbf{0}$ m s$^{-2}$

   (b) $\mathbf{x}(3) = \begin{pmatrix} 4 \\ -25 \\ -25 \end{pmatrix}$ m, $\mathbf{v}(3) = \begin{pmatrix} 0 \\ -10 \\ -10 \end{pmatrix}$ m s$^{-1}$, $\mathbf{a}(3) = \mathbf{0}$ m s$^{-2}$.

   (c) $\mathbf{x}(\frac{1}{2}) = \begin{pmatrix} 4 \\ 0 \\ 0 \end{pmatrix}$ m, $\mathbf{v}(\frac{1}{2}) = \begin{pmatrix} 0 \\ -10 \\ -10 \end{pmatrix}$ m s$^{-1}$, $\mathbf{a}(\frac{1}{2}) = \mathbf{0}$ m s$^{-2}$

3. $\mathbf{x}(t) = t\mathbf{u} + \begin{pmatrix} 1 \\ 1\frac{1}{2} \end{pmatrix} t^2 + \mathbf{x}_0, \mathbf{v}(t) = \mathbf{u} + t\begin{pmatrix} 2 \\ 3 \end{pmatrix}$

4. $\mathbf{v}(t) = \begin{pmatrix} v\cos\alpha + 10t \\ 10t \\ v\sin\alpha - 10t \end{pmatrix}, \mathbf{x}(t) = \begin{pmatrix} v\cos\alpha t + 5t^2 \\ 5t^2 \\ v\sin\alpha t - 5t^2 \end{pmatrix}$

### Exercise 9*b*, page 149

1. $u = 5$ m s$^{-1}$, $\beta = 53{\cdot}1°$, $R = 2{\cdot}45$ m, $T = 0{\cdot}82$ s, $h = 0{\cdot}82$ m
2. $\mathbf{u} = \begin{pmatrix} 5{\cdot}26 \\ 2{\cdot}72 \end{pmatrix}$ m s$^{-1}$, $R = 2{\cdot}97$ m, $T = 0{\cdot}56$ s, $h = 0{\cdot}38$ m.
3. 6·06 m up the plane after 0·74 s
4. 42·3 m up the plane after 2·21 s; vertical height 15·4 m after 1·77 s
5. (i) $(g\sqrt{a^2 + h^2} + a)^{\frac{1}{2}}$, (ii) $(g\sqrt{a^2 + h^2} - a)^{\frac{1}{2}}$.

### 9.4 Miscellaneous Exercises 9, page 150

1. 20·1 m up line of projection, after 1·19 s  2. (b) $\alpha = 45°$ or $\alpha = 63{\cdot}4°$
3. $l = 2\lambda u^2 \sin\theta\,(1 + \lambda\cos\theta)/g$; $\theta = 60°$; $1/4\sqrt{3} = 0{\cdot}144 \approx 1/7$
4. $a \leqq \sqrt{\dfrac{2V^2}{g}\left(\dfrac{V^2}{2g} - b\right)}$  5. 0·2%  6. 53° 8′
8. $v > \sqrt{4b^2g^2 + u^4}/2u$; least when $u = \sqrt{2bg}$

## Chapter 10

### Exercise 10*a*, page 156

1. (a) 63·6°, (b) 100·8°  2. (a) no solution, (b) $b = 2$  3. (a) 82·0°, (b) 2·47
4. $(4{\cdot}33 + 3{\cdot}06) \times 10^5 = 7{\cdot}39 \times 10^5$ J  5 456 J, 274 W  6. −5·80

### Exercise 10*b*, page 160

1. $2\mathbf{x} = 3\mathbf{y}$  2. (a) $|\mathbf{x}| = 3$, (b) $|\mathbf{x} - \hat{\mathbf{a}}| = \sqrt{6}$ and $|\mathbf{x} + \hat{\mathbf{a}}| = \sqrt{14}$,
   (c) $\cos\theta = 4/\sqrt{21}$  3. $\mathbf{a}.\mathbf{b} = 4$ and $(\mathbf{a} + \mathbf{b}).(\mathrm{a} + \mathbf{b}) = |\mathbf{a} + \mathbf{b}|^2 = 28$

**Exercise 10*c*, page 163**

1. (a) 60°, (b) and (d) are perpendicular, (c) 95·8°
2. (a) $\frac{1}{\sqrt{2}}\hat{\mathbf{i}} - \frac{1}{\sqrt{2}}\hat{\mathbf{j}}$ (b) $\frac{1}{\sqrt{11}}\hat{\mathbf{i}} + \frac{1}{\sqrt{11}}\hat{\mathbf{j}} + \frac{3}{\sqrt{11}}\hat{\mathbf{k}}$
   (c) $\frac{2}{\sqrt{62}}\hat{\mathbf{i}} - \frac{3}{\sqrt{62}}\hat{\mathbf{j}} + \frac{7}{\sqrt{62}}\hat{\mathbf{k}}$ 3. (a) 114·6°
   (b) $|\mathbf{a} + \mathbf{b}| = \sqrt{15} \approx 3{\cdot}87, |\mathbf{a} - \mathbf{b}| = \sqrt{35} \approx 5{\cdot}92$ (c) 107·8°.
4. (ii) BY = 2 m, OY = 5·29 m 5. The scalar products are 53, 477 and 0 respectively.
   Area = $79\frac{1}{2}$

**10.9 Miscellaneous Exercises 10, page 163**

1. 6080 N (3S) at 34·7° to smaller force. Work done = 24 300 J 2. (a) $\mathbf{a}\,.\,\mathbf{a} = 4$, $\mathbf{a}\,.\,\mathbf{b} = 5{\cdot}20$, $\mathbf{b}\,.\,\mathbf{b} = 9$ (b) $(\mathbf{a} + \mathbf{b})\,.\,(\mathbf{a} - 2\mathbf{b}) = -19{\cdot}2$ 3. (a) $1/\sqrt{2} \approx 0{\cdot}707$; (b) 45°; (c) $(\hat{\mathbf{a}} - \mathbf{b})^2 = \frac{1}{2}$, $(\hat{\mathbf{a}} + \mathbf{b})^2 = 5/2$; (d) 63·4° 4. (a) Obtuse, (b) $\alpha = 14/5$, (c) $(\hat{\mathbf{i}} + 12\hat{\mathbf{j}} - 5\hat{\mathbf{k}})/\sqrt{170}$ 6. 22·2° 7. $\mathbf{i} = \mathbf{u}/\sqrt{3} + \mathbf{v}\sqrt{\frac{2}{3}} + 0\mathbf{w}$
8. Force $20\mathbf{i} - 10\mathbf{j}$ N. Work 0 J

## Chapter 11

**Exercise 11*a*, page 168**

1. (a) $(8/3)\hat{\mathbf{i}} - 4\hat{\mathbf{j}} + 2\hat{\mathbf{k}}$ N s, (b) $(56/3)\hat{\mathbf{i}} - 12\hat{\mathbf{j}} + 58\hat{\mathbf{k}}$ N s
   $\mathbf{v}(0) = -(8/9)\hat{\mathbf{i}} + (4/3)\hat{\mathbf{j}} - (2/3)\hat{\mathbf{k}}$ m s$^{-1}$,
   $\mathbf{v}(4) = (56/3)\hat{\mathbf{i}} - 12\hat{\mathbf{j}} + 58\hat{\mathbf{k}}$ m s$^{-1}$
2. 515 N, 26/9 m s$^{-1}$ 3. (a) $13\frac{1}{8}$ m s$^{-1}$, (b) 9·28 m s$^{-1}$, time 0·3 s 4. 1·44 s, 1·40 s

**Exercise 11*b*, page 173**

1. Total time 20 s, final speed 1/15 m s$^{-1}$ 2. $(9/5)\hat{\mathbf{i}} + \hat{\mathbf{j}}$ m s$^{-1}$, $(21/5)\hat{\mathbf{i}} - \hat{\mathbf{j}}$ m s$^{-1}$
4. 0·2 s after the string becomes taut

**Exercise 11*c*, page 177**

1. 9 m, ratio $2:\sqrt{3}$ or 1·15:1 2. 5·53 m horizontally each time
3. (a) speed of mass $m$ is $17u/24$, of mass $2m$ is $43u/48$
4. 3 kg mass has velocity $\frac{1}{4}\begin{pmatrix}17\\2\end{pmatrix}$ m s$^{-1}$; the other has velocity $\frac{1}{4}\begin{pmatrix}17\\-10\end{pmatrix}$ m s$^{-1}$
5. Velocity of B after impact is $\begin{pmatrix}3\frac{1}{2}\\2\frac{1}{2}\\0\end{pmatrix}$m s$^{-1}$. Impulse $\begin{pmatrix}-6\\6\\0\end{pmatrix}$N s.
   Line of centres is in direction $\begin{pmatrix}-1\\1\\0\end{pmatrix}$. $e = \frac{3}{4}$

**Exercise 11*d*, page 179**

1. 229 500 N 2. 46·5 N 3. 1·47 m 4. 1·49 m s$^{-2}$ 5. $U + u\ln(1/k)$

**11.7 Miscellaneous Exercises 11, page 180**

1. 54·9 N; momentum 275 N s, velocity 137 m s$^{-1}$ down the slope; frictional force 20·6 N.
2. Momentum 30 N s, velocity 15 m s$^{-1}$ in the direction 090°. Magnitude of velocity 65 m s$^{-1}$. 3. Time 2·29 s; magnitude of impulse $8{\cdot}91 \times 10^4$ N s.

4. Velocity of B is $-\mathbf{i} + \mathbf{j} + \mathbf{k}$ units; impulse $4\mathbf{i} + 8\mathbf{j} - 4\mathbf{k}$ units; direction of line of centres $\mathbf{i} + 2\mathbf{j} - \mathbf{k}$. 5. Velocity: (a) $40{\cdot}8\ \mathrm{m\,s^{-1}}$, (b) $36{\cdot}7\ \mathrm{m\,s^{-1}}$. Time $5{\cdot}1$ s.
6. Magnitude of impulse $m\sqrt{[2gh\,1 + f^2)]}$, $d = 2f\sqrt{(Hh - h^2)}$.
7. New velocities $10\ \mathrm{m\,s^{-1}}$ and $7{\cdot}5\ \mathrm{m\,s^{-1}}$ 8. (i) $51°$, (ii) $5{\cdot}3v$
9. (a) speeds $2u/5$ and $7u/5$, (b) $e = 5/8$.

# Chapter 12

### Exercise 12*a*, page 185

Most of these questions are answered in subsequent sections.

3. $\mathbf{F} \wedge \mathbf{x}$ is the moment of the force $\mathbf{F}$ about the point X. The given equation states that the sum of the moments of two forces about a point is equal to the moment of their resultant about that point.

### Exercise 12*b*, page 189

1. (a) $\begin{pmatrix} 9 \\ -15 \\ -24 \end{pmatrix}$ (b) $\begin{pmatrix} 10 \\ -12 \\ 15 \end{pmatrix}$ (c) $\begin{pmatrix} 36 \\ -22 \\ -1 \end{pmatrix}$

2. (a) $\dfrac{1}{\sqrt{133}}\begin{pmatrix} 4 \\ -9 \\ -6 \end{pmatrix}$ (b) $\dfrac{1}{\sqrt{312}}\begin{pmatrix} 9 \\ -16 \\ -5 \end{pmatrix}$ (c) $\dfrac{1}{\sqrt{507}}\begin{pmatrix} -17 \\ 13 \\ 7 \end{pmatrix}$

3. (a) $\begin{pmatrix} 0 \\ 0 \\ -7 \end{pmatrix}$ (b) $\begin{pmatrix} 0 \\ 0 \\ 18 \end{pmatrix}$ (c) $\begin{pmatrix} 0 \\ 0 \\ -4 \end{pmatrix}$

4. (a) $\begin{pmatrix} 0 \\ 0 \\ -5 \end{pmatrix}$ (b) $\begin{pmatrix} 0 \\ 0 \\ -9 \end{pmatrix}$ (c) $\begin{pmatrix} 0 \\ 0 \\ 26 \end{pmatrix}$

5. (a), (b) and (c) $\begin{pmatrix} 0 \\ 0 \\ 1 \end{pmatrix}$

6. $(\mathbf{f} \wedge \mathbf{g}) \wedge \mathbf{h} = \begin{pmatrix} 21 \\ 28 \\ 0 \end{pmatrix} = 10\mathbf{f} + \mathbf{g}$;

$\mathbf{f} \wedge (\mathbf{g} \wedge \mathbf{h}) = \begin{pmatrix} -15 \\ 10 \\ 0 \end{pmatrix} = \mathbf{g} + 4\mathbf{h}$

7. Converse false

8. (a) $\hat{\mathbf{b}} = \begin{pmatrix} 3/5 \\ 4/5 \\ 0 \end{pmatrix}$

(b) $(\mathbf{c} - \mathbf{a}) \wedge \hat{\mathbf{b}} = \begin{pmatrix} 0 \\ 0 \\ 14/5 \end{pmatrix}$

(c) $|(\mathbf{c} - \mathbf{a}) \wedge \hat{\mathbf{b}}| = 14/5$ = perpendicular distance from C to line through A parallel to $\mathbf{b}$.

9. $3\sqrt{3/14}$.

10. $\sin\theta = \dfrac{\sqrt{(a_2b_3 - a_3b_2)^2 + (a_3b_1 - a_1b_3)^2 + (a_1b_2 - a_2b_1)^2}}{\sqrt{a_1^2 + a_2^2 + a_3^2}\,\sqrt{b_1^2 + b_2^2 + b_3^2}}$

### 12.5 Miscellaneous Exercises 12, page 190

1. (a) Interchanging two adjacent columns reverses the sign of a determinant.
   (b) A determinant with two equal columns is zero.
   (c) $\begin{vmatrix} \hat{\mathbf{i}} & a_1 & b_1 + c_1 \\ \hat{\mathbf{j}} & a_2 & b_2 + c_2 \\ \hat{\mathbf{k}} & a_3 & b_3 + c_3 \end{vmatrix} = \begin{vmatrix} \hat{\mathbf{i}} & a_1 & b_1 \\ \hat{\mathbf{j}} & a_2 & b_2 \\ \hat{\mathbf{k}} & a_3 & b_3 \end{vmatrix} + \begin{vmatrix} \hat{\mathbf{i}} & a_1 & c_1 \\ \hat{\mathbf{j}} & a_2 & c_2 \\ \hat{\mathbf{j}} & a_3 & c_3 \end{vmatrix}$
   (d) Multiplying a column by a scalar multiplies the value of the determinant by that scalar.

2. (a) $\mathbf{0}$, (b) $\mathbf{0}$, (c) $\mathbf{p} \wedge \mathbf{q} = -\mathbf{q} \wedge \mathbf{p} = \begin{pmatrix} -8 \\ 4 \\ 5 \end{pmatrix}$,
   (d) $\begin{pmatrix} -16 \\ 8 \\ 10 \end{pmatrix}$, (e) $\begin{pmatrix} -176 \\ 88 \\ 110 \end{pmatrix}$, (f) $(\alpha\delta - \beta\gamma)\begin{pmatrix} -8 \\ 4 \\ 5 \end{pmatrix}$

3. (a) (ii) $\lambda(\mathbf{i} + \mathbf{j} + 2\mathbf{k}) - \mathbf{k}$
   (b) $\mathbf{h} = -2m(1 + t^2)\mathbf{k}$; $\mathbf{F} = 2m\hat{\mathbf{i}}$; $\dfrac{\mathrm{d}h}{\mathrm{d}t} = \mathbf{r} \wedge \mathbf{F} = -4mt\,\mathbf{k}$

4. (a) $\mathbf{x} = \mathbf{b} - \dfrac{1}{2a^2}(\mathbf{a} \,.\, \mathbf{b})\mathbf{a}$
   (b) $\mathbf{p} = \pm\dfrac{3}{\sqrt{2}}(\mathbf{i} + \mathbf{j})$, $\mathbf{q} = \pm\dfrac{1}{\sqrt{2}}(\mathbf{i} - \mathbf{j})$, $\mathbf{r} = \pm 6(\mathbf{i} - \mathbf{j}) \pm 3\mathbf{k}$,
   where the last $\pm$ is independent of the first

6. (i) $\lambda = d/a^2$; (ii) $\mu = 0$, $\nu = -1/(ac)$

## Chapter 13

### Exercise 13*a*, page 192

1. (a) $\sqrt{13}$, (b) 5, (c) $\sqrt{38}$, (d) $2\sqrt{38}$  2. $a = -83/8$  3. (a) $3\mathbf{a} - \frac{1}{2}\mathbf{b}$,
   (b) $\frac{1}{4}(10\mathbf{a} + 3\mathbf{b})$, (c) $-7\mathbf{b}$, (d) $7(\mathbf{a} - \mathbf{b})/3$  4. $\mathbf{g}_1 = (\mathbf{a} + \mathbf{b} + \mathbf{d})/3$,
   $\mathbf{g}_2 = (\mathbf{c} + \mathbf{b} + \mathbf{d})/3$, $G_1G_2 : H_1H_2 : AC = 3:4:9$
5. (a) $\mathbf{r} = (2\hat{\mathbf{i}} - 3\hat{\mathbf{j}} + 7\hat{\mathbf{k}}) + t(\hat{\mathbf{i}} + 6\hat{\mathbf{j}} - 8\hat{\mathbf{k}})$
   (b) $\mathbf{a} \wedge \mathbf{b} = -18\hat{\mathbf{i}} + 23\hat{\mathbf{j}} + 15\hat{\mathbf{k}}$, for example
   (c) $\mathbf{r} = \frac{5}{2}\hat{\mathbf{i}} + 3\hat{\mathbf{k}} + u(-18\hat{\mathbf{i}} + 23\hat{\mathbf{j}} + 15\hat{\mathbf{k}})$
6. (a) $\dfrac{1, 2, 9}{\sqrt{86}}$, (b) $\dfrac{5, -12, 13}{13\sqrt{2}}$, (c) $\dfrac{-40, 9}{41}$
7. Scalar products: (a) 98, (b) $-33$, (c) 11, (d) $-112$.
   Vector products: (a) $\begin{pmatrix} 134 \\ 32 \\ -22 \end{pmatrix}$ (b) $\begin{pmatrix} 0 \\ 0 \\ 47 \end{pmatrix}$ (c) $\begin{pmatrix} 0 \\ 0 \\ 16 \end{pmatrix}$ (d) $\mathbf{0}$

### Exercise 13*b*, page 195

1. (i): (a) (12/5, 13/5, 1), (b) (11/5, 9/5, 2)
   (ii) (8, 0, 3)
   (iii) (7, 8/3, 2/3),
2. AB (5/2, 3, $\frac{1}{2}$), AC (4, 3/2, 2), AD (5/2, $\frac{1}{2}$, 5/2), AE ($\frac{1}{2}$, $-\frac{1}{2}$, 11/2), AF (2, 2, 2)
3. (i) $G_1$ (4, 7/3, 1/3), $G_2$ (8/3, 0, 11/3), $G_3$ (5/3, 1, 8/3), $G_4$ ($\frac{8}{3}$, $\frac{5}{3}$, $\frac{7}{3}$).
   (ii), (iii) all answers (11/4, 9/4, 5/4).
   (iv) The medians of a tetrahedron JKLM are concurrent at a point which divides each in the ratio 1:3.

4. (ii): (a) A, (b) B, (c) mid-point, (d) point dividing AB in ratio 2:3, (e) point dividing AB in ratio 3:2, (f) point C such that A is mid-point of BC, (g) point C such that AC:CB = −1:2.
5. (a) 1:3, (b) 2:−1, (c) 3:−2, (d) 5:−2, (e) −1:3, (f) −2:7
6. AC $\sqrt{21}$, BC $3\sqrt{3}$, DC $\sqrt{14}$, EC $\sqrt{114}$, FC $\sqrt{17}$
7. $\cos(\widehat{AOC}) = 17/\sqrt{574}$, $\cos(\widehat{BOC}) = 26/\sqrt{1458}$, $\cos(\widehat{DOC}) = 20/\sqrt{533}$. $\cos(\widehat{EOC}) = -2/\sqrt{2829}$, $\cos(\widehat{FOC}) = 19/\sqrt{574}$.

**Exercise 13*c*, page 198**

1. (i) $\dfrac{10, -3, 4}{5\sqrt{5}}$, (ii) $\dfrac{2, -2, 1}{3}$, (iii) $\dfrac{1, 2, 3}{\sqrt{14}}$

2. (i) $\dfrac{x+1}{10} = \dfrac{y-3}{-3} = \dfrac{z+2}{4}$ (ii) $\dfrac{x-4}{2} = \dfrac{y+3}{-2} = \dfrac{z-7}{1}$

(iii) $\dfrac{x-2}{1} = \dfrac{y-4}{2} = \dfrac{z-6}{3}$ (iv) $x = 2,\ \dfrac{y-4}{9} = \dfrac{z-6}{-1}$

(v) $\dfrac{x-4}{1} = \dfrac{y+5}{3} = \dfrac{z+3}{2}$. (Other forms are possible for each part.)

3. (i) $\dfrac{x-4}{10} = \dfrac{y+3}{-3} = \dfrac{z-7}{4}$ (ii) $\dfrac{x-2}{2} = \dfrac{y-4}{-2} = \dfrac{z-6}{1}$

4. (i) $\dfrac{x-2}{2} = \dfrac{y-3}{3} = \dfrac{z-4}{4}$, (ii) $x - 2 = y - 3 = z - 4$ or $x = y - 1 = z - 2$

5. The lines do not meet 6. (i) $\dfrac{-1, 3, -2}{\sqrt{14}}$ (ii) $\dfrac{6, 7, 8}{\sqrt{149}}$

**Exercise 13*d*, page 202**

1. $p = 2\sqrt{2}$, $q = \sqrt{10} = r = t$, $s = 2\sqrt{5}$, $u = \sqrt{13}$
2. $\cos(\widehat{POQ}) = 2/\sqrt{5}$, $\cos(\widehat{POR}) = 2/\sqrt{5}$, $\cos(\widehat{POS}) = 1/\sqrt{10}$, $\cos(\widehat{POT}) = 1/\sqrt{5}$, $\cos(\widehat{POU}) = -5/\sqrt{26}$
3. For example, $\left\{\hat{\mathbf{p}} = \begin{pmatrix} 1/\sqrt{2} \\ 1/\sqrt{2} \end{pmatrix}, \hat{\mathbf{v}} = \begin{pmatrix} 1/\sqrt{2} \\ -1/\sqrt{2} \end{pmatrix}\right\}$
   This set is not unique, and the other solutions will depend on the set chosen
6. (a) No, (b) yes, (c) no

**Exercise 13*e*, page 208**

1. $5/\sqrt{29}$ 2. $2x - y + 5z = 6$ 3. $14x + 11y + 2z = 27$ 4. $2x - 5y + 3z = -3$
5. $3x - 17y + 2z = 0$ 6. $x + y + z = -2$ 7. $\arccos(-12/\sqrt{906})$ 8. $10/\sqrt{41}$
9. (a) $z = 0$, (b) $x + y + z = 1$ 10. (a) $3x + 4y + 5z = 25\sqrt{2}$, (b) $2x + 3y + 4z = 29$ 11. (52/31, 43/31, 30/31)

**Exercise 13*g*, page 215**

1. Tangent $x - ty + at^2 = 0$, normal $y + tx = 2at + at^3$
2. $\hat{\mathbf{s}} = \begin{pmatrix} 1 \\ 0 \end{pmatrix}$, $\hat{\mathbf{c}} = \dfrac{1}{t^2+1}\begin{pmatrix} t^2 - 1 \\ 2t \end{pmatrix}$, $\hat{\mathbf{u}} = \dfrac{1}{(1+t^2)^{1/2}}\begin{pmatrix} t \\ 1 \end{pmatrix}$

   $\hat{\mathbf{s}} \cdot \hat{\mathbf{u}} = \dfrac{t}{(1+t^2)^{1/2}} = \hat{\mathbf{c}} \cdot \hat{\mathbf{u}}$ which implies that a ray of light from a distance, striking the parabola at P, will be reflected through the focus

3. Tangent $\dfrac{x\cos\theta}{a} + \dfrac{y\sin\theta}{b} = 1$, normal $xa\sin\theta - yb\cos\theta = \frac{1}{2}(a^2 - b^2)\sin 2\theta$

5. Tangent $x + t^2y = 2ct$, normal $t^2x - y = ct^3 - c/t$

6. Tangent $y = mx \pm a(1 + m^2)^{\frac{1}{2}}$

**Exercise 13*h*, page 218**

1. $y^2 + z^2 = 4ax$ 2. $\dfrac{x^2}{a^2} + \dfrac{y^2 + z^2}{b^2} = 1$ 3. $3x + 4y + 22z = 398$

4. $3(x^2 + y^2 + z^2) = 4(X + y + z)^2$

**13.10 Miscellaneous Exercises 13, page 218**

1. (i) perpendicular distance 9, volume 15
   (ii) direction cosines $\dfrac{5, 2, -1}{\sqrt{30}}$, point $(5/3, 2/3, -1/3)$

2. (i) $(-24, -18, 0)$, (ii) $x/4 = y/3 = (z - 12)/2$, (iii) $\dfrac{4, 3, 2}{\sqrt{29}}$, (iv) $26\frac{1}{2}°$, $33\frac{1}{2}°$

3. Holds in three dimensions; $\sqrt{5}$ 4. (a) (i) $-3$, (b) 106·3 or 1·7

5. $x + 2y + 3z = 6$, $(3/7, 6/7, 9/7)$ 6. $(4/3, -2/3, 4/3)$

7. $5\lambda = 2\mu$, $\begin{pmatrix} x \\ y \\ z \end{pmatrix} = \begin{pmatrix} 3/2 \\ 15/2 \\ 0 \end{pmatrix} + t\begin{pmatrix} 5 \\ 29 \\ 2 \end{pmatrix}$

8. Cone $(ax + by + cz)^2 = (x^2 + y^2 + z^2)(a^2 + b^2 + c^2)\cos^2\alpha$

9. $\mathbf{PQ} = a(\mathbf{i} + \mathbf{j} + 2\mathbf{k})$, $\mathbf{PR} = a(2\mathbf{j} + 2\mathbf{k})$, $\mathbf{QR} = a(-\mathbf{i} + \mathbf{j})$
   $\mathbf{P} = 30°$, $Q = 90°$, $R = 60°$.
   Unit normal $\dfrac{1}{\sqrt{3}}(\mathbf{i} + \mathbf{j} - \mathbf{k})$, plane $x + y - z = a$ 10. $x^2 + y^2 + z^2 = (x + y + z)^2$

11. $10/\sqrt{66}$ 12. $\begin{pmatrix} 3 \\ 2 \\ 1 \end{pmatrix}, \begin{pmatrix} 3 \\ 1 \\ 2 \end{pmatrix}$

13. $3x - 2y - z = 3$, $5\sqrt{14}/7$, $x - 1 = \frac{1}{4}(y - 1) = (z + 2)/(-5)$

14. $\mathbf{r}\cdot(3\mathbf{i} + \mathbf{j}) = 6$, $\mathbf{r}\cdot(\mathbf{i} + 3\mathbf{j}) = 6$ 15. $\dfrac{x - 2}{6} = y + 1 = \dfrac{z}{4}$

## Chapter 14

**Exercise 14*a*, page 229**

1. (a) and (b) 49 J, (c) 28 J 2. KE $5mg(4 - \sqrt{3})/8$, work $5mg\sqrt{3}/8$, KE $5mg/2$
3. 3 kg 4. Tractive force 3610 N, braking force 1820 N 5. (a) $528g \approx 5180$ J, (b) $4\sqrt{30g}/5 \approx 13{\cdot}7$ m s$^{-1}$, (c) $4\sqrt{15g}/5 \approx 9{\cdot}70$ m s$^{-1}$ 6. 0·487
7. 27·1 m s$^{-1}$ 8. Speed $\sqrt{u^2 + 2ga}$, impulse $m\sqrt{2(u^2 + ga)}$, direction arctan $(u/\sqrt{u^2 + 2ga})$ with velocity at bottom. 9. Force $mu_1^2/2d$; distance $(M - m)d/M$
10. Coefficient of restitution $\frac{1}{2}$, height 1 m.

**Exercise 14*b*, page 232**

1. SHM period $2\pi\sqrt{(3/10g)}$, centre 0·3 m below the end of the unstretched spring.
2. Extension in each string $= a$. SHM period $4\pi\sqrt{(a/g)}$, centre the equilibrium position.

**Exercise 14*c*, page 234**

1. (a) 5·4 J, (b) 2·75 J  2. $\frac{1}{2}$  3. 26·8%

**Exercise 14*d*, page 237**

1. (a) 3680 W, (b) 7400 W  2. speed $67\frac{1}{2}$ km h$^{-1}$ = $18\frac{3}{4}$ m s$^{-1}$, acceleration 0·04 m s$^{-2}$

3. (a) 1640 W, (b) 600 kW  4. $\dfrac{uv}{2v - u}$  5. (a) $66\frac{2}{3}$ s, (b) $64\frac{2}{7}$ s

6. First $\frac{1}{4}$ km: $\dfrac{50m}{P}\left(\dfrac{3P}{2m}\right)^{2/3}$; Next $1\frac{1}{4}$ km: $\dfrac{1}{8}\left(\dfrac{2m}{3P}\right)^{1/3}$; Last $\frac{1}{4}$ km: $\dfrac{m}{5}\left(\dfrac{3P}{2m}\right)^{2/3}$

**14.9 Miscellaneous Exercises 14, page 239**

1. (i) 13 500 J, (ii) 6·72 m s$^{-1}$  2. $-2g/5$  3. 24:1  4. 16 kW, $\frac{1}{4}$ m s$^{-2}$
7. 25 N s s$^{-1}$ = 25 N. The 25 W motor is sufficient. Speed 0·85 m s$^{-1}$
8. $mgd + \frac{1}{2}mv^2 = Td$, $g(h - d) = \frac{1}{2}mv^2$  9. $a = \frac{1}{40}g$  10. 0, $x^2 + \frac{1}{2}y^2$

# Bibliography

## I. Preliminary knowledge

We assume the reader to be familiar with the contents of some modern Ordinary level course, and possibly of a modern Additional Mathematics course. In this section, we list some books which cover the relevant ground.

1. *The Contemporary School Mathematics Series*, published by Edward Arnold, London. Particularly:
Brand, T. E., Wade, D. W. M. and Sherlock, A. J., *Mathematics 4.*
Matthews, G., *Matrices 1* and *Matrices 2.*
Brand, T. E., and Wade, D. W. M., *Exercises 2.*

2. Heritage, R. S. and Edge, J. D. *Vectors, Transformations and Matrices*. Penguin, London.

3. Clarke, L. H. *Additional Pure Mathematics*. Heinemann, London.

4. Clarke, L. H. and Norton, F. G. J. *Additional Applied Mathematics.*

## II. Other sixth form books

We assume also that the reader is following a sixth form course in pure mathematics which will provide the necessary knowledge of calculus, etc., for coping with the problems in this book. In this section, we list some books which could prove useful either for covering topics in other branches of mathematics, or for providing a back-up for the material we cover.

1. The other books in the Contemporary Mathematics series, published by Edward Arnold, particularly:
Brand, T. E. and Sherlock, A. J. *Matrices: Pure and Applied.* This contains the necessary matrix work, and much more besides.

2. Ellis, A. S. and Treeby, T. P., *Algebraic Structure*, John Murray, London. This gives a full treatment of the structural ideas mentioned in this volume, as well as other structural concepts.

3. Quadling, D. A. and Ramsey, A. R. D. *Elementary Mechanics 1*, *Elementary Mechanics 2*, and *An Introduction to Advanced Mechanics*. Bell, London. These three volumes give a full and alternative treatment to the mechanics of this book, as well as going beyond the level of this volume.

4. Boys, G. R. H. *Problems in Applied Mathematics*. Arnold, London. A collection of examination questions in mechanics, probability and statistics, from modern Advanced level syllabuses.

5. Palmer, A. H. G. and Snell, K. S. *Mechanics*. University of London Press, London.

6. Matthews, G. *Calculus.* John Murray, London. A comprehensive sixth form calculus course.

7. Backhouse, J. K. and Houldsworth, S. P. T. *Pure Mathematics, a First Course.* Longman, London.

Backhouse, J. K., Houldsworth, S. P. T. and Cooper, B. E. D. *Pure Mathematics, a Second Course*, Longman, London. These two volumes provide a comprehensive sixth form pure mathematics course.

8. Siddons, A. W., Snell, K. S. and Morgan, J. B. *A New Calculus* (three volumes). Cambridge University Press, Cambridge. An extensive calculus course, reaching beyond University scholarship level.

9. Parsonson, S. L. *Pure Mathematics 1 and 2.* Cambridge University Press, Cambridge. A modern course of Pure Mathematics, calculus excluded.

10 Cleaves, H. F. *An Introduction to Differential Equations.* Oliver and Boyd, Edinburgh. A full treatment of the differential equations required at this level.

11. *School Mathematics Project, Various Advanced Level Texts.* Cambridge University Press, Cambridge.

## III. Further reading

In this section, we list some books which provide reading in the subject beyond the level normally reached in the sixth form, and naturally includes books we have found useful in our preparation of this volume.

1. Weatherburn, C. E., *Elementary Vector Analysis.* Bell, London.

2. Weatherburn, C. E., *Advanced Vector Analysis.* Bell, London.

3. Synge, J. L. and Griffith, B. A., *Principles of Mechanics.* McGraw-Hill, London.

4. Margenau, H. and Murphy, G. M., *The Mathematics of Physics and Chemistry.* van Nostrand, London.

5. Rutherford, D. E. *Vector Methods.* Oliver and Boyd, Edinburgh.

# Index

Definitions and important references are indicated by the use of bold type e.g. **182**.
Illustrations, especially by worked examples, are indicated by the use of italic type, e.g. *183*